METHOD OF LEAST SQUARES AND PRINCIPLES OF THE THEORY OF OBSERVATIONS

PUBLISHER'S NOTICE
TO REVIEWERS AND READERS

CONCERNING THE QUALITY OF PRODUCTION AND PUBLISHED PRICE OF THIS WORK

We much regret that in the interest of speedily making available the information contained in this publication, it has been necessary to produce the text by non-letterpress setting and photo lithography, with the result that the quality of production is not as high as the public have come to associate with and expect from the Pergamon Press.

To have re-set this manuscript by letterpress would have delayed its appearance by many months and the price would have had to be increased further.

The cost of translating scientific and technical works from the Russian in time, money, and publishing effort is very considerable. In the interest of getting the Soviet Authorities eventually to pay the usual authors' royalties to Western authors, the Pergamon Press is voluntarily paying to Russian authors the usual authors' royalties on this publication, in addition to the translators' and editors' fees. This and the somewhat limited market and the lack of any kind of subsidy accounts for what may appear to be a higher than usual published price.

I. R. Maxwell
Publisher at Pergamon Press

Method of Least Squares and Principles of the Theory of Observations

by

YU. V. LINNIK

Translated from the Russian by
REGINA C. ELANDT, *Ph.D.*
Department of Biometry,
Agricultural College, Poznan

Edited by
N. L. JOHNSON, *M.Sc., Ph.D., F.I.A.*
Reader in Statistics at the University of London

PERGAMON PRESS

OXFORD · LONDON · NEW YORK · PARIS

1961

PERGAMON PRESS LTD.,
Headington Hill Hall, Oxford.
4 and 5 Fitzroy Square, London W.1.

PERGAMON PRESS INC.,
122 East 55th Street, New York 22, N.Y.
Statler Center — 640,
900 Wilshire Blvd, Los Angeles 17, Calif.

PERGAMON PRESS S.A.R.L.
24 Rue des Ecoles, Paris Ve.

PERGAMON PRESS G.m.b.H.
Kaiserstrasse 75, Frankfurt-am-Main.

A translation of the original volume
'*Metod naimen'shikh kvadratov i osnovy matematiko-statisticheskoi teorii obrabotki nablyudenii*'

(Fizmatgiz, Moscow, 1958)

Library of Congress Card Number: 60-13826

Printed in Great Britain by
PERGAMON PRINTING & ART SERVICES LTD.,
LONDON

CONTENTS

PREFACE

At the present time the method of least squares is widely applied in the treatment of quantitative results from experimental work in natural science, technical data, astronomical and geodetic observations and measurements. Following the classical work of Markov[37], a certain number of handbooks in Russian have appeared, setting out the theory of this method (see, for example, Chebotariev [51], Edelson [19], Yushchenko [56]). In these are detailed accounts of the calculations associated with the method, and also many applications and examples. However, in these books the mathematical and statistical aspects of the work are treated essentially in the classical spirit of the last century, without taking account of the ideas and achievements of modern mathematical statistics, in which the method of least squares can be included naturally as part of the theory of estimation of parameters. The small book by Romanovski [44] is excluded from these comments, but it deals with only a part of the method of least squares.

In these applications, modern mathematical statistics makes full and accurate utilization of the information derived from the observations by the method of least squares, and deepens the understanding of the real meaning and importance of the results obtained by this method. Hence it is useful practically, as well as theoretically.

The present book deals with the theory of the method of least squares with emphasis on the mathematico-statistical interpretation of the results obtained from the data by this method (which, of course, only has a meaning on the basis of the natural assumption that the errors of measurement can be regarded as random quantities).

The basic schemes of calculation used in applying the method are also described (in section 12, chapter IV, and in many examples).

Following the introduction, which contains a series of practical examples and arbitrary applications of the method of least squares to them, chapters I, II and III contain brief accounts of necessary results in algebra, probability theory and mathematical statistics, including the elements of the modern theory of estimation of parameters.

The theory of the treatment of direct measurements is given in chapters IV and V; here, in particular, there is a description of a useful method of treating groups of direct measurements, so that information on the common accuracy of each group is extracted. In chapter VI indirect unconditional observations are treated; chapters VII and VIII are on fitting by the use of elements and correlates. In all cases the construction of confidence intervals for estimating the measured quantities, and the accuracy of measurements, is described. The work of Neyman and David on the estimation of linear forms in the parameters is described in chapter IX. In chapter X some problems in geodesy, and, in chapter IX, a special theory of direction-finding, are discussed. Among the new results in this chapter is the application of confidence intervals in the theory of direction-finding. The fundamentals of Chebyshev's theory of parabolic interpolation are set out in chapter XII, while chapter XIII contains Wald's results on fitting a series of observations by a straight line when the measurements of the abscissae, and not only of the ordinates, are subject to error. The final chapter gives some additional information about the method of least squares - the general construction of confidence ellipsoids, theorems relating to the close connection between the method of least squares and the normal law of error, the theorem of Kolmogorov, Petrov and Smirnov and the application of Cauchy's method to the analysis of observations.

The development of the theory is given in matrix form: the necessary knowledge of matrices is collected together in chapter I. It should be noted that this way of approach is now conventional, and generally accepted in similar mathematical works, because of its brevity and ease of writing; it has also penetrated into astronomy and geodesy (see, for example, the Finnish work on geodesy [50]). However, in view of the fact that matrix calculation is still not habitual for everybody, some paragraphs are inserted at the end of certain chapters, containing the principal results and rules, without using matrices; besides this, there is a relatively large number of examples in which matrices are only little used.

The most important results are given as numbered theorems.

A.P.Khousou has been of great help in compiling this book: she wrote section 12 of chapter VI, carried out calculations for many of the examples, and prepared the tables: for this I express to her my deep gratitude.

Yu.V.Linnik

INTRODUCTION

1. Outline of Problems and Some Typical Examples

The best and most natural way of appreciating present-day problems and mathematical techniques in the method of least squares is to consider some real examples.

Example 1. (Markov [37]). In "Foundations of Chemistry" by Mendeléjev (1936) there are some data on the solubility of sodium nitrate, $NaNO_3$, in relation to water temperature. At the temperatures shown below, the following parts of $NaNO_3$ dissolve in 100 parts of water:

0°	4°	10°	15°	21°	29°	36°	51°	68°
66·7	71·0	76·3	80·6	85·7	92·9	99·4	113·6	125·1

Theoretical considerations lead us to think that the quantitative aspect of this phenomenon can be described sufficiently exactly by the linear relationship

$$y = a + bx, \tag{0.1.1}$$

where x is the temperature in degrees and y is the relative solubility in 100 parts of water.
However, if we try to determine the coefficients a and b in (0.1.1) putting $x = x_i = 0°, 4°, 10°, ...$ and $y = y_i = 66·7;\ 71·0;\ 76·3$ ... we obtain 9 equations

$$y_i = a + bx_i \qquad (i = 1, 2, \ldots, 9) \tag{0.1.2}$$

for two parameters a and b, and these equations are incompatible. This incompatibility of the equations can be explained either on the ground of inadequacy of the theoretical assumption of linearity of dependence, or by errors of observations, or by both. We can, however, suppose that the quantitative corrections to the theory and to observations are not very large and try, at any rate approximately, to explain the observations in times of the linear relationship (0.1.1).

terms

Then, we try to find values of the coefficients a and b such that the absolute values of the "errors"

$$\eta_i = y_i - (a + bx_i) \qquad (i = 1, 2, \ldots, 9), \qquad (0.1.3)$$

form, in some sense, a set of small values. The method of calculation of the coefficients a and b and the values obtained will depend on the meaning, which we attach to the idea of a set of small values $|\eta_i|$. We can, for instance, estimate a and b from the condition

$$\sum_{i=1}^{9} |\eta_i| = \min \qquad (0.1.4)$$

but we soon find that this task is not easy and leads to a good deal of calculation, because of the introduction into the work of an analytically awkward (not everywhere differentiable) function $|y - (a + bx)|$. The method of least squares in the present case, consists in the determination of a and b from the condition

$$Q = \sum_{i=1}^{9} \eta_i^2 = \min. \qquad (0.1.5)$$

Without additional knowledge of the theory of errors of observations, formula (0.1.5) is just as arbitrary as, for example, (0.1.4).

Later, we will see that for a very wide class of problems formula (0.1.5) is, in a certain sense, the best. Thus, we shall see that the present example (and all later examples) can quite straightforwardly be included in this class of problems. For the time being we can convince ourselves that calculation by the method of least squares is appropriate to the calculation of the relationship. To find values a and b satisfying (0.1.5) we form the equations

$$\left.\begin{aligned} \frac{\partial Q}{\partial a} &= -2 \sum_{i=1}^{9} (y_i - a - bx_i) = 0, \\ \frac{\partial Q}{\partial b} &= -2 \sum_{i=1}^{9} x_i (y_i - a - bx_i = 0. \end{aligned}\right\} \qquad (0.1.6)$$

It is convenient to introduce the following notations

$$\bar{x} = \frac{1}{9} \sum_{i=1}^{9} x_i; \quad \bar{y} = \frac{1}{9} \sum_{i=1}^{9} y_i; \quad S_1 = \frac{1}{9} \sum_{i=1}^{9} x_i y_i;$$

$$S_2 = \frac{1}{9} \sum_{i=1}^{9} x_i^2.$$

From (0.1.6) we obtain the equations

$$a + b\bar{x} = \bar{y}; \quad a\bar{x} + bS_2 = S_1. \tag{0.1.7}$$

Hence

$$b = \frac{S_1 - \bar{x}\bar{y}}{S_2 - \bar{x}^2}; \quad a = \bar{y} - b\bar{x}. \tag{0.1.8}$$

We see that a and b are defined from (0.1.6) uniquely, so that the minimum value of Q, if it exists, must be unique and corresponds to the values of (a, b) given by (0.1.8). The existence of a minimum is evident from the formula

It is easy to see that the formula (0.1.8) can be written in the form

$$b = \frac{\sum_{i=1}^{9} (x_i - \bar{x})(y_i - \bar{y})}{\sum_{i=1}^{9} (x_i - \bar{x})^2}; \quad a = \bar{y} - b\bar{x}. \tag{0.1.9}$$

Subtracting from (0.1.1) the second of the equations (0.1.9) we find the required "least squares straight line fit" from the expression

$$y - \bar{y} = b(x - \bar{x}), \tag{0.1.10}$$

where b is given by (0.1.9). The calculation can be done according to the scheme shown in Table 1.

TABLE 1

x_i	y_i	$x_i - \bar{x}$	$(x_i - \bar{x})^2$	$y_i - \bar{y}$	$(x_i - \bar{x})(y_i - \bar{y})$
0	66·7	—26	676	—23·4	608·4
4	71·0	—22	484	—19·1	420·2
10	76·3	—16	256	—13·8	220·8
15	80·6	—11	121	—9·5	104·5
21	85·7	—5	25	—4·4	22·0
29	92·9	3	9	2·8	8·4
36	99·4	10	100	9·3	93·0
51	113·6	25	625	23·5	587·5
68	125·1	42	1764	35·0	1470·0
Sum. 234	811 3		4060		3534 8

Consequently

$$\bar{x}=\frac{234}{9}=26, \quad \bar{y}=\frac{811\ 3}{9}=90{\cdot}1,$$

whence we have

$$y-90{\cdot}1=\frac{3534{,}8}{4060}(x-26),$$

or

$$y=67{\cdot}5+0{\cdot}87x \qquad (0.1.11)$$

which was obtained by Mendeléjev as early as 1881.

Having obtained the straight line (0.1.11) we can discuss, for the moment by visual comparison with the experimental data, how satisfactorily it represents the observed phenomena. We denote by y'_i the results calculated for given x_i $(i=1, 2, \ldots, 9)$ on the basis of (0.1.11). We get the table

x_i	y_i	y'_i
0	66·7	67·5
4	71·0	71·0
10	76·3	76·2
15	80·6	80·6
21	85·7	85·8
29	92·9	92·5
36	99·4	98·8
51	113·6	111·87
68	125·1	126·6

We notice that the apparently satisfactory agreement for $i=2, 3, \ldots, 7$ is somewhat spoilt at the extremes of range of temperatures. Not having any further information and a definite, i.e. mathematico statistical model for the phenomena we cannot estimate more exactly the accuracy of fit.

In the above example we considered an apparently sufficiently correct functional connexion between temperature and solubility; only in the errors of the observations do we encounter any random elements (in the sense of the theory of probability). In the following example this factor is present in the phenomenon itself.

Example 2. (Ezekiel[54], the data are transformed from the English system of measurement to the metric). In an investigation of street traffic, observations were made of the stopping distance of a car, after a given signal, in relation to its velocity (Table 2).

TABLE 2

Velocity in km/hr	Stopping distance in metres	Calculated value	Difference
6,44	0,61; 3,05	—0,56	1,17; 3,61
11,26	1,22; 6,71	3,03	—1,81; 3,68
12,87	4,88	4,23	0,65
14,48	3,05	5,43	—2,38
16,09	7,93; 5,49; 10,37	6,63	1,30; —1,14; 3,74
17,70	8,54; 5,18	7,83	0,71; —2,65
19,31	6,10; 4,27; 7,32; 8,54	9,03	—2,93; —4,76; —1,71; —0,49
20,92	10,37; 7,93; 10,37; 14,03	10,23	0,14; —2,30; 0,14; 3,80
22,53	10,98; 7,93; 18,30; 24,40	11,43	—0,45; —3,50; 6,87; 12,97
24,14	16,47; 7,93; 6,10	12,63	3,84; —4,70; —6,53
25,74	9,76; 12,20	13,82	—4,06; —1,62
27,35	15,25; 12,20; 9,76	15,02	0,23; —2,82; —5,26
28,96	17,08; 25,62; 23,18; 12,81	16,22	0,86; 9,40; 6,96; —3,41
30,57	20,74; 14,03; 10,98	17,42	3,32; —3,39; —6,44
32,18	14,64; 17,08; 19,52; 15,86; 9,76	18,62	—3,98; —1,54; 0,90; —2,76, —8.86
35,40	20,13	21,03	—0,90
37,01	16,47	22,23	—5,76
38,62	28,36; 21,35; 36,60; 28,06	23,43	4,93; —2,08; 13,17; 4,63
40,23	25,92	24,63	1,29

Denoting the velocity by x_i and the stopping distance by y_i we see that the data cannot be expressed by a single valued function (and certainly not a linear function). For $x_i = 6\cdot44$ we have: $y_i = 0\cdot61$; $3\cdot05$; for $x_i = 11\cdot26$ we have $y_i = 1\cdot22$; $6\cdot71$ etc.). We can, however, try to study the dependence of stopping distance on velocity as an approximate relation $y = ax + b$, finding a and b by the method of least squares and then, to compare the obtained data with the observations, leaving the more detailed examination for the future. Later the most convenient schemes of calculation will also be shown. For the present we notice that in similar calculations it is often convenient to use prepared tables of squares. Formulae (0.1.8) and (0.1.9), with the number of observations changed from $N = 9$ to $N = 50$ are suitable also in this case. From (0.1.8) we find

$$b = \frac{50\sum x_i y_i - \sum x_i \sum y_i}{50\sum x_i^2 - (\sum x_i)^2}, \qquad (0.1.12)$$

where the summation is from $i = 1$ to $i = 50$, including repeated values (e.g.

$$x_1 = x_2 = 6.44;\ x_3 = x_4 = 11.26 \quad \text{etc.}).$$

We have

$$\sum x_i = 1238.98;\ \sum y_i = 655.43;\ \sum x_i^2 = 34\,248{,}4;$$
$$\sum x_i y_i = 18\,885{,}2;$$
$$\bar{x} = 24.780;\quad \bar{y} = 13.109;\quad b = 0{,}7454;\quad a = -5.362,$$

therefore

$$y = -5.362 + 0.7454x. \tag{0.1.13}$$

Comparison with observed values is given in Table 2.

We see that the nature of the relationship is described only approximately by (0.1.13) (later we will introduce a more precise meaning for this description). Some fitted values do not agree too badly with the observations, but there are also some absurd results, such as, for instance, the negative value of y_i for $i = 1$.

Nevertheless, the calculations described above are useful to the extent to which their actual meaning can be made precise.

In the previous examples we have considered the description of observations in terms of linear dependence or, as is often said, the reduction of the observations by a straight line. We will now consider a more complicated case of reduction, by fitting a curve, as in the following example, by fitting a parabola.

Example 3. (Ezekiel [54]). We consider observations on two variables: the protein content x in the seeds of wheat and the percentage content of "vitreous kernels" y in the same seeds. Both variables characterize the quality of the wheat; to determine x it is necessary to carry out a complicated chemical analysis, but y can be determined in a very much simpler manner and without special apparatus. The results of 20 observations are given in Table 3

TABLE 3

No	Contents (%)	
	protein	vitreous kernels
1	10.3	6
2	12.2	75
3	14.5	87
4	11.1	55
5	10.9	34
6	18.1	98
7	14.0	91
8	10.8	45
9	11.4	51
10	11.0	17
11	10.2	36
12	17.0	97
13	13.8	74
14	10.1	24
15	14.4	85
16	15.8	96
17	15.6	92
18	15.0	94
19	13.3	84
20	19.0	99

We will try to fit these observations by the parabola

$$y = a + bx + cx^2. \tag{0.1.14}$$

In the present case the method of least squares leads to the condition: a, b, c must satisfy

$$Q = \sum_i \left[y_i - \left(a + bx_i + cx_i^2\right)\right]^2 = \min. \tag{0.1.15}$$

We again find that it is possible to attain the minimum of Q by satisfying the equations

$$\frac{\partial Q}{\partial a} = 0; \quad \frac{\partial Q}{\partial b} = 0; \quad \frac{\partial Q}{\partial c} = 0. \tag{0.1.16}$$

We introduce the notations

$$x_i^2 = z_i;\quad S_1 = \sum x_i y_i;\quad S_2 = \sum x_i^2;\quad T_1 = \sum x_i z_i;\quad T_2 = \sum z_i^2;$$
$$V_1 = \sum y_i z_i;\quad \bar{x} = \frac{1}{N}\sum x_i;\quad \bar{y} = \frac{1}{N}\sum y_i;\quad \bar{z} = \frac{1}{N}\sum z_i$$
$$(i = 1, 2, \ldots, 20);\quad N = 20.$$

Then

$$y_i = a + bx_i + cz_i, \tag{0.1.17}$$

and from (0.1.16) it is easy to get the following equations for b, c, a:

$$\left.\begin{aligned} S_2 b + T_1 c &= S_1;\\ T_1 b + T_2 c &= V_1;\\ a &= \bar{y} - b\bar{x} - c\bar{z}. \end{aligned}\right\} \tag{0.1.18}$$

This is a particular case of the so-called "normal equations". A convenient method of solution of normal equations (due to Doolittle) will be presented later. Here we give only the final results of the calculations viz.:

$$a = 11.56;\quad b = -0.088;\quad c = 0.00144,$$

so that

$$y = 11.56 - 0.088x + 0.00144x^2. \tag{0.1.19}$$

The agreement of the values, y^i, calculated from (0.1.19) with the observations can be seen in Table 4.

TABLE 4

Contents in %		Estimated values of protein content in % (minus 10)	Difference
vitreous kernels	protein (minus 10)		
6	0.3	1.08	—0.78
75	2.2	3.06	—0.86
87	4.5	4.80	—0.30
55	1.1	1.08	0.02
34	0.9	0.23	0.67
98	8.1	6.79	1.31
91	4.0	5.50	—1.50
45	0.8	0.52	0.28
51	1.4	0.83	0.57
17	1.0	0.48	0.52
36	0.2	0.26	—0.06
97	7.0	6.60	0.40
74	3.8	2.95	0.85
24	0.1	0.28	—0.18
85	4.4	4.51	—0.11
96	5.8	6.41	—0.61
92	5.6	5.68	—0.08
94	5.0	6.04	—1.04
84	3.3	4.35	—1.05
99	9.0	6.99	2.01

This agreement gives the impression that the choice of the parabola (0.1.19) was reasonable satisfactory. Looking at the calculations, it may be noted that it was not an essential condition that $z_i = x_i^2$; the values z_i in (0.1.17) could be any given set of values, in general independent of the set of values x_i. Using, instead of the quadratic parabola (0.1.14), the cubic parabola

$$y = a_0 + a_1 x + a_2 x^2 + a_3 x^3, \qquad (0.1.20)$$

we can try to fit the data of Table 3 by this parabola; putting $x_i = x_{1i}$; $x_i^2 = x_{2i}$; $x_i^3 = x_{3i}$, we would obtain the system of incompatible equations

$$y_i = a_0 + a_1 x_{1i} + a_2 x_{2i} + a_3 x_{3i} \qquad (i = 1, 2, \ldots, 20), \qquad (0.1.21)$$

and we could estimate (0.1.20) by the method of least squares. We can deal with example 2 in the same way. However, in cases where, as in example 2, there is not a single-valued functional relationship in the data, the calculations are much more complicated.

Example 4. The measurements of three angles A_1, A_2, A_3 of a plane triangle are:

$$A_1 = 54°5'; \quad A_2 = 50°1'; \quad A_3 = 76°6'.$$

The sum of these values is $A_1 + A_2 + A_3 = 180°12'$ giving a discrepancy of 12′ which arises from observational error. We try to remove this discrepancy by changing A_i to $A_i + \lambda_i = A_i'$, so that $A_1' + A_2' + A_3' = 180°$. Then we must have

$$\lambda_1 + \lambda_2 + \lambda_3 = -0°12'. \qquad (0.1.22)$$

Thus, the relationship (0.1.22) has been imposed on the quantities λ_1, λ_2, λ_3 but in other respects they are undefined. In this case the method of least squares leads to the requirement

$$Q = \lambda_1^2 + \lambda_2^2 + \lambda_3^2 = \min \qquad (0.1.23)$$

subject to the condition (0.1.22). This is a problem of conditional minimization which is solved, in the general case, by using Lagrange's auxiliary multipliers. In the present case it is possible to obtain the solution without differentiation. We put $\bar{\lambda} = \frac{1}{3}(\lambda_1 + \lambda_2 + \lambda_3)$. Then, it is easy to see that

$$Q = \lambda_1^2 + \lambda_2^2 + \lambda_3^2 = \sum_{i=1}^{3} (\lambda_i - \bar{\lambda})^2 + 3\bar{\lambda}^2.$$

From (0.1.22) we see that $\bar{\lambda} = -0°4'$, so that

$$Q = \sum_{i=1}^{3} (\lambda_i + 0°4')^2 + 3 \cdot (0°4')^2.$$

Hence it can be seen that Q attains a unique minimum at $\lambda_i = -0°4'$, so that

$$A_1' = 54°1'; \quad A_2' = 49°57'; \quad A_3' = 76°2'. \qquad (0.1.24)$$

Here we have an example of the application of the method of least squares to observations connected by some conditions. The angles A_1', A_2', A_3' give no discrepancy; the real meaning of the corrections introduced will be explained later.

Example 5. From some points on a plane, $M_1, M_2, \ldots, M_s$ bearings are taken on a certain point O (Fig. 1), say visually, phonometrically or in some other way. The bearings constitute a series of

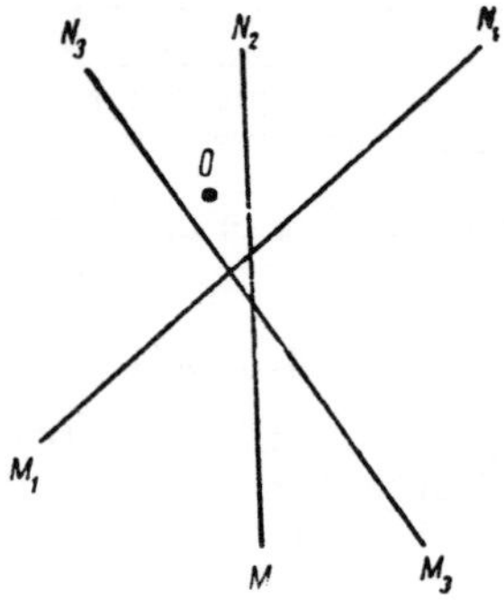

Fig. 1

directions M_iN_i. Due to errors of observation the straight lines M_iN_i do not intersect in a single point. It is necessary to find an approximation to the required point O on the basis of the observed directions M_iN_i.

It would be possible to apply the method of least squares in the following way. Let $d_i(X)$ denote the distance of a point X from the straight line M_iN_i. We will determine X by the condition

$$\sum d_i^2(X) = \min. \qquad (0.1.25)$$

As we shall see later (Chapter XI) another approach, also of the least squares type, is appropriate.

Problems relating to bearings in space (e.g. on aircraft) can be constructed in a similar way.

Example 6. In the mathematico-statistical description of the unevenness of profiles of surfaces the concept of the mean line of random profile plays an important role in the work (Linnik and Khousou [33]). In a very simplified form the problem of finding the mean profile can be presented in the following way. In the plane XOY there are given a series of points (x_i, y_i) $(i = 1, 2, \ldots, s)$. We want to find the straight line $y = ax + b$ for which the sum of squares of distances of the points (x_i, y_i) from this line is a minimum.

We can interpret this problem in terms of mechanics. We ascribe a unit mass to the point (x_i, y_i) and want to find the axis of rotation with respect to which the given system of points has the least moment of inertia (i.e. the least kinetic energy of rotation for a given angular velocity). From elementary courses in mechanics we know that this axis passes through the centre of gravity of the system and that the perpendicular axis through the centre of gravity gives, for this system of points, the maximum moment of inertia. It is easy to see that there can be many such axes (e.g. if the points lie on the vertices of a regular polygon, or generally, if the system of points is superposed on itself after rotation through some acute angle).

Further, from the basic properties of continuous functions it is clear that at least one such axis exists. We will prove that it passes through the centre of gravity of the system of points (x_i, y_i), which, of course, has the co-ordinates $(\bar{x}, \bar{y})$*

We denote our axis by $O'U$ and draw the perpendicular axis $O'V$ (Fig. 2). Let the co-ordinates of points (x_i, y_i) in this new system

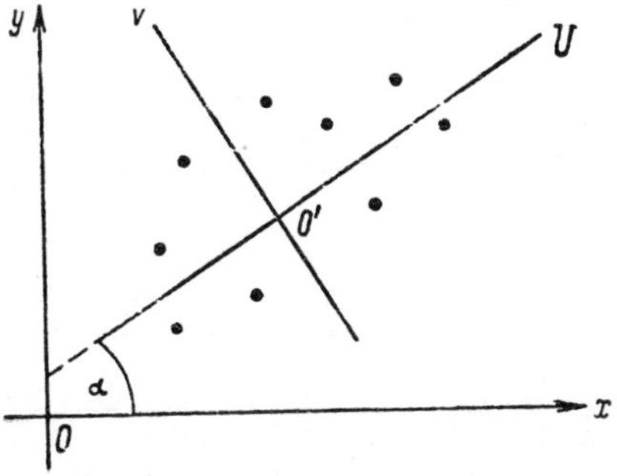

Fig. 2

* This assertion is equivalent to the well-known Steiner's theorem in mechanics.

of co-ordinates be (u_i, v_i). From the equation $\sum(v_i-\bar{v})^2=\sum v_i^2-n\bar{v}^2$ we conclude that if $\bar{v}\neq 0$, then by changing the axis $O'U$ to $v=\bar{v}$, we reduce the moment of inertia, which is impossible. Hence $\bar{v}=0$, and so the axis $O'U$ passes through the centre of gravity $(\bar{u}, \bar{v})$, which has the old co-ordinates $(\bar{x}, \bar{y})$. We come to the conclusion that the origin O' of the system $(O'U, O'V)$ coincides with $(\bar{x}, \bar{y})$. It remains to find the condition satisfied by the angle of inclination α between the new and old systems.

We have

$$Q=Q(\alpha)=\sum v_i^2=\min, \tag{0.1.26}$$

whence

$$\sum v_i\frac{dv_i}{d\alpha}=0. \tag{0.1.27}$$

Further, putting

$$x_i'=x_i-\bar{x};\qquad y_i'=y_i-\bar{y},$$

we obtain, by the formulae for transformation of co-ordinates,

$$\left.\begin{aligned} u_i&=x_i'\cos\alpha+y_i'\sin\alpha,\\ v_i&=-x_i'\sin\alpha+y_i'\cos\alpha.\end{aligned}\right\} \tag{0.1.28}$$

Hence $\frac{dv_i}{d\alpha}=-u_i$, and so (0.1.27) can be written in the form

$$\sum u_iv_i=0.$$

Inserting this result in (0.1.28) we have

$$(\cos^2\alpha-\sin^2\alpha)\sum x_i'y_i'-\sin\alpha\cos\alpha\sum(x_i'^2-y_i'^2)=0.$$

Hence

$$\operatorname{tg}2\alpha=\frac{2\sum x_i'y_i'}{\sum x_i'^2-\sum y_i'^2}=\frac{2\sum(x_i-\bar{x})(y_i-\bar{y})}{\sum(x_i-\bar{x})^2-\sum(y_i-\bar{y})^2}. \tag{0.1.29}$$

We see that, generally, $\operatorname{tg}2\alpha$, is defined uniquely by (0.1.29), so that the angle α can have any one of four values. At first sight it seems difficult to agree to this, in view of what was said above about the multiples axes of symetry. But this can be explained by the fact that in similar cases the expression (0.1.29) must present indeterminacy of type $\frac{0}{0}$.

In cases arising in the theory of quality of preparation of surfaces the points (x_i, y_i) are not far from a certain straight line and the angle α is determined uniquely from (0.1.29).

We now compare formula (0.1.29) with formula (0.1.9). From (0.1.9) we have $b=\operatorname{tg}\alpha'$, where α' is the angle of slope of the axis obtained by the method of least squares to the axis OX. Since

$$\operatorname{tg} 2\alpha' = \frac{2\operatorname{tg}\alpha'}{1-\operatorname{tg}^2\alpha'},$$

we find from (0.1.9)

$$\operatorname{tg} 2\alpha' = \frac{2\sum(x_i-\bar{x})(y_i-\bar{y})\sum(x_i-\bar{x})^2}{\left(\sum(x_i-\bar{x})^2\right)^2-\left(\sum(x_i-\bar{x})(y_i-\bar{y})\right)^2}. \qquad (0.1.30)$$

The actual line so determined, is called the orthogonal regression line.

Examining the examples given above, we can satisfy ourselves that the mathematical structure of most of these problems can be expressed in the following form (method of least squares): there is given a set of numbers x_{ki} $(k=1, 2, \ldots, n; i=1, 2, \ldots, N)$; $w_i>0$ $(i=1, 2, \ldots, N)$. It is required to find numbers $a_1, a_2, \ldots, a_n$, for which

$$Q=\sum_{i=1}^{N} w_i\left(\eta_i-\sum_{k=1}^{n} a_k x_{ki}\right)^2=\min \qquad (0.1.31)$$

which satisfy some supplementary conditions

$$F_j(a_1, a_2, \ldots, a_n)=0 \qquad (j=1, 2, \ldots, m). \qquad (0.1.32)$$

where the F_j's are known functions with n arguments.

In most cases there is presupposed the existence of a definite probability model, in which the quantities η_i (and sometimes x_{ki}) are regarded as random variables subjected to definite requirements. In such cases the values of the quantities $a_1, a_2, \ldots, a_n$ obtained by the method of least squares are also random variables. The description of their behaviour and examination of their optimal properties with respect to other quantities which are, in a certain sense, admissible constitutes the probabilistic part of the theory of the method of least squares and clarifies the real probabilistic meaning of calculations by this method. The question of finding the values $a_1, a_2, \ldots, a_n$ from (0.1.31), if the quantities x_{ki}, η_i, w_i, F_j, are given, constitutes the algebraic and computational part of the theory. For this some geometrical concepts are useful.

In view of this, before the presentation of the general theory, we shall give, in chapters I, II and III, a short account of necessary results from algebra, probability theory and mathematical statistics.

2. Brief Historical Outline

The first presentation of elements of the method of least squares was given in 1806 by Legendre [30] in connection with the problems of calculation of orbits of comets.

In 1809 Gauss [7] gave the first probabilistic basis for the method of least squares and in 1810 he worked out more thoroughly the computational techniques associated with this problem and introduced symbols and notations which are still in use up to the present. A series of important new results were discovered by Gauss in 1821 [9].

In 1812 Laplace, in his fundamental work on the theory of probability, obtained a series of important results and applied them to the method of least squares. Further important results in the theory of the method of least squares were obtained in 1859 by Chebyshev while working out the theory of interpolation by the method of least squares, using orthogonal polynomials, which is named after him.

Markov, in 1898, in the paper [26] and in his course on the theory of probability, already mentioned in section 1, introduced many very important ideas into mathematical statistics, which clarified the concepts of the method of least squares.

Much work on the development of applications of the method of least squares in astronomy and geology was done by Helmert at the end of the last century.

Following the work of Markov in the first twenty years of the present century the method of least squares was included in mathematical statistics, as an important and natural part of the theory of estimation of parameters (see chapter III). In this connection a series of interesting and important results were obtained by Neyman and David (see chapter VII), Aitken [55] and Rao [41].

In 1946 Kolmogorov [22] gave an elegant geometrical presentation of the method of least squares.

In recent years matrix calculus has penetrated more and more into the method of least squares and its applications. This permits us to express calculations and results conveniently and briefly, and in later chapters will be used systematically.

CHAPTER I

NECESSARY KNOWLEDGE OF ALGEBRA

1. Vectors

In the present chapter will be given briefly, without proofs, some algebraic results which are necessary for the deduction and convenient expression of results in the method of least squares. Proofs of the theorems given below, and some other useful theorems, can be found, for example, in books by Gantmacher [6] Curosh [28], and Maltsev [35].

The ordered set of n real numbers $(x_1, x_2, \ldots, x_n)$ we will call a (n-dimensional) vector and denote by X. A vector can be multiplied by a scalar, c, and then we obtain the new vector $cX = (cx_1, cx_2, \ldots, cx_n)$. Two vectors $X = (x_1, x_2, \ldots, x_n)$ and $Y = (y_1, y_2, \ldots, y_n)$, can be added, giving, by definition, the new vector $Z = X + Y = (x_1 + y_1, x_2 + y_2, \ldots, x_n + y_n)$; we can also add more than two vectors. The scalar product of two vectors, which we will denote by Gauss' symbol $[X \cdot Y]$, is defined as the number equal to

$$[X \cdot Y] = x_1 y_1 + x_2 y_2 + \ldots + x_n y_n,$$

so that

$$[X \cdot Y] = [Y \cdot X].$$

For $n = 1, 2, 3$ this product has an intuitive geometrical meaning. The vectors X and Y are called orthogonal, if $[X \cdot Y] = 0$; for $n = 2, 3$ we get ordinary mutually perpendicular vectors.

Linear combinations of the vectors $X_1, X_2, \ldots, X_s$ of the form $c_1 X_1 + \ldots + c_s X_s$, where $c_1, \ldots, c_s$ may be any arbitary real numbers, form the vector space $\mathcal{X}_s$.

If from the relation $c_1 X_1 + \ldots + c_s X_s = 0$ it follows that $c_1 = c_2 = \ldots = c_s = 0$, then the vectors $X_1, \ldots, X_s$ are called linearly independent. In every vector space $\mathcal{X}_s$ we can choose a basis of t linearly independent vectors $Z_1, Z_2, \ldots, Z_t$ $(t \leqslant s)$, i.e. we can find a system of such vectors Z_i $(i = 1, 2, \ldots, t)$ that every element of the vector space is represented uniquely in the form $b_1 Z_1 + \ldots + b_t Z_t$ (b_i's are real numbers). It is said that the vector space $\mathcal{X}_s$ has the dimension t.

If we have two systems of vectors: $X_1, \ldots, X_s$ and $Y_1, \ldots, Y_v$ and $[X_i \cdot Y_j] = 0$ $(i = 1, 2, \ldots, s;\ j = 1, 2, \ldots, v)$, then the spaces $\mathcal{X}_s$ and $\mathcal{Y}_v$, formed by these vectors, are called orthogonal.

If several vectors are orthogonal in pairs, then they are linearly independent.

We now recall the important inequality of Buniakovski-Cauchy*

$$[X \cdot Y]^2 \leqslant [X \cdot X] \cdot [Y \cdot Y], \qquad (1.1.1)$$

i.e. the absolute value of a scalar product does not exceed the square root of the product of scalar squares. More precisely we can write

$$\left(\sum_{i=1}^{n} x_i y_i\right)^2 \leqslant \left(\sum_{i=1}^{n} x_i^2\right)\left(\sum_{i=1}^{n} y_i^2\right). \qquad (1.1.2)$$

2. Linear Equations. Matrices

A system of m linear equations in n unknowns $x_1, \ldots, x_n$ is of the form

$$\left.\begin{aligned} a_{11}x_1 + a_{12}x_2 + \ldots + a_{1n}x_n &= b_1, \\ a_{21}x_1 + a_{22}x_2 + \ldots + a_{2n}x_n &= b_2, \\ \cdots\cdots\cdots\cdots\cdots\cdots &\cdots \\ a_{m1}x_1 + a_{m2}x_2 + \ldots + a_{mn}x_n &= b_m. \end{aligned}\right\} \qquad (1.2.1)$$

If $b_1 = b_2 = \ldots = b_m = 0$, the system is called homogeneous. Introducing vectors $a_i = (a_{i1}, \ldots, a_{in})$ $(i = 1, 2, \ldots, m)$ and $X = (x_1, \ldots, x_n)$, we can write the system in the form

$$[a_i \cdot X] = b_i \qquad (i = 1, 2, \ldots, m). \qquad (1.2.2)$$

Thus, in the case of a homogeneous system ($b_i = 0$; $i = 1, 2, \ldots, m$) the problem of solution of the system is equivalent to the problem of constructing a certain vector space orthogonal to the space constructed on the vectors $a_1, \ldots, a_m$.

With the introduction of matrices by Cayley **) the study of systems of linear equations as a part of the theory of linear transformations became, extraordinarily deeper and simpler. Since, in the method of least squares, we are always dealing with linear equations, the application of matrices is very appropriate.

The rectangular table of real numbers a_{ik} of the form

$$A = \left\| \begin{matrix} a_{11} & a_{12} & \ldots & a_{1n} \\ a_{21} & a_{22} & \ldots & a_{2n} \\ \cdots & \cdots & \cdots & \cdots \\ a_{m1} & a_{m2} & \ldots & a_{mn} \end{matrix} \right\|$$

* B.Y. Buniakovski (1804-1889) - Russian mathematician; O.Cauchy (1789-1857) - French mathematician.

** A.Cayley (1821-1895) - English mathematician.

or, briefly, $A = \| a_{ik} \|$ is called a matrix of type $m \times n$.

To emphasize that the matrix A has m rows and n columns, sometimes we will write $A = A_{mn}$. We will identify the matrix $A_{11} = \| a_{11} \|$ with the ordinary number a_{11}. An element a_{rs} of the matrix A we denote by the symbol $\{A\}_{rs}$ *).

Two matrices A_{mn} and $B_{m_1 n_1}$ are regarded as equal, if and only if $m = m_1$, $n = n_1$ and $\{A\}_{rs} = \{B\}_{rs}$ for all possible r and s. The zero matrix $0 = 0_{mn}$ is that matrix for which $\{0\}_{rs} = 0$ for all possible r and s.

The matrices: $X_{1n} = \| x_{11}, \ldots, x_{1n} \|$ and $X_{n1} = \begin{Vmatrix} x_{11} \\ x_{21} \\ \cdot \\ \cdot \\ x_{n1} \end{Vmatrix}$ can be regarded as n-dimensional vectors.

The elements $\{A\}_{rr}$ $(r = s)$ are called diagonal, and the diagonal on which they lie, is called the principal diagonal.

If we reflect the matrix

$$A_{mn} = \begin{Vmatrix} a_{11} & a_{12} & \cdots & a_{1n} \\ a_{21} & a_{22} & \cdots & a_{2n} \\ \cdot & \cdot & \cdots & \cdot \\ a_{m1} & a_{m2} & \cdots & a_{mn} \end{Vmatrix}$$

in the principal diagonal, we obtain the matrix

$$B_{nm} = \begin{Vmatrix} a_{11} & a_{21} & \cdots & a_{m1} \\ a_{12} & a_{22} & \cdots & a_{m2} \\ \cdot & \cdot & \cdots & \cdot \\ a_{1n} & a_{2n} & \cdots & a_{mn} \end{Vmatrix},$$

in which the rows of A_{mn} are changed into columns and conversely. The matrix B_{nm} is called the transposed matrix of A_{mn} and it is denoted by $B_{nm} = A^T_{mn}$.

Evidently

$$B^T_{nm} = \left(A^T_{mn}\right)^T = A_{mn}.$$

Multiplication by any arbitrary real number α is defined for all matrices A:

$$\alpha A = \alpha \| a_{rs} \| = \| \alpha a_{rs} \|.$$

For matrices with equal numbers of rows, m, and columns, n, there is defined the sum. If

$$A_{mn} = \| a_{rs} \|, \quad B_{mn} = \| b_{rs} \|,$$

then

$$A_{mn} + B_{mn} = \| a_{rs} + b_{rs} \|.$$

---

*) This symbol was first introduced by the Soviet mathematician I.A.Lappo-Danilevski (1895-1931)

By virtue of these definitions the matrices $A = A_{mn}$ form a certain vector space: in particular, using the matrices

$$X_{n1} = \begin{Vmatrix} x_1 \\ \vdots \\ x_n \end{Vmatrix} \quad \text{and} \quad X_{1n} = \| x_1, \ldots, x_n \|$$

we can represent n-dimensional vectors.

The product of two matrices A_{mn} and B_{uv} is defined only for the case, when $u = n$ (the number of columns of matrix A_{mn} is equal to the number of rows of matrix B_{uv}). Their product

$$C_{mv} = A_{mn} B_{nv}$$

is defined by

$$C_{mv} = \| c_{rs} \|,$$

where

$$c_{rs} = a_{r1} b_{1s} + a_{r2} b_{2s} + \ldots + a_{rn} b_{ns} = \sum_{i=1}^{n} a_{ri} b_{is}.$$

The meaning of this definition of the product will be made quite clear by comparison of matrices with the linear transformations, from which they arose. If

$$X = \begin{Vmatrix} x_1 \\ x_2 \\ \vdots \\ x_v \end{Vmatrix}, \quad B = B_{nv} = \| b_{rs} \|, \quad Y = \begin{Vmatrix} y_1 \\ \vdots \\ y_n \end{Vmatrix},$$

then the equation

$$Y = B \cdot X \tag{1.2.3}$$

expresses in very convenient and compact form the linear transformation

$$\left.\begin{aligned} y_1 &= b_{11} x_1 + b_{12} x_2 + \ldots + b_{1v} x_v, \\ &\cdots\cdots\cdots\cdots\cdots \\ y_n &= b_{n1} x_1 + b_{n2} x_2 + \ldots + b_{nv} x_v. \end{aligned}\right\} \tag{1.2.4}$$

If, as well as (1.2.4), we have also the transformation

$$Z = A \cdot Y, \tag{1.2.5}$$

where

$$Z = \begin{Vmatrix} z_1 \\ \vdots \\ z_m \end{Vmatrix}, \quad A = A_{mn} = \| a_{rs} \|,$$

corresponding to the equations

$$\left.\begin{aligned} z_1 &= a_{11} y_1 + \ldots + a_{1n} y_n, \\ &\cdots\cdots\cdots\cdots\cdots \\ z_m &= a_{m1} y_1 + \ldots + a_{mn} y_n, \end{aligned}\right\} \tag{1.2.6}$$

then the result of putting (1.2.4) into (1.2.6) is the new transformation

$$Z = C \cdot X. \tag{1.2.7}$$

Here

$$C = C_{mv} = A_{mn} B_{nv}, \tag{1.2.8}$$

which is not surprising, since the product (1.2.8) was defined just in this way to obtain this relationship. The operation of multiplication of two matrices corresponds exactly to the successive application of two linear transformations. In view of this we naturally have the following laws for the multiplication of matrices:

associative law: $(A_{mn} B_{nv}) C_{vw} = A_{mn} (B_{nv} C_{vw})$;

distributive law: $A_{mn} (B_{nv} + C_{nv}) = A_{mn} \cdot B_{nv} + A_{mn} C_{nv}$,
$(A_{mn} + B_{mn}) C_{nv} = A_{mn} C_{nv} + B_{mn} C_{nv}$.

These laws can be generalized to an arbitrary number of multiplicands or summands.

It is also natural, in view of the relationships obtained above for linear transformations, that the commutative (change of order) law, which is true for ordinary real numbers, is not, in general, true for matrices, i.e. $AB \neq BA$. If $A = A_{mn}$, $B = B_{nv}$, then the product AB is defined, but BA is not defined, if $v \neq m$; if, however, $v = m$, then BA exists, but, in general, is different from AB.

The rule for transposing a product has the form

$$(AB)^T = B^T A^T,$$

i.e. in transposing, the multiplicands are reversed in order and transposed (automatically, this multiplication becomes possible). This rule can be generalized to any arbitrary number of multiplicands.

A matrix, $A = A_{nn}$, which has the same number of rows and columns, is called a square matrix.

The square matrix of the form

$$D = D_{nn} = \begin{Vmatrix} d_1 & 0 & \dots & 0 \\ 0 & d_2 & \dots & 0 \\ \cdot & \cdot & \cdot & \cdot \\ 0 & 0 & \dots & d_n \end{Vmatrix},$$

where all elements, except those on the principal diagonal, are equal to 0, is called a diagonal matrix. If $d_i \geqslant 0$ $(i = 1, 2, \dots, n)$, then we can introduce the concept of the fractional power of a diagonal matrix, which is convenient for the technique of the method of least squares. Let $\alpha > 0$. We will denote by D^{α} the matrix

$$D^{\alpha}=\left\|\begin{matrix} d_1^{\alpha} & 0 & \dots & 0 \\ 0 & d_2^{\alpha} & \dots & 0 \\ \cdot & \cdot & \cdot & \cdot \\ 0 & 0 & \dots & d_n^{\alpha} \end{matrix}\right\|. \tag{1.2.9}$$

If $\alpha>0$ and $\beta>0$ we have the obvious equation

$$D^{\alpha}\cdot D^{\beta}=D^{\alpha+\beta}.$$

In particular, $D^{\frac{1}{2}}\cdot D^{\frac{1}{2}}=D$.

The diagonal matrix in which all diagonal elements are equal to one; $d_i=1$ $(i=1,2,\dots,n)$ we call the unit matrix. We will denote it by E or E_{nn}. We have

$$A_{mn}E_{nn}=A_{mn};\quad E_{mm}A_{mn}=A_{mn}$$

for any arbitrary matrix A_{mn}.

Sometimes there arises the necessity to partition the square matrix $Q=Q_{nn}$ into separate matrices, from which it is constructed according to the model

$$Q=Q_{nn}=\left\|\begin{array}{c:c} A_{rr} & B_{rk} \\ \hdashline C_{kr} & D_{kk} \end{array}\right\|;\quad n=r+k.$$

Such a matrix we will call a partitioned matrix. The dotted line shows how the partitioning has been done. If we have also a matrix $Q'=Q'_{nn}$, partitioned in the same way as Q, i.e.

$$Q'=Q'_{nn}=\left\|\begin{array}{c:c} A'_{rr} & B'_{rk} \\ \hdashline C'_{kr} & D'_{kk} \end{array}\right\|$$

then we have the important formula

$$QQ'=\left\|\begin{array}{c:c} A_{rr} & B_{rk} \\ \hdashline C_{kr} & D_{kk} \end{array}\right\|\cdot\left\|\begin{array}{c:c} A'_{rr} & B'_{rk} \\ \hdashline C'_{kr} & D'_{kk} \end{array}\right\|=$$

$$=\left\|\begin{array}{c:c} A_{rr}A'_{rr}+B_{rk}C'_{kr} & A_{rr}B'_{rk}+B_{rk}D'_{kk} \\ \hdashline C_{kr}A'_{rr}+D_{kk}C'_{kr} & C_{kr}B'_{rk}+D_{kk}D'_{kk} \end{array}\right\|, \tag{1.2.10}$$

i.e. we obtain the correct result by multiplying the sub-matrices as if they were numbers.

An important role in the theory of square matrices is played by their determinants. If $A=A_{nn}=\|a_{rs}\|$, then we will denote the determinant

$$\left|\begin{matrix} a_{11} & a_{12} & \dots & a_{1n} \\ a_{21} & a_{22} & \dots & a_{2n} \\ \cdot & \cdot & \cdot & \cdot \\ a_{n1} & a_{n2} & \dots & a_{nn} \end{matrix}\right|$$

by $\det(A)$. We assume the basic rules of operations on determinants to be known.

If, in the matrix $A=\|a_{rs}\|$ we select an arbitrary element a_{rs} and remove from this matrix the rth row and the sth column (at the intersection of which is the element a_{rs}), then we obtain a new square matrix $A_{n-1,\,n-1}$. Its determinant is called the minor of the element a_{rs} and is denoted by $M^{(r,\,s)}$. The quantity $D^{(r,\,s)}=(-1)^{r+s}\cdot M^{(r,\,s)}$ is called the cofactor of a_{rs}.

There is a formula

$$\det(A)=\sum_{s=1}^{n} a_{rs}D^{(r,\,s)}=\sum_{r=1}^{n} a_{rs}D^{(r,\,s)}.$$

The concepts given above can be generalized in the following way. If, in the matrix $A=A_{nn}$, we select the rows with numbers $i_1, i_2, \ldots, i_k$ and columns with numbers $j_1, j_2, \ldots, j_k$, then taking elements lying on the intersections of these rows and columns we obtain the new matrix A'_{kk}; its determinant M' is called a minor of the kth order. If also $i_1=j_1, i_2=j_2, \ldots, i_k=j_k$, then the minor is called the principal minor. If we remove rows with numbers $i_1, \ldots, i_k$ and columns with numbers $j_1, \ldots, j_k$, then we get a new matrix $A''_{n-k,\,n-k}$; its determinant M'' is called the complementary minor to the minor M'.

The quantity $(-1)^{i_1+i_2+\ldots+i_k+j_1+j_2+\ldots+j_k}\cdot M''$ is called the cofactor of the minor M'. There is the important theorem:

Laplace's theorem. From the matrix $A=A_{nn}$ suppose there are selected arbitrarily k rows (or k columns), $k\leqslant n$. The sum of products of all minors of the kth order, included in the selected rows (or columns), with their cofactors, is equal to $\det(A)$.

If, from the matrix $A_{nn}=A=\|a_{rs}\|$ we construct the new matrix $A^*=\|a^*_{rs}\|$, where $a^*_{rs}=D^{(s,\,r)}$ (the cofactor of the element a_{sr}), which is called the adjugate matrix to A then

$$AA^*=A^*A=(\det(A))\cdot E \qquad (1.2.11)$$

If $\det(A)\neq 0$, then the matrix A is called non-singular. For a non-singular matrix A we can construct a matrix

$$B=\frac{1}{\det(A)}A^*. \qquad (1.2.12)$$

From (1.2.11) we have

$$AB=BA=E.$$

It is natural to call B the reciprocal matrix to A, and denote it by A^{-1}. We have $AA^{-1}=A^{-1}A=E$; further

$$(AB)^{-1}=B^{-1}A^{-1}, \qquad (1.2.13)$$

and the last rule can be generalized on any arbitrary number of non-singular multiplicands.

The matrix symbols and technique allow us to write the solution of linear equations and to examine their properties in a very simple way; in this lies their special value for the method of least squares. On the basis of the results given above, we can, for example, express the system of equations (1.2.11) in the form

$$AX = B, \tag{1.2.14}$$

where

$$A = A_{mn} = \|a_{rs}\|; \quad X = X_{n1} = \begin{Vmatrix} x_1 \\ \vdots \\ x_n \end{Vmatrix},$$

$$B = B_{m1} = \begin{Vmatrix} b_1 \\ \vdots \\ b_m \end{Vmatrix}.$$

If $m = n$, so that $A = A_{nn}$, and $\det(A) \neq 0$, then the matrix A^{-1} exists; multiplying (1.2.14) by A^{-1}, on the left we find the unique solution of the system as

$$A^{-1}(AX) = X = A^{-1} \cdot B. \tag{1.2.15}$$

If $Z = Z_{1n} = \|z_1, \ldots, z_n\|$, then the system of equations

$$\begin{array}{c} a_{11}z_1 + \ldots + a_{1n}z_n = b_1 \\ \cdots\cdots\cdots\cdots \\ a_{m1}z_1 + \ldots + a_{mn}z_n = b_m \end{array}$$

can be written in the form

$$ZA^T = B^T.$$

Multiplying this by $(A^T)^{-1}$, on the right we find

$$Z = B^T (A^T)^{-1}. \tag{1.2.16}$$

But by virtue of the uniqueness of solution of our systems the matrix Z must represent the same system of numbers as X only replacing rows by columns, so that we must have

$$Z = X^T = (A^{-1}B)^T = B^T (A^{-1})^T.$$

Indeed, it is easy to prove that the relation

$$(A^{-1})^T = (A^T)^{-1}. \tag{1.2.17}$$

is satisfied.

Now we consider the important concept of rank of the matrix $A = A_{mn}$. The least order of minors which are not all zero, contained in the matrix A we call the rank of this matrix. This number we will write in the form: rank (A).

Suppose there is a matrix

$$A = \begin{Vmatrix} a_{11} & a_{12} & \dots & a_{1n} \\ a_{21} & a_{22} & \dots & a_{2n} \\ \cdot & \cdot & \cdot & \cdot \\ a_{m1} & a_{m2} & \dots & a_{mn} \end{Vmatrix}$$

The columns of this matrix present n vectors $\begin{Vmatrix} a_{1s} \\ \vdots \\ a_{ms} \end{Vmatrix}$ $(s = 1, 2, \dots, n)$, and the rows - m vectors $\| a_{r1}, a_{r2}, \dots, a_{rn} \|$ $(r = 1, 2, \dots, m)$.

There is an important theorem:

The greatest number of linearly independent columns of a matrix, considered as vectors, is equal to the greatest number of linearly independent rows, and is equal to the rank of the matrix.

This may be expressed in other words: the n columns of the matrix A define a linear vector space with dimensions equal to rank (A), the same assertion is true for the m rows.

Further, the following theorem will be important to us.

The rank of the product of a number of matrices does not exceed the least rank of individual multiplicands.

If $A_1, A_2, \dots, A_k$ are matrices which it is possible to multiply, then this assertion may be written in the form

$$\text{rank}\,(A_1 A_2 \dots A_k) \leqslant \min\,(\text{rank}\,(A_1), \dots, \text{rank}\,(A_k)). \tag{1.2.18}$$

3. Some Theorems About Determinants. The Gram Determinant

Some theorems in determinants will be important to us. Some part of these which are well known, and are presented in books on higher algebra, have been mentioned in section 1; one of these theorems is well known, but is of rather special nature, and we present its proof.

If $A_1, A_2, \dots, A_k$ are square matrices of type $n \times n$, then

$$\det(A_1 A_2 \dots A_k) = \det(A_1) \cdot \det(A_2) \dots \det(A_k). \tag{1.3.1}$$

Suppose we have a system of Cartesian co-ordinates in n-dimensional space.

We will consider n vectors $(\xi_{11}, \dots, \xi_{1n}), \dots, (\xi_{n1}, \dots, \xi_{nn})$ and construct the matrix

$$\Xi = \begin{Vmatrix} \xi_{11} & \dots & \xi_{1n} \\ \cdot & \cdot & \cdot \\ \xi_{n1} & \dots & \xi_{nn} \end{Vmatrix}.$$

Then, the volume of the parallelopiped constructed from these vectors is equal to

$$|\det(\Xi)|.$$

In particular, for linear dependence of our n vectors, it is necessary and sufficient that $\det(\Xi)=0$, which is also clear geometrically. This circumstance is important in the calculation of multiple integrals.

Suppose we have n infinitely small vectors in an n-dimensional Cartesian system of co-ordinates:

$$(dx_1;\ 0,\ \ldots,\ 0);\ (0,\ dx_2,\ 0,\ \ldots,\ 0);\ \ldots;\ (0,\ \ldots,\ 0,\ dx_n), \quad (1.3.2)$$

where $dx_i > 0$ ($i=1, 2, \ldots, n$). The volume of the parallelopiped constructed on them is equal, of course, to $dx_1 \ldots dx_n$. If we introduce a linear, non-singular transformation

$$\begin{Vmatrix} dy_1 \\ \vdots \\ dy_n \end{Vmatrix} = A \cdot \begin{Vmatrix} dx_1 \\ \vdots \\ dx_n \end{Vmatrix}, \quad A=A_{nn},\ \det(A)\neq 0,$$

then the volume of the parallelopiped constructed on the new, infinitely small vectors into which the old vectors (1.3.2) have been transformed, is equal to

$$|\det(A)|\,dx_1 \ldots dx_n. \quad (1.3.3)$$

Suppose there are given n vectors

$$x_j=(x_{1j},\ \ldots,\ x_{Nj});\quad j=1, 2, \ldots, n;\ N \geqslant n. \quad (1.3.4)$$

We construct all possible scalar products of these vectors

$$[x_i x_j]=\sum_{r=1}^{n} x_{ri}x_{rj};\quad i,\ j=1, \ldots, n, \quad (1.3.5)$$

and form the determinant

$$G(x_1, \ldots, x_n)=\begin{vmatrix} [x_1x_1] & [x_1x_2] & \ldots & [x_1x_n] \\ [x_2x_1] & [x_2x_2] & \ldots & [x_2x_n] \\ \cdot & \cdot & \cdot & \cdot \\ [x_nx_1] & [x_nx_2] & \ldots & [x_nx_n] \end{vmatrix}.$$

This determinant is called the Gram determinant of the system of vectors $x_1, \ldots, x_n$. If we introduce the matrix

$$X_{Nn}=X=\begin{Vmatrix} x_{11} & x_{12} & \ldots & x_{1n} \\ x_{21} & x_{22} & \ldots & x_{2n} \\ \cdot & \cdot & \cdot & \cdot \\ x_{N1} & x_{N2} & \ldots & x_{Nn} \end{Vmatrix}, \quad (1.3.7)$$

it is easy to see that

$$X^T X=\begin{Vmatrix} [x_1x_1] & [x_1x_2] & \ldots & [x_1x_n] \\ [x_2x_1] & [x_2x_2] & \ldots & [x_2x_n] \\ \cdot & \cdot & \cdot & \cdot \\ [x_nx_1] & [x_nx_2] & \ldots & [x_nx_n] \end{Vmatrix} \quad (1.3.8)$$

Thus, we have the following expression for the Gram determinant

$$G(x_1, \ldots, x_n) = \det(X^T X). \tag{1.3.9}$$

If $N = n$, then the matrices X and X^T are square and, from the known equation $\det(X^T) = \det(X)$ we obtain, from (1.3.9)

$$G(x_1, \ldots, x_n) = [\det(X)]^2. \tag{1.3.10}$$

Thus, in the case $n = N$, the Gram determinant $G(x_1, \ldots, x_n)$ is equal to the square of the volume of the parallelopiped constructed on the vectors $x_1, \ldots, x_n$, given in Cartesian co-ordinates of n-dimensional space.

In the method of least squares the generalization of this theorem to the case $N > n$ is important.

Theorem 1.3.1

For $N \geqslant n$ we have the equation

$$G(x_1, \ldots, x_n) = \sum_k \delta_k^2, \tag{1.3.11}$$

where δ_k runs through all C_N^n minors of nth order included in the matrix $X = X_{Nn}$.

Proof. We construct the auxiliary square matrix

$$Y_{N+n,\, N+n} = Y = \left\| \begin{array}{cccc:c} 1 & 0 & \ldots & 0 & \\ 0 & 1 & \ldots & 0 & X_{Nn} \\ \cdot & \cdot & \cdot & \cdot & \\ 0 & 0 & \ldots & 1 & \\ \hdashline & (X_{Nn})^T & & & 0_{nn} \end{array} \right\| \tag{1.3.12}$$

We calculate the value of $\det(Y)$ in two ways. The first way, using the known rules for calculation of determinants, consists in multiplication of the columns of the matrix

$$\left\| \begin{array}{cccc} 1 & 0 & \ldots & 0 \\ 0 & 1 & \ldots & 0 \\ 0 & 0 & \ldots & 1 \\ \hdashline & (X_{Nn})^T & & \end{array} \right\| \tag{1.3.13}$$

successively as follows: the first column by $-x_{11}, -x_{12}, \ldots, -x_{1n}$, the second by $-x_{21}, -x_{22}, \ldots, -x_{2n}, \ldots$, the Nth column by $-x_{N1}, -x_{N2}, \ldots, -x_{Nn}$ and adding to the corresponding columns of the matrix

$$\left\| \begin{array}{c} X_{Nn} \\ \hdashline 0_{nn} \end{array} \right\|.$$

Considering carefully the results of these operations we can see that the matrix

$$Y_1 = \left\| \begin{array}{ccc:c} 1 & 0 \dots & 0 & \\ 0 & 1 \dots & 0 & 0_{Nn} \\ 0 & 0 \dots & 1 & \\ \hdashline & (X_{Nn})^T & & -(X_{Nn})^T X_{Nn} \end{array} \right\| \begin{array}{l} \left.\right\} N \\ \left.\right\} n \end{array}$$

is obtained. Hence

$$\det(Y_1) = \det(Y) = (-1)^n \det(X^T \cdot X). \qquad (1.3.14)$$

On the other hand this determinant may be calculated using Laplace's theorem. For this we develop $\det(Y)$ in terms of the minors in the last rows. Let us take the minor corresponding to these rows, with the columns $j_1, j_2, \dots, j_n$ $(j_1 < j_2 < \dots < j_n)$. We can consider $j_n \leqslant N$, for otherwise we would have a minor with zero column from 0_{nn}, which would thus be equal to zero. Therefore, we cross out the columns $j_1, j_2, \dots, j_n$ only from the matrix (1.3.13) so that from (1.3.12) we obtain a square matrix of type $N \times N$. It has the form

$$Y_2 = \| A_{N, N-n} \vdots X_{Nn} \| .$$

Here, in the matrix $A_{N, N-n}$ the rows numbered $j_1, j_2, \dots, j_n$ will consist entirely of zeros and the remaining rows will have one element equal to one and $(N - n - 1)$ zeros. We will be interested in $\det(Y_2)$ which is the minor complementary to our minor. To calculate it we multiply those columns of the matrix $A_{N, N-n}$, in which there is one number equal to one and $(N - 1)$ zeros, by the corresponding elements of columns of X_{Nn} and subtract these columns from X_{Nn}. Thus, instead of X_{Nn} we get the matrix X'_{Nn}, which will have rows with all elements equal to zeros which, from the method of construction, will be different from $j_1, j_2, \dots, j_n$. We obtain the new matrix

$$Y_3 = \| A_{N, N-n} \vdots X'_{Nn} \| ,$$

where the zero rows of $A_{N, N-n}$ will have numbers $j_1, j_2, \dots, j_n$ and where the zero rows of X'_{Nn} have different numbers from these. Also $\det(Y_3) = \det(Y_2)$.

For the calculation of $\det(Y_3)$ we apply again Laplace's theorem, developing by minors of the n last columns of the matrix Y_3. But only one of these minors will differ from zero - that with rows numbered $j_1, j_2, \dots, j_n$.

By removing these rows from the matrix Y_3, the matrix $A_{N, N-n}$ is converted into a unit matrix $E_{N-n, N-n}$. The cofactor of our minor equals to

$$(-1)^{j_1+j_2+\dots+j_n+N-n+1+N-n+2+\dots+N} \det(E_{N-n, N-n}) =$$
$$= (-1)^{j_1+\dots+j_n+N-n+1+\dots+N}$$

This minor, evidently, is equal to the original minor of order n of the matrix $(X_{Nn})^T$, which we will denote by δ_k. The product of δ_k by its cofactor is equal to

$$\delta_k(-1)^{N+1+\dots+N+n+j_1+\dots+j_n+j_1+\dots+j_n+N-n+1+\dots+N} =$$
$$= \delta_k(-1)^{n^2} = \delta_k(-1)^n.$$

Hence

$$\det(Y) = (-1)^n \sum_k \delta_k^2. \quad (1.3.15)$$

Comparing with (1.3.14) we obtain the statement of theorem 1.3.1.

It is necessary also to generalize this theorem a little.

Let

$$P_{NN} = P = \left\| \begin{matrix} p_1 & 0 & \dots & 0 \\ 0 & p_2 & \dots & 0 \\ \cdot & \cdot & \cdot & \cdot \\ 0 & 0 & \dots & p_N \end{matrix} \right\| \quad (1.3.16)$$

be a diagonal matrix in which $p_i > 0 \quad (i = 1, 2, \dots, N)$.

We will denote the minor obtained from n columns and n rows, each numbered $j_1, j_2, \dots, j_n$ of the matrix X_{Nn}, by $\delta_{j_1 \dots j_n}$.

Theorem 1.3.2.

We have
$$\det(X^T P X) = \sum p_{j_1} p_{j_2} \dots p_{j_n} \delta^2_{j_1 \dots j_n}, \quad (1.3.17)$$

where the summation is over all possible minors of the type given above.

Proof. We introduce the matrix $P^{\frac{1}{2}}$ (see formula (1.2.9)) and put $Y = P^{\frac{1}{2}} X$. Hence $Y^T = X^T \left(P^{\frac{1}{2}}\right)^T = X^T P^{\frac{1}{2}}$, since $\left(P^{\frac{1}{2}}\right)^T = P^{\frac{1}{2}}$. Further,

$$X^T P X = Y^T Y.$$

Therefore we apply theorem 1.3.1 replacing X by Y. But the matrix Y differs from X in that the rth row is multiplied by $p_r^{\frac{1}{2}}$, so that (1.3.17) follows immediately from (1.3.11).

We also need some knowledge about the invariants of square matrices.

For the theory of the method of least squares only the concept of the trace, Sp(A *)of the square matrix A is essential.

The sum of diagonal elements of matrix $A_{nn} = A = \|a_{rs}\|$ is called the trace

---

* The symbol Sp(A) is derived from the German word "Spur"

$$\mathrm{Sp}\,(A) = \sum_{r=1}^{n} a_{rr}.$$

There is a theorem about the invariance of Sp (A): if $F = F_{nn}$ is a non-singular matrix and $A' = FAF^{-1}$, then

$$\mathrm{Sp}\,(A') = \mathrm{Sp}\,(A). \tag{1.3.18}$$

It is easy to prove this theorem by consideration of the " λ - matrix" $A - \lambda E$.

4. Symmetrical Matrices. Quadratic Forms. Orthogonal Matrices.

A square matrix is called symmetrical, if it is symmetrical about the principal diagonal, i.e. if $A^T = A$, or $\{A\}_{rs} = \{A\}_{sr}$ for all possible r and s.

If $A = A_{mn}$ is an arbitrary matrix, then the matrices $C_1 = AA^T$ and $C_2 = A^T A$ are always symmetrical.

Indeed

$$C_1^T = (AA^T)^T = AA^T = C_1;$$

and, in exactly the same way $C_2^T = C_2$, which proves the symmetry of the matrices C_1 and C_2.

A function of the vector $X_{n1} = X = \begin{Vmatrix} x_1 \\ \vdots \\ x_n \end{Vmatrix}$, of the form

$$Q = \sum_{r=1}^{n} \sum_{s=1}^{n} a_{rs} x_r x_s,$$

where $a_{rs} = a_{sr}$ is called a quadratic form Q.

Introducing the symmetrical matrix $A = \|a_{rs}\|$, it is easy to see that Q can be written in the form

$$Q = X^T A X. \tag{1.4.1}$$

A is called the matrix of the quadratic form Q.

The equation (1.4.1) is very useful in the theory of the method of least squares, in which quadratic forms play a fundamental role.

If A is a diagonal matrix, then the corresponding quadratic form will be called diagonal. In the particular case of a diagonal matrix, where $A = E = E_{nn}$, we have

$$Q = X^T E X = X^T X = x_1^2 + \ldots + x_n^2. \tag{1.4.2}$$

If, in place of the vector $X = X_{n1}$ we introduce a new vector $Y = Y_{n1}$, corresponding to the linear transformation

$$X_{n1} = O_{nn} Y_{n1}, \tag{1.4.3}$$

where $G_{nn} = G$ is any arbitrary square matrix, then, from (1.4.1) we obtain

$$Q = X^T AX = Y^T G^T AGY = Y^T BY, \tag{1.4.4}$$

where

$$B = G^T AG. \tag{1.4.5}$$

Evidently, $B^T = (G^T AG)^T = G^T A^T G = G^T AG$, is also a square matrix, so that Q will be a quadratic form in Y, and the relationships (1.4.4) and 1.4.5) exhibit the rules of transformation of a quadratic form by linear substitutions.

In the method of least squares we meet essentially positive definite and semi-definite quadratic forms.

The form $Q = X^T AX$ is called semi-definite or non-negative, if $Q \geqslant 0$ for all X. The form Q is called positive definite, if $Q > 0$ for any arbitrary, non-zero vector X. If the form Q can take values with different signs, then we call it non-definite.

A very important definite form is $Q = X^T X = x_1^2 + \dots + x_n^2$. Geometrically we can interpret it as the squared distance of the point $(x_1, \dots, x_n)$ from the origin of co-ordinates in n-dimensional space.

If we substitute (1.4.3) into X then the quadratic form is transformed into the form $Q = Y^T BY$, where $B = G^T G$. If G is a matrix such that

$$B = G^T G = E, \tag{1.4.6}$$

then Q is transformed into $Y^T Y = y_1^2 + y_2^2 + \dots + y_n^2$. This kind of transformation (1.4.3) describes rotations and reflections in n-dimensional space, or orthogonal transformations of the space. If $G = \| g_{rs} \|$, then the explicit form of condition (1.4.6) will be

$$\sum_{s=1}^{n} g_{rs}^2 = 1 \quad (r = 1, 2, \dots, n); \quad \sum_{s=1}^{n} g_{rs} g_{r_1 s} = 0 \qquad (r \neq r_1).$$

From $G^T G = E$ it follows that $G^T = G^{-1}$; $GG^T = E$. Matrices G, satisfying the condition $GG^T = G^T G = E$ we call orthogonal.

Example. The matrix

$$G = \begin{Vmatrix} \cos a & -\sin a \\ \sin a & \cos a \end{Vmatrix}$$

in the transformation $Y = Y_{21} = GX_{21}$ describes a rotation through an angle a. It is easy to see that

$$GG^T = G^T G = \begin{Vmatrix} 1 & 0 \\ 0 & 1 \end{Vmatrix}.$$

The following property of orthogonal transformations is very important: every quadratic form $Q = X^T AX$ can be reduced to diagonal form by means of orthogonal transformations of the vector X. More exactly, for every symmetrical matrix $A_{nn} = A$ we can find an orthogonal matrix F such that $B = F^T AF$ is a diagonal matrix.

If a symmetrical matrix A is non-singular, $(\det(A) \neq 0)$, then A has a reciprocal matrix A^{-1} which is also symmetrical as can be seen from the relation $(A^{-1})^T = (A^T)^{-1} = A^{-1}$. We can construct a quadratic form $Q = X^T A^{-1} X$, which is called the reciprocal to the form $Q = X^T AX$. If a symmetrical matrix A is singular $(\det(A) = 0)$, then the corresponding form $Q = X^T AX$ is called degenerate. By some orthogonal transformation (1.4.3) we can reduce a degenerate quadratic form to the diagonal form $Q = \varkappa_1 y_1^2 + \ldots + \varkappa_r y_r^2$, where $r < n$, and r is such that no non-singular linear transformation $Y = FX$, can reduce Q to a diagonal form with fewer components $\varkappa_i y_i^2$. It can be shown that this number is equal to the rank of the matrix A, rank $(A) = r$. This is also called the rank of the quadratic form Q.

Let Q be a quadratic form with matrix $A_{nn} = A = \| a_{rs} \|$.

The necessary and sufficient condition that the quadratic form is semi-definite is that the principal minors of the matrix of its coefficients must be non-negative:

$$\begin{vmatrix} a_{i_1 i_1} & \ldots & a_{i_1 i_k} \\ \cdot & \cdot & \cdot \\ a_{i_k i_1} & \ldots & a_{i_k i_k} \end{vmatrix} \geqslant 0 \quad (1 \leqslant i_1 < i_2 < \ldots < i_k \leqslant n,\ k = 1, 2, \ldots, n).$$

If the form $Q = X^T AX$ is semi-definite, i.e. always $Q \geqslant 0$, then we write, symbolically: $A \geqslant 0$.

The necessary and sufficient condition for the positive definite form $Q = X^T AX$, is

$$\begin{vmatrix} a_{11} & \ldots & a_{1k} \\ \cdot & \cdot & \cdot \\ a_{k1} & \ldots & a_{kk} \end{vmatrix} > 0 \qquad (k = 1, 2, \ldots, n). \tag{1.4.7}$$

In this case we write, symbolically: $A > 0$.

If $Q \geqslant 0$, then $a_{ii} \geqslant 0$ $(i = 1, 2, \ldots, n)$. In fact, if $a_{i_0 i_0} < 0$, then putting $x_{i_0} = 1$; $x_i = 0$ $(i \neq i_0)$, we would have $Q = X^T AX = a_{i_0 i_0} < 0$, which is impossible.

We remember one other important property: if $Q = X^T AX \geqslant 0$, i.e. if Q is a semi-definite form and $\det(A) > 0$, then Q is a positive definite form.

In fact, we put $X = FY$, where F is a orthogonal matrix such that

$$F^T AF = \begin{Vmatrix} d_1 & 0 & \ldots & 0 \\ 0 & d_2 & \ldots & 0 \\ \cdot & \cdot & \cdot & \cdot \\ 0 & 0 & \ldots & d_n \end{Vmatrix}.$$

We have, of course, $d_i \geqslant 0$. But $\det(A) = \det(F^T A F) = d_1 d_2 \ldots$ $\ldots d_n > 0$, so that $d_i > 0$ $(i = 1, 2, \ldots, n)$. But then, of course, Q must be a positive definite form.

CHAPTER II

NECESSARY KNOWLEDGE OF THE THEORY OF PROBABILITY

1. Random Variables

It is supposed that we know the theoretical concepts of random events and random variables in one- and n- dimensions (random vectors) and the relation of these concepts to reality, and also the concept of statistical independence and some elementary theorems in the theory of probability.

Here will be given, briefly, some further necessary results in probability theory. Most of them are well-known; proofs can be found, for example, in the book by Gnedenko [11]. Other known, but more specialized, results will be given with proofs.

The general concept of a random variable calls for the introduction of Stieltjes' integral, and we will not use it. The random variables which will be of fundamental interest to us are errors of measurements or rounding errors; therefore we will consider random variables of two types only: discrete random variables, and random variables possessing continuous density distributions (chiefly the latter).

A discrete random variable X is defined by a series of values x_k $(k=1, 2, \ldots)$ and corresponding probabilities $p_k=P(X=x_k)$ (in future the symbol $P(\ldots)$ will denote the probability of the random event, enclosed in the brackets). We will give some examples of discrete variables.

Example 1. The last rounded figure in a long series of observations by the same observer is noted. To a first approximation it can be regarded as a quantity X, taking the values $0, 1, \ldots, 9$, with probabilities $p_i=\frac{1}{10}$ $(i=1, 2, \ldots, 10)$.

More detailed examination shows that there exist circumstances in which there are different probabilities for different figures, because, for example, of unconscious preference of the observer for certain numbers (0.5).

In Table 5 are given data for 4 observers, who had made about

1000 observations each (Kendall [20]).

TABLE 5

Distribution of the last figure in measurements by 4 observers A, B, C, D

Last figure	No. of occurrences in 1000 measurements			
	A	*B*	*C*	*D*
0	158	122	251	358
1	97	98	37	49
2	125	98	80	90
3	79	90	72	63
4	76	100	55	37
5	71	112	222	211
6	90	98	71	62
7	56	99	75	70
8	126	101	72	44
9	129	81	65	16
Sum	1001	999	1000	1000

Example 2. (Multinomial distribution). Suppose there are n independent trials in each of which a particle (or other object) can fall in some one of k areas $Z_1, Z_2, \ldots, Z_k$. In each trial the probability of the particle falling in zone Z_i is p_i and $p_1+p_2+\ldots+p_k=1$. After n trials there are, say $m_1, m_2, \ldots, m_k$ particles in zones $Z_1, Z_2, \ldots, Z_k$ respectively, with the sum of the m's equal to n. The random vector $X=\|m_1, m_2, \ldots, m_k\|$ represents this distribution of particles among the zones. If $n_1, n_2, \ldots, n_k$ are given numbers with sum equal to n then

$$P(X=\|n_1, n_2, \ldots, n_k\|)=\frac{n!}{n_1!\, n_2! \ldots n_k!}\, p_1^{n_1} \ldots p_k^{n_k}.$$

In the special case $k=2$ we can suppose, for example, that Z_1 is a certain circle on a shooting target, and Z_2 is all areas outside this; $p_1=p$ is the probability of falling in the circle Z_1, $p_2=1-p$. The result of n shots can be sufficiently described by one-dimensional quantity X in terms of m_1 $(m_2=n-m_1)$. instead of the vector m_1, m_2 Here

$$P(X=n_1)=\frac{n!}{n_1!\, n_2!}\, p^{n_1}(1-p)^{n-n_1}.$$

We now proceed to an example of random variables and vectors with continuous probability density functions.

Consider the n-dimensional random vector $X=\|x_1, \ldots, x_n\|$, defined over the whole n-dimensional space. If we have a n-dimensional parallelopiped $I_\Delta=[\alpha_i, \alpha_i+\Delta_i]$ $(i=1, 2, \ldots, n)$, where $\|\alpha_1, \ldots, \alpha_n\|$ is an arbitrary fixed point and Δ_i an arbitrary positive number, then we will suppose that there is defined the probability $P(X \in I_\Delta)$ *) and the limit

$$\lim_{\Delta_1, \ldots \Delta_n \to 0} \frac{P(X \in I_\Delta)}{\Delta_1 \Delta_2 \ldots \Delta_n} = f(\alpha_1, \alpha_2, \ldots, \alpha_n),$$

where $f(\alpha_1, \alpha_2, \ldots, \alpha_n)$ is the continuous density function of X.

If Ω is a region in space over which it is possible to integrate, then

$$P(X \in \Omega) = \int_\Omega \ldots \int f(x_1, x_2, \ldots, x_n)\, dx_1 \ldots dx_n. \qquad (2.1.1)$$

If Ω, extends over the whole n-dimensional space R_n, the integral (2.1.1) is equal to unity.

Example 3. The normal random variable X has the probability density function

$$f(x) = \frac{1}{\sqrt{2\pi}\sigma} \exp - \frac{(x-a)^2}{2\sigma^2}, \qquad (2.1.2)$$

(The symbol $\exp x$ denotes e^x; this is convenient, when the exponent is a long expression). We will denote the family of normal laws (2.1.2) by $N(a, \sigma)$ and write $X \in N(a, \sigma)$.

We take note of some quantitative facts about the normal law (2.1.2.) For a normal random variable $X \in N(a, \sigma)$ we have

$$P\{|X-a| \leqslant 1{,}96\sigma\} \approx 0.95, \qquad (2.1.3)$$

$$P\{|X-a| \geqslant 3\sigma\} \approx 0.0027. \qquad (2.1.4)$$

The latter inequality is often called the "rule of 3σ ".

Very many of the quantitive measurements met in practice follow, approximately, the normal distribution, i.e. among a sufficiently large number of independent observations, the relative frequency of values falling in a given interval is approximately equal to the probability that a random normal variable $X \in N(a, \sigma)$ with appropriate values of the parameters a and σ will fall in the same interval. Such quantities may be the errors of observations of a single observer, the linear dimensions of some details of mass produced articles, the projection, on some axis, of segments from the centre of a shooting target to the points of impact of repeated shots by the same firer with fixed sights.

The application of the normal law to the description of the behaviour of errors of observations is well illustrated from Table 6

---

* The symbol $\in$ means "belongs to"

(Edelson [18]).

TABLE 6

λ_i	N_i	N'_i
0″.1	94	95
0.2	182	184
0.3	260	262
0.4	318	327
0.5	369	376
0.6	405	411
0.7	431	436
0.8	445	451
0.9	455	460
1.0	462	465
1.4	470	470

Here N_i is the number of observations of the angle of direct ascension of Sirius for which the deviations, λ, from their arithmetic mean do not exceed λ_i in absolute value. The overall number of observations is $N=470$; N'_i is the number of observations obtained from the normal law with parameters (0; 0.391) calculated from the formula

$$N'_i = NF(\lambda_i),$$

where

$$F(\lambda_i) = \frac{1}{\sqrt{2\pi}\sigma} \int_{-\lambda_i}^{\lambda_i} e^{-\frac{t^2}{2\sigma^2}} dt,$$

$\sigma = 0.391$.

From Table 6 it can be seen that the normal law $N(0;\ 0.391)$ describes the errors of observations quite well; the fundamental role played by this law in the theory of the method of least squares is thus apparent. Later (in section 1 of this chapter and in chapter III) some theoretical bases for the role of the normal law in the theory of errors of observations will be put forward.

It will also be necessary to use later on the concept of a random matrix. A random matrix $X_{mn} = X = \|x_{rs}\|$ is a random vector with mn components arranged in a table in the form of the matrix X. The addition and multiplication of random matrices is defined in the same way as for ordinary matrices; it must be understood that the problem of the distribution of a resultant matrix can be solved only if we know the joint distribution of the matrices from which it is constructed.

The application of such matrices sometimes shortens the calculations and also makes their expression more compact.

We recall some properties of moments of random variables.

The mathematical expectation (sometimes also called the central, or mean value) of a random variable X will be denoted by $E(X)$, and also by M. E. X. If X has a probability density function $\varphi(x)$ $(x \in (-\infty, \infty))$, then

$$m = E(X) = \int_{-\infty}^{\infty} x\varphi(x)\, dx. \tag{2.1.5}$$

It is also assumed that the integral (2.1.5) is absolutely convergent.

The variance (dispersion) of X, if it exists, will be denoted $D(X)$. By definition

$$D(X) = E(X - m)^2 = \int_{-\infty}^{\infty} (x - m)^2 \varphi(x)\, dx. \tag{2.1.6}$$

Here $m = E(X)$, as in (2.1.5). The quantity

$$\sigma(X) = \sqrt{D(X)}. \tag{2.1.7}$$

is called the standard deviation.
For the normal density function, $f(x)$, when $X \in N(a, \sigma)$, putting $f(x)$ in place of $\varphi(x)$ in (2.1.5), (2.1.6), (2.1.7) gives

$$m = E(X) = a; \qquad D(X) = \sigma^2; \quad \sigma(X) = \sigma. \tag{2.1.8}$$

The concept of moments can also be introduced for the n-dimensional vector $X = (X_1, X_2, \ldots, X_n)$, having a probability density function $f(x_1, x_2, \ldots, x_n)$ see (2.1.1). The first moments are the mathematical expectations of the components of X

$$a_i = E(X_i) = \int_{R_n} \cdots \int x_i f(x_1, \ldots, x_n)\, dx_1 \ldots dx_n \tag{2.1.9}$$

(R_n is the whole n-dimensional space of the points $(x_1, \ldots, x_n)$).

The second moments, b_{rs}, are defined by the formula

$$b_{rs} = \int_{R_n} \cdots \int (x_r - a_r)(x_s - a_s) f(x_1, \ldots x_n)\, dx_1 \ldots dx_n$$

$$(r, s = 1, 2, \ldots, n) \tag{2.1.10}$$

(provided the integrals are absolutely convergent). We see that $b_{rs} = b_{sr}$ and $b_{rr} \geqslant 0$.

The symetrical matrix

$$B_{nn} = B_X = \|b_{rs}\| \tag{2.1.11}$$

is called the correlation matrix of the random vector X. It can be conveniently expressed as a random matrix. We call the matrix $E(Y) = \|E(y_{rs})\|$, composed of the mathematical expectations of the elements y_{rs}, the mathematical expectation of the random matrix $Y = \|y_{rs}\|$. Putting

$$X = X_{n1} = \begin{Vmatrix} x_1 \\ \vdots \\ x_n \end{Vmatrix}, \tag{2.1.12}$$

we can write

$$E(X) = \begin{Vmatrix} a_1 \\ \vdots \\ a_n \end{Vmatrix} = A \tag{2.1.13}$$

and

$$B = B_X = E\left((X-A)(X-A)^T\right). \tag{2.1.14}$$

In fact, we have

$$(X-A)(X-A)^T = \left\|(x_r - a_r)(x_s - a_s)\right\|. \tag{2.1.15}$$

We introduce the auxiliary vector $Z_{n1} = Z = \begin{Vmatrix} z_1 \\ \vdots \\ z_n \end{Vmatrix}$ and construct the "correlation quadratic form"

$$\sum_{r=1}^{n} \sum_{s=1}^{n} b_{rs} z_r z_s = Z^T B Z.$$

This form is positive definite or semi-definite, since $Z^T B Z \geqslant 0$ for all Z. In fact, by reason of (2.1.10), we have for any Z

$$Z^T B Z = \sum_{r=1}^{n} \sum_{s=1}^{n} b_{rs} z_r z_s =$$

$$= \int_{R_n} \cdots \int f(x_1, \ldots, x_n) \left[\sum_{r=1}^{n} \sum_{s=1}^{n} z_r (x_r - a_r) z_s (x_s - a_s) \right] dx_1 \ldots dx_n =$$

$$= \int_{R_n} \cdots \int f(x_1, \ldots, x_n) \left(\sum_{i=1}^{n} z_i (x_i - a_i) \right)^2 dx_1\, dx_2 \ldots dx_n \geqslant 0,$$

since $f(x_1, \ldots, x_n) \geqslant 0$.

If B is non-singular, so that $\det(B) \neq 0$, then the correlation quadratic form will be positive definite; if $\det(B) = 0$, it will be semi-definite. This follows from the remarks at the end of section 4 of chapter I.

We state another important inequality which is essentially an altered form of the Buniakovski-Cauchy inequality.

If $X = \left\| \begin{matrix} x_1 \\ x_2 \end{matrix} \right\|$ is a two-dimensional random vector, then

$$\left(E(x_1 x_2)\right)^2 \leqslant E\,|x_1 x_2|^2 \leqslant \left(Ex_1^2\right)\left(Ex_2^2\right). \tag{2.1.16}$$

The following are some important properties of the moments $E(X)$ and $D(X)$. For independent variables X and Y we have

$$E(XY) = E(X)\,E(Y), \tag{2.1.17}$$

if all these quantities exist. For variables $X_1, X_2, \ldots, X_n$ which are pairwise independent

$$D(X_1 + \ldots + X_n) = D(X_1) + \ldots + D(X_n), \tag{2.1.18}$$

provided the quantities on the right hand side exist.

Chebyshev's inequality, connecting $D(X)$ and $E(X)$ is also important; for any $t > 0$

$$P\{|X - E(X)| \geqslant t\} \leqslant \frac{D(X)}{t^2}. \tag{2.1.19}$$

2. A Normal Random Vector

In practice we very often meet vectors which are approximately normal.

Such are, for example, the vectors joining the centre of a shooting target with the sights, the results of repeated observations of average velocity of wind at a given point on the surface of the earth, the set of observed errors of replicated measurements of a system of physical quantities $X_1, X_2, \ldots, X_n$ by the same observer.

The random normal n-dimensional vector $X = (X_1, \ldots, X_n)$ is an immediate generalization of the concept of a random normal variable.

Let $Q=Z^T\Lambda Z=\sum_{r=1}^{n}\sum_{s=1}^{n}\lambda_{rs}z_rz_s$ be a positive definite quadratic form in n variables $z_1, \ldots, z_n$ with the matrix $\Lambda_{nn}=\Lambda=\|\lambda_{rs}\|$; and

$$A_{n1}=A=\left\|\begin{matrix}a_1\\ \vdots\\ a_n\end{matrix}\right\|$$ be a vector.

The normal n-dimensional vector $X=X_{n1}$, corresponding to the given vector of mean values of A and to the positive definite matrix Λ, is defined as a vector with probability density function*

$$f(x_1, \ldots, x_n)=C_0\exp-\frac{1}{2}(X-A)^T\Lambda(X-A), \qquad (2.2.1)$$

where C_0 is a constant defined by the equation

$$C_0\cdot\int_{R_n}\cdots\int\exp-\frac{1}{2}[(X-A)^T\Lambda(X-A)]\,dx_1\ldots dx_n=1. \qquad (2.2.2)$$

To study the operation of matrix technique in calculations we will consider, how to express the constant C_0 in terms of Λ, and also we will find an expression for the correlation matrix of the vector X in terms of Λ and we will show that $E(X)=A$ (see, for example, Rao [42], p.51-2).

Theorem 2.2.1.

$$C_0=\frac{[\det(\Lambda)]^{\frac{1}{2}}}{(2\pi)^{\frac{n}{2}}}, \qquad (2.2.3)$$

$$E(X)=A; \qquad (2.2.4)$$

$$B_X=\Lambda^{-1}, \qquad (2.2.5)$$

where B_X is the correlation matrix of vector X. Thus, the non-singular matrix B_X is the reciprocal matrix of Λ.

Proof. First we will prove (2.2.3). We put

---

* Here and in many other places we denote the vector X and its value by the same letter, which should not lead to misunderstanding

$Y_{n1} = Y = X - A = \begin{Vmatrix} y_1 \\ \vdots \\ y_n \end{Vmatrix}$. From (2.2.2) we find

$$C_0 \int_{R_n} \ldots \int \exp -\frac{1}{2} Y^T \Lambda Y \, dy_1 \ldots dy_n = 1. \tag{2.2.6}$$

It is known, from section 4, chapter I, that the quadratic form $Y^T \Lambda Y$ can be reduced to diagonal form by an orthogonal transformation

$$Y = FZ; \quad Z = Z_{n1} = \begin{Vmatrix} z_1 \\ \vdots \\ z_n \end{Vmatrix}, \quad F = F_{nn}, \quad F^T = F.$$

We get

$$Y^T \Lambda Y = Z^T F^T \Lambda F Z = Z^T D Z,$$

where

$$D = \begin{Vmatrix} d_1 & 0 & \ldots & 0 \\ 0 & d_2 & \ldots & 0 \\ \cdot & \cdot & \cdot & \cdot \\ 0 & 0 & \ldots & d_n \end{Vmatrix}$$

is a diagonal matrix. We have also

$$\det(D) = \det(F^T) \det(\Lambda) \det(F) = \det(\Lambda) > 0,$$

so that $d_i > 0$ $(i = 1, 2, \ldots, n)$. If we also introduce the

transformation $Z = D^{-\frac{1}{2}} W$, $W = \begin{Vmatrix} w_1 \\ \vdots \\ w_n \end{Vmatrix}$,

then by virtue of $\left(D^{-\frac{1}{2}}\right)^T = D^{-\frac{1}{2}}$

we obtain

$$Y^T \Lambda Y = Z^T D Z = W^T D^{-\frac{1}{2}} D D^{-\frac{1}{2}} W = W^T W = \sum_{i=1}^{n} w_i^2. \tag{2.2.7}$$

We have

$$Y = FZ = FD^{-\frac{1}{2}}W \qquad (2.2.8)$$

and

$$\det\left(FD^{-\frac{1}{2}}\right) = \det\left(D^{-\frac{1}{2}}\right) = d_1^{-\frac{1}{2}} \ldots d_n^{-\frac{1}{2}} = [\det(D)]^{-\frac{1}{2}} = = [\det(\Lambda)]^{-\frac{1}{2}}. \qquad (2.2.9)$$

To calculate the integral in (2.2.6) we transform to variables $w_1, \ldots, w_n$.

The region of integration is again the space R_n $(-\infty < w_i < \infty)$. In transforming to new variables, it is known, from the theory of multiple integrals, that $dy_1 \ldots dy_n$ in (2.2.6) must be transformed into $dw_1 \ldots dw_n$, multiplied by the absolute value of the jacobian $|\det(J)|$, where $J = \left\| \frac{\partial y_r}{\partial w_s} \right\|$. In this case we have

$$Y = FD^{-\frac{1}{2}}W,$$

so that

$$y_r = \sum_{m=1}^{n} \left\{ FD^{-\frac{1}{2}} \right\}_{rm} w_m, \text{ and } \frac{\partial y_r}{\partial w_s} = \left\{ FD^{-\frac{1}{2}} \right\}_{rs}.$$

This means that $J = FD^{-\frac{1}{2}}$ and

$$|\det(J)| = \left|\det\left(FD^{-\frac{1}{2}}\right)\right| = [\det(\Lambda)]^{-\frac{1}{2}}. \qquad (2.2.10)$$

Making the transformation of variables in the integral (2.2.6) we obtain

$$C_0[\det(\Lambda)]^{-\frac{1}{2}} \int_{R_n} \cdots \int \exp -\frac{1}{2}(W^T W)\, dw_1 \ldots dw_n = \qquad (2.2.11)$$

but $W^T W = w_1^2 + \ldots + w_n^2$, so that

$$\int_{R_n} \cdots \int \exp -\frac{1}{2}(W^T W)\, dw_1 \ldots dw_n =$$

$$= \int_{-\infty}^{\infty} \exp\left(-\frac{1}{2} w_1^2\right) dw_1 \ldots \int_{-\infty}^{\infty} \exp\left(-\frac{1}{2} w_n^2\right) dw_n = (2\pi)^{\frac{n}{2}},$$

since

$$\int_{-\infty}^{\infty} \exp\left(-\frac{1}{2} x^2\right) dx = \sqrt{2\pi}.$$

Substituting into (2.2.6) we find

$$C_0\,[\det(\Lambda)]^{-\frac{1}{2}}(2\pi)^{\frac{n}{2}}=1;\quad C_0=[\det(\Lambda)]^{\frac{1}{2}}(2\pi)^{-\frac{n}{2}}, \tag{2.2.12}$$

which proves (2.2.3).

We will find the probabilistic meaning of the vector A in the expression for the normal probability density function (2.2.1). We will prove that $a_i=E(X_i)$ $(i=1, 2, \ldots, n)$.

We have

$$E(X_i)=C_0\int\limits_{R_n}\cdots\int x_i\exp-\frac{1}{2}(X-A)^T\Lambda(X-A)\,dx_1\ldots dx_n.$$

Putting $X-A=Y$, т. е. $x_j=y_j+a_j$ $(j=1, 2, \ldots, n)$, we find

$$\begin{aligned}E(X_i)&=C_0\int\limits_{R_n}\cdots\int (y_i+a_i)\exp-\frac{1}{2}(Y^T\Lambda Y)\,dy_1\ldots dy_n=\\&=C_0\int\limits_{R_n}\cdots\int y_i\exp-\frac{1}{2}(Y^T\Lambda Y)\,dy_1\ldots dy_n+\\&+a_iC_0\int\limits_{R_n}\cdots\int\exp-\frac{1}{2}(Y^T\Lambda Y)\,dy_1\ldots dy_n.\end{aligned} \tag{2.2.13}$$

Further we will prove that

$$C_0\int\limits_{R_n}\cdots\int y_i\exp-\frac{1}{2}(Y^T\Lambda Y)\,dy_1\ldots dy_n=0. \tag{2.2.14}$$

In fact, the quadratic form $Y^T\Lambda Y=\sum\lambda_{rs}y_ry_s$ is an even function of y_i and the expression $y_i\exp-\frac{1}{2}(Y^T\Lambda Y)$ is an odd function of y_i while the other variables can take any arbitrary fixed values. And since our integral for y_i is taken from $-\infty$ to ∞, it is equal to zero.

Further, from (2.2.6), the second term in (2.2.13) is equal to a_i. Using (2.2.14), we obtain the required equation

$$a_i = E(X_i), \tag{2.2.15}$$

so that we have $A = E(X)$, which proves (2.2.4).

Now we will find the relationship between the correlation matrix B_X of the vector X and the corresponding matrix Λ in the expression (2.2.1) of the probability density function. We must calculate the matrix

$$B_X = E(YY^T) = C_0 \int_{R_n} \cdots \int YY^T \exp -\frac{1}{2}(Y^T \Lambda Y)\, dy_1 \ldots dy_n, \tag{2.2.16}$$

and we should interpret this expression as follows: each element of the matrix YY^T is multiplied by $C_0 \exp -\frac{1}{2}(Y^T \Lambda Y)$ and integrated over the space R_n; the results obtained constitute the new matrix B_X.

To calculate the matrix (2.2.16) we introduce, as before, the transformation

$$Y = FD^{-\frac{1}{2}} W;$$

to simplify the writing we put $FD^{-\frac{1}{2}} = G$. Hence we have

$$Y = GW; \quad G^T \Lambda G = E; \quad Y^T \Lambda Y = W^T W = \sum_{i=1}^{n} w_i^2.$$

Further,

$$YY^T = GW(GW)^T = GWW^T G^T. \tag{2.2.17}$$

Substituting this into (2.2.12) and 2.2.9) we find

$$B_X = C_0 \det(G) \int_{R_n} \cdots \int GWW^T G^T \exp -\frac{1}{2}(W^T W)\, dw_1 \ldots dw_n.$$

Or, from (2.2.12) and (2.2.9)

$$B_X = (2\pi)^{-\frac{n}{2}} \int_{R_n} \cdots \int GWW^T G^T \exp -\frac{1}{2}(W^T W)\, dw_1 \ldots dw_n =$$

$$= G(2\pi)^{-\frac{n}{2}} \int_{R_n} \cdots \int WW^T \exp -\frac{1}{2}(W^T W)\, dw_1 \ldots dw_n G^T. \tag{2.2.18}$$

We will prove that

$$(2\pi)^{-\frac{n}{2}} \int_{R_n} \cdots \int WW^T \exp -\frac{1}{2}(W^T W)\, dw_1 \ldots dw_n = E_{nn},$$

where E_{nn} is a unit matrix. Our integral is a matrix $U = \|u_{rs}\|$ with the elements

$$u_{rs} = (2\pi)^{-\frac{n}{2}} \int_{R_n} \dots \int w_r w_s \exp - \frac{1}{2}(w_1^2 + \dots + w_n^2)\, dw_1 \dots dw_n.$$

This expression, of course, is equal to zero for $r \neq s$. For $r = s$ we have

$$u_{rs} = u_{sr} = (2\pi)^{-\frac{n}{2}} \int_{R_n} \dots \int w_r^2 \exp - \frac{1}{2}(w_1^2 + \dots + w_n^2)\, dw_1 \dots dw_n =$$

$$= \frac{1}{\sqrt{2\pi}} \int_{-\infty}^{\infty} w_r^2 \exp - \frac{1}{2} w_r^2\, dw_r = 1$$

By virtue of the properties of the random variable $X \in N(0, 1)$ (see 2.1.8) this means that

$$U = \|u_{rs}\| = E,$$

which proves our assertion. From (2.2.18) we find $B_X = GG^T$ But we have earlier shown that $G^T \Lambda G = E$, so that $G^T = G^{-1}\Lambda^{-1}$, and

$$B_X = GG^T = GG^{-1}\Lambda^{-1} = \Lambda^{-1}.$$

Thus

$$B_X = \Lambda^{-1};\ \Lambda = B_X^{-1},$$

which proves (2.2.5) and completes the proof of theorem 2.2.1.

Thus, by using the correlation matrix $B_X = B$ the normal probability density function can be expressed in the form

$$f(x_1, \dots, x_n) = (2\pi)^{-\frac{n}{2}} [\det(B)]^{-\frac{1}{2}} \exp - \frac{1}{2}\left[(X - A)^T B^{-1} (X - A)\right] \tag{2.2.19}$$

For an example we will consider the two-dimensional normal vector $X = \left\| \begin{matrix} x_1 \\ x_2 \end{matrix} \right\|$. We put

$$E(x_i - a_i)^2 = \sigma_i^2 \quad (i = 1, 2), \qquad E(x_1 - a_1)(x_2 - a_2) = \rho\sigma_1\sigma_2;\ |\rho| < 1.$$

(as is known from elementary courses in probability theory (see Gnedenko[11]), ρ is called the correlation coefficient between x_1 and x_2).

As it is easy to calculate

$$B=\left\| \begin{matrix} \sigma_1^2 & \rho\sigma_1\sigma_2 \\ \rho\sigma_1\sigma_2 & \sigma_2^2 \end{matrix} \right\|; \quad B^{-1}=\frac{1}{1-\rho^2}\left\| \begin{matrix} \frac{1}{\sigma_1^2} & -\frac{\rho}{\sigma_1\sigma_2} \\ -\frac{\rho}{\sigma_1\sigma_2} & \frac{1}{\sigma_2^2} \end{matrix} \right\|;$$

$$\det(B)=\sigma_1^2\sigma_2^2(1-\rho^2)>0;$$

$$f(x_1, x_2)=\frac{1}{2\pi\sigma_1\sigma_2(1-\rho^2)^{1/2}}\exp -\frac{1}{2(1-\rho^2)}\left(\frac{1}{\sigma_1^2}(x_1-a_1)^2- -\frac{2\rho}{\sigma_1\sigma_2}(x_1-a_1)(x_2-a_2)+\frac{1}{\sigma_2^2}(x_2-a_2)^2\right). \quad (2.2.20)$$

For $n=1$ we obtain the normal variable, the concept of which was introduced earlier.

From formula (2.2.19) it is clear that it is possible to construct a normal n-dimensional density function immediately from the vector of mean values of A and the correlation matrix B with $\det(B)>0$. We note that, from this result, any arbitrary, symmetrical matrix $B=B_{nn}$ corresponding to a positive definite quadratic form Y^TBY, can be the correlation matrix of an n-dimensional random vector. We can take, for example $A=\left\| \begin{matrix} 0 \\ \vdots \\ 0 \end{matrix} \right\|$, and put $\Lambda=B^{-1}$, then the required density function is defined by the equation (2.2.1) with $C_0=(2\pi)^{-\frac{n}{2}}[\det(B)]^{-\frac{1}{2}}$.

3. Linear Functions of an n-Dimensional Normal Vector

In applications of the method of least squares we will often deal with an n-dimensional vector $X=\left\| \begin{matrix} x_1 \\ \vdots \\ x_n \end{matrix} \right\|$, the components of which will represent random errors of observations. In connection with them we have often to form linear combinations of observations, and their errors, of the type

$$u_i=a_{i1}x_1+a_{i2}x_2+\ldots+a_{in}x_n \qquad (i=1, 2, \ldots, k). \quad (2.3.1)$$

Introducing the vector $U=U_{k1}=\left\| \begin{matrix} u_1 \\ \vdots \\ u_k \end{matrix} \right\|$ and the matrix

$A=A_{kn}=\|a_{rs}\|$,

we can write (2.3.1) in the form

$$U = AX, \tag{2.3.2}$$

where U is a linear vector function of the random vector X. If $k = 1$, then we have a scalar function of the vector X.

As can be seen from (2.3.1) the components $u_i = [A_i \cdot X]$ are, geometrically, the scalar products of vector X by k fixed vectors $A_i = (a_{i1}, \ldots, a_{in})$ $(i = 1, 2, \ldots, k)$, i.e. they are proportional to the projections of X in k fixed directions.

We will distinguish two cases. If the linear forms (2.3.1) are linearly independent (see section 2, chapter I), i.e. if the rank of the matrix $A = A_{kn}$ is equal to k, then we will call a linear vector function U a non-degenerate vector; in the other case (the rank $(A) < k$) we call it a degenerate vector.

First we study non-degenerate vectors U. We start from a particular case $k = n$, so that $A = A_{nn}$, rank $(A) = n$. We will prove that in this case vector U, and also X, is a non-dimensional normal random vector.

Let $v_1, \ldots, v_n$ be given values and $dv_1, \ldots, dv_n$; positive increments; we are interested in the event

$$\mathfrak{A}: \{v_1 \leqslant u_1 < v_1 + dv_1, \ldots; v_n \leqslant u_n < v_n + dv_n\} \tag{2.3.3}$$

and in its probability

$$P\{\mathfrak{A}\} = P\{v_1 \leqslant u_1 < v_1 + dv_1, \ldots; v_n \leqslant u_n < v_n + dv_n\} \tag{2.3.4}$$

for sufficiently small dv_i $(i = 1, 2, \ldots, n)$.

First we will consider a similar problem for the case $n = 1$ and for the general (non-linear) functional relationship of random variables.

Let X be a random variable distributed on the whole axis or on some segment with a probability density $f(x)$, and $Y = g(X)$ a function such that the derivative $g'(x) = \frac{dg(x)}{dx}$ exists and is continuous. Let x be any arbitrary number, dx a small increment, and $dy = g'(x)\,dx$. We want to find the probability density of the distribution of Y, $\varphi(y)$ (if it exists). For this purpose we must study the ratio

$$\frac{P\{y \leqslant Y < y + \Delta y\}}{\Delta y} \text{ for } \Delta y \to 0.$$

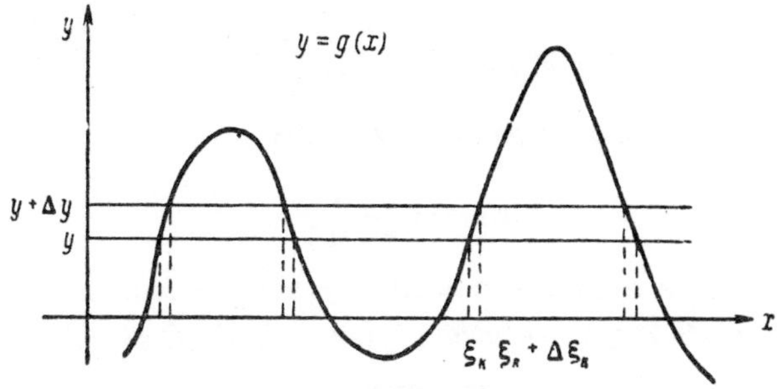

Fig. 3a

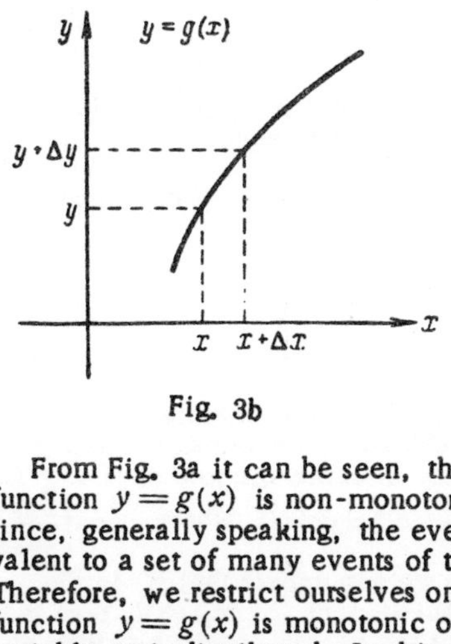

Fig. 3b

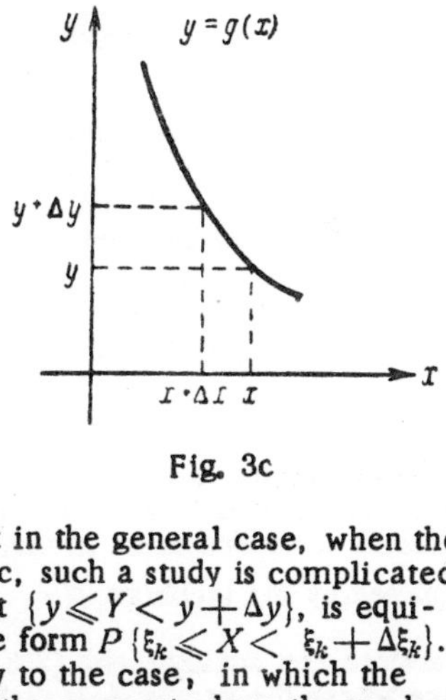

Fig. 3c

From Fig. 3a it can be seen, that in the general case, when the function $y = g(x)$ is non-monotonic, such a study is complicated since, generally speaking, the event $\{y \leqslant Y < y + \Delta y\}$, is equivalent to a set of many events of the form $P\{\xi_k \leqslant X < \xi_k + \Delta\xi_k\}$. Therefore, we restrict ourselves only to the case, in which the function $y = g(x)$ is monotonic on the segment where the random variable X is distributed. In this case we have: $g'(x) > 0$ (Fig. 3b) or $g'(x) < 0$ (Fig. 3c) on this segment, and (for the case in Fig. 3b) as is easily appreciated

$$P\{y \leqslant Y < y + \Delta y\} = P\left\{x \leqslant X < x + \frac{dy}{g'(x)}\right\}$$

with accuracy of a higher order of smallness than dx and dy. But for small δ we have $P\{x \leqslant X < x + \delta\} = f(x) \cdot \delta$ with accuracy to a higher order of smallness than δ, which we write

$$P\{x \leqslant X < x + \delta\} \approx f(x)\,\delta.$$

Hence

$$P\left\{x \leqslant X < x + \frac{dy}{g'(x)}\right\} \approx f(x)\,\frac{dy}{g'(x)}.$$

Thus

$$P\{y \leqslant Y < y+\Delta y\} \approx \frac{f(x)}{g'(x)} \Delta y.$$

Consequently, Y has the probability density

$$\varphi(y) = \frac{f(x)}{g'(x)},$$

where x must be expressed in terms of y from the formula $y = g(x)$. For the case in Fig. 3c we have $\varphi(y) = -\frac{f(x)}{g'(x)}$ (here $g'(x) < 0$), so that in the general case we obtain

$$\varphi(y) = \frac{f(x)}{|g'(x)|}. \tag{2.3.5}$$

The case of a monotonic function is different from the case in Fig. 3a, in that $g'(x) \neq 0$ over the whole segment.

Now we pass to the case of a vector function U of the random vector X:

$$U = g(X) = \begin{Vmatrix} g_1(x_1, \ldots, x_n) \\ \cdots\cdots \\ g_n(x_1, \ldots, x_n) \end{Vmatrix}.$$

Let the vector X have the probability density function $f(x_1, \ldots, x_n)$. It is known, that in the theory of transformations of variables and substitution in multiple integrals the role of $y' = g'(x)$ is played by the jacobian $J(x_1, \ldots, x_n) = \det(I)$, where $I = \left\| \frac{\partial g_r}{\partial x_s} \right\|$. Therefore, by analogy with (2.3.5) we can expect that if, in the space where the vector X is distributed, $J(x_1, \ldots x_n) \neq 0$, then the probability density $\varphi(u_1, \ldots, u_n)$ of the vector U, will be given by

$$\varphi(u_1, u_2, \ldots, u_n) = \frac{f(x_1, \ldots, x_n)}{|J(x_1, \ldots, x_n)|}, \tag{2.3.6}$$

where x_i must be expressed in terms of u_j from the formula $u_j = g_j(x_1, \ldots, x_n)$ $(j = 1, 2, \ldots, n)$.

This is, in fact, true and we will soon prove it for the linear transformation $U = AX$, introduced above, where $A = A_{nn}$ is a non-singular matrix. In the inverse linear transformation $X = A^{-1}U$ there will correspond, to the parallelopiped connected with the event $\mathfrak{A}$ in (2.3.3), some oblique angled parallelopiped of volume

$$\frac{du_1 \cdots du_n}{|\det(A)|} \tag{2.3.7}$$

(see section 3, chapter I, in particular (1.3.3)). Therefore, $P(\mathfrak{A})$ is equal to the probability that the vector X falls in the oblique-angled parallelopiped with volume (2.3.7), i.e.

$$P(\mathfrak{A}) = \frac{f(x_1, \ldots, x_n)}{|\det(A)|} du_1 \cdots du_n. \tag{2.3.8}$$

Thus, the vector U is a random vector having the probability density

$$\varphi(u_1, \ldots, u_n) = \frac{f(x_1, \ldots, x_n)}{|\det(A)|}, \tag{2.3.9}$$

where x_i must be expressed in terms of u_j. But X is a normal vector, so that, according to (2.2.19)

$$f(x_1, \ldots, x_n) = \frac{1}{(2\pi)^{\frac{n}{2}} [\det(B)]^{\frac{1}{2}}} \exp - \frac{1}{2}\left(Y^T B^{-1} Y\right), \tag{2.3.10}$$

where $Y = X - M$, M is a vector of mean values and B is a correlation matrix.

We have $U = AX = A(Y + M)$, whence

$$Y = A^{-1}U - M = A^{-1}(U - AM); \quad Y^T = (U - AM)^T (A^T)^{-1},$$

so that putting $U - AM = V$, $Y = A^{-1}V$, we find

$$\varphi(u_1, \ldots, u_n) = \frac{1}{(2\pi)^{\frac{n}{2}} |\det(A)| (\det(B))^{\frac{1}{2}}} \exp - \frac{1}{2}\left(V^T (A^T)^{-1} B^{-1} A^{-1} V\right).$$

Therefore, by (2.3.10) and theorem 2.2.1 we conclude that U is an n-dimensional normal random vector with the vector of mean values AM and correlation matrix

$$B_U = AB_X A^T, \tag{2.3.11}$$

$$\det(B_U) = (\det(A))^2 \det(B) \quad \text{and} \quad [\det(B_U)]^{\frac{1}{2}} = |\det(A)| (\det B)^{\frac{1}{2}}.$$

We will now calculate directly the correlation matrix of the vector $U = AX$ without any arbitrary supposition about the rank of the matrix $A = A_{kn}$. According to section 1 of this chapter [see formulae (2.1.13) and (2.1.14)] we have

$$E(U) = E(AX) = AE(X) = AM;$$
$$B_U = E(U - AM)(U - AM)^T = E\left(A(X - M)(A(X - M))^T\right) =$$
$$= E\left(A(X - M)(X - M)^T A^T\right) = AE(X - M)(X - M)^T A^T = AB_X A^T.$$

Here A and A^T are constant matrices which, in the calculation of the mathematical expectations of the matrices, are placed outside the sign of mathematical expectations. We return to (2.3.11).

In the more general case, when $k < n$, $A = A_{kn}$, rank $(A) = k$, there is a theorem:

Theorem 2.3.1.

The vector $U = AX$ is a k-dimensional random vector with the vector of mean values, AM, and the correlation matrix $B_U = AB_X A^T$.

We will not give here the proof of this theorem, which calls for very painstaking matrix calculation, and will only give its general idea.*

The vector

$$U = U_{k1} = \begin{Vmatrix} u_1 \\ \vdots \\ u_k \end{Vmatrix}.$$

is extended to the vector

$$U'_{n1} = U' = \begin{Vmatrix} u_1 \\ \vdots \\ u_k \\ u_{k+1} \\ \vdots \\ u_n \end{Vmatrix}$$

just as the matrix A is extended to a matrix $A' = A'_{nn}$; rank $(A') = n$. On the basis of previous work we obtain the normal n-dimensional vector U', for which we can write the probability density function, $\varphi(y_1, \ldots, y_n)$. As a result of this, the event $\mathfrak{A}$:

$$(y_1 \leqslant u_1 < y_1 + dy_1, \ldots, y_k \leqslant u_k < y_k + dy_k)$$

is replaced by the equivalent event, $\mathfrak{A}_1$:

$$(y_1 \leqslant u_1 < y_1 + dy_1, \ldots, y_k \leqslant u_k < y_k + dy_k;$$
$$-\infty < u_{k+1} < \infty, \ldots, -\infty < u_n < \infty).$$

Hence

$$P(\mathfrak{A}) = dy_1 \ldots dy_k \int_{R_{n-k}} \cdots \int \varphi(y_1, \ldots, y_n)\, dy_{k+1} \ldots dy_n,$$

where R_{n-k} denotes $(n-k)$-dimensional space. From this it is easy to find the probability density function of the initial vector U, giving it as a k-dimensional normal vector. By the arguments given above the vector of mean values must be equal to AM, and the

---

* For the detailed matrix proof see, for example, the book by Rao [42], p.53-4.

correlation matrix is $B_U = AB_X A^T$. Now we consider the case of a degenerate linear vector function, where in the expression $U = AX$ the rank of the matrix, $A = A_{kn}$ is less than k. This will always happen, if $k > n$. In this case (see section 2, chapter I) there are

linear dependences between the components of the vector $U = \begin{Vmatrix} u_1 \\ \vdots \\ u_k \end{Vmatrix}_k$

which may be written in the form $\sum_{j=1} c_{ij} u_j = 0$, or $CU = 0$, where

$C = C_{mk}$ is a certain matrix.

Geometrically, the condition $CU = 0$ means that the vector U lies in some sub-space R_k, and from the probabilistic point of view this condition means that the distribution of the vector is concentrated in this sub-space. In this case we can describe the behaviour of the linear vector function $U = AX$ in the following way. We select the maximum number of linear independent components, say, $u_1, \ldots, u_l$;

$l < k$ and we construct the vector $U' = \begin{Vmatrix} u_1 \\ \vdots \\ u_l \end{Vmatrix}$ This is an l-dimen-

sional vector, and the components $u_{l+1}, \ldots, u_k$ are known linear functions of the components $u_1, \ldots, u_l$.

All components are random normal variables. We will not prove this (see, for example, Rao [12], Cramér [25]).

We will prove some more theorems about normal vectors, which will be useful later.

Theorem 2.3.2. (Fisher's theorem).

If X is a normal n-dimensional vector with zero mean vector and with independent, equally distributed components, and $F = F_{nn}$ is any arbitrary orthogonal transposition, then the n-dimensional normal vector $Y = FX$ has the same distribution as the vector X.

Proof. We have $E(X) = 0$, $B_X = \sigma^2 E$, where σ^2 is the common variance of each component of X. From theorem 2.3.1 $Y = FX$ is a n-dimensional normal vector. Here

$$E(Y) = E(FX) = FE(X) = F0 = 0;$$
$$B_Y = FB_X F^T = F\sigma^2 E \cdot F^T = \sigma^2 FF^T = \sigma^2 E = B_X,$$

since $FF^T = E$ by virtue of the orthogonality of F. Thus,

* R.A. Fisher (born 1890) - English statistician

$E(Y)=E(X)$; $B_Y=B_X$; this means that the vector Y is also distributed in the same way as X, which was to be proved.

Let

$$Y_1=A_1X; \quad Y_2=A_2X, \tag{2.3.12}$$

where A_1 is a matrix of a type $(m_1\times n)$, and A_2 a matrix of type $(m_2\times n)$, be two linear vector functions of the n-dimensional normal vector X. There is the following theorem:

Theorem 2.3.3.

A necessary and sufficient condition that $Y_1=A_1X$ and $Y_2=A_2X$ will be statistically independent is

$$A_1B_XA_2^T=0. \tag{2.3.13}$$

Proof. Without loss of generality, we can suppose $E(X)=M=0$. In fact, if this is not true, we introduce the vector $Z=X-M$. Then, $B_X=B_Z$, so that the condition (2.3.13) has its previous form, and the vectors $Y_1'=A_1(X-M)$ and $Y_2'=A_2(X-M)$, of course are statistically independent, if and only if Y_1 and Y_2. are independent. Now, assuming $E(X)=0$, we prove the necessity of the condition (2.3.13). Because $B_X=E(XX^T)$, (2.3.13) can be expressed as:

$$A_1E(XX^T)A_2^T=E\left((A_1X)(A_2X)^T\right)=0,$$

or, by virtue of (2.3.12)

$$E\left(Y_1Y_2^T\right)=0. \tag{2.3.14}$$

Accordingly, Y_1 and Y_2 will be normal vectors with

$$E(Y_i)=A_iE(X)=0; \qquad i=1,\ 2. \tag{2.3.15}$$

Let

$$Y_1=\begin{Vmatrix} y_{11}\\ y_{12}\\ \vdots\\ y_{1m_1}\end{Vmatrix}; \qquad Y_2=\begin{Vmatrix} y_{21}\\ y_{22}\\ \vdots\\ y_{2m_2}\end{Vmatrix}. \tag{2.3.16}$$

If Y_1 and Y_2 are independent, then the arbitrary pair of components y_{1i} and y_{2j} are a pair of independent normal random variables so that

$$E(y_{1i}y_{2j})=E(y_{1i})E(y_{2j})=0 \tag{2.3.17}$$

by virtue of (2.3.15) and (2.3.17). But (2.3.17) means precisely that

$$E\left(Y_1 Y_2^T\right) = 0.$$

This proves the equation (2.3.14), which is equivalent to (2.3.13). To prove the sufficiency of (2.3.13) is more difficult. First of all we select a non-singular matrix $G_{nn} = G$ such that

$$G B_X G^T = E. \qquad (2.3.18)$$

We have seen earlier that G can be chosen in the form $G = D_0 \cdot F_0$, where D_0 is a extended non-singular matrix, and F_0 is an orthogonal matrix. In fact, taking an orthogonal matrix F_0 such that

$$F_0 B_X F_0^T = D_1,$$

we note that

$$D_1 = \begin{Vmatrix} d_1 & 0 & \dots & 0 \\ 0 & d_2 & \dots & 0 \\ \cdot & \cdot & \cdot & \cdot \\ 0 & 0 & \dots & d_n \end{Vmatrix},$$

where $d_i > 0$ $(i = 1, 2, \dots, n)$, since B_X is a non-singular matrix. Taking $G = D_1^{-\frac{1}{2}} F_0$; $G^T = F_0^T D_1^{-\frac{1}{2}}$, we obtain what is required. Now suppose the condition (2.3.13) is satisfied. We have

$$A_1 G^{-1} G B G^T \left(G^T\right)^{-1} A_2^T = A_1 G^{-1} \left(A_2 G^{-1}\right)^T = 0. \qquad (2.3.19)$$

Further,

$$Y_1 = A_1 G^{-1} G X; \quad Y_2 = A_2 G^{-1} G X. \qquad (2.3.20)$$

We introduce the notations: $GX = Z$; $A_1 G^{-1} = A_3$; $A_2 G^{-1} = A_4$. Then

$$Y_1 = A_3 Z; \quad Y_2 = A_4 Z; \quad A_3 A_4^T = 0, \qquad (2.3.21)$$

and Z is an n-dimensional random vector with $E(Z) = 0$; $B_Z = E$. We have to prove the independence of Y_1 and Y_2. Let

$$A_3 = \begin{Vmatrix} a_{11} & \dots & a_{1n} \\ \cdot & \cdot & \cdot \\ a_{m_1 1} & \dots & a_{m_1 n} \end{Vmatrix}; \quad A_4 = \begin{Vmatrix} b_{11} & \dots & b_{1n} \\ \cdot & \cdot & \cdot \\ b_{m_2 1} & \dots & b_{m_2 n} \end{Vmatrix}. \qquad (2.3.22)$$

We will consider the row $(a_{i1}, \dots, a_{in})$ as a vector and denote it by a_i and the row $(b_{j1}, b_{j2}, \dots, b_{jn})$ as a vector b_j $(i = 1, 2, \dots, m_1;$ $j = 1, 2, \dots, m_2)$. The condition $A_3 A_4^T = 0$ denotes pair-wise orthogonality of these vectors

$$[a_i b_j] = 0 \quad (i = 1, 2, \dots, m_1;\ j = 1, 2, \dots, m_2). \qquad (2.3.23)$$

Among vectors a_i and among vectors b_j there may be some linear dependence. Let rank $(A_3) = \mu$, rank $(A_4) = \nu$. We note that rank (A_3) = rank (A_1) and rank (A_4) = rank (A_2). This follows from the relationship (1.2.18), since $A_3 = A_1G$, $A_1 = A_3G^{-1}$; rank $(G) = n$, rank $(A_1) \leqslant n$; the same holds for the matrices A_2 and A_4.

We will select in A_3 a system of μ linearly independent rows, and in A_4 a system of ν linearly independent rows; let the corresponding vectors be $a_{\alpha_1}, a_{\alpha_2}, \ldots, a_{\alpha_\mu}$ and $b_{\beta_1}, \ldots, b_{\beta_\nu}$, respectively, so that

$$[a_{\alpha_i} \cdot b_{\beta_j}] = 0 \quad (i = 1, 2, \ldots, \mu; \ j = 1, 2, \ldots, \nu). \qquad (2.3.24)$$

Evidently, the relationships (2.3.23) are consequences of the relationships (2.3.24), because the vectors a_i are linear combinations of the vectors a_{α_i} and b_j linear combinations of vectors b_{β_j}. We have, corresponding to (2.3.16) for $Z = (z_1, \ldots, z_n)$ *)

$$y_{1i} = [a_i \cdot z]; \quad y_{2j} = [b_j \cdot z]. \qquad (2.3.25)$$

In view of this, of course, all components y_{1i} are linear combinations of components $y_{1\alpha_i}$; all components y_{2j} are linear combinations of components $y_{2\beta_j}$. We introduce the new vectors

$$Y_1' = \begin{Vmatrix} y_{1\alpha_1} \\ \vdots \\ y_{1\alpha_\mu} \end{Vmatrix}, \quad Y_2' = \begin{Vmatrix} y_{2\beta_1} \\ \vdots \\ y_{2\beta_\nu} \end{Vmatrix}. \qquad (2.3.26)$$

If we prove that Y_1' and Y_2' are statistically independent, then, of course, we prove that Y_1 and Y_2 are independent because Y_1 and Y_2 are vector functions of Y_1' and Y_2', respectively. We can write

$$Y_1' = A_5Z; \qquad Y_2' = A_6Z, \qquad (2.3.27)$$

where A_5 is constructed from the rows $\alpha_1, \ldots, \alpha_\mu$ of matrix A_3, and A_6 from the rows $\beta_1, \ldots, \beta_\nu$ of matrix A_4. Evidently,

$$A_5A_6^T = 0, \qquad (2.3.28)$$

since this equation is equivalent to (2.3.24). From theorem 2.3.1, Y_1' is a μ-dimensional, and Y_2' is a ν-dimensional normal vector. Now we construct a new random vector from all components of Y_1' and Y_2'

---

* Here, and sometimes later, we will write the vector in this way:

$$Z = \begin{Vmatrix} z_1 \\ \vdots \\ z_n \end{Vmatrix}.$$

$$Y = \begin{Vmatrix} y_{1\alpha_1} \\ \vdots \\ y_{1\alpha_\mu} \\ y_{2\beta_1} \\ \vdots \\ y_{2\beta_\nu} \end{Vmatrix}. \qquad (2.3.29)$$

We have

$$Y = AZ; \qquad A = \begin{Vmatrix} A_5 \\ \cdots \\ A_6 \end{Vmatrix}. \qquad (2.3.30)$$

We will prove that Y is a $(\mu+\nu)$-dimensional normal vector (so that $\mu+\nu \leqslant n$). It is clear, that Y is a normal vector (theorem 2.3.1); the number of its components is equal to $\mu+\nu$. To prove Y is a $(\mu+\nu)$-dimensional normal vector, it sufficient to be convinced, that its correlation matrix B_Y is non-singular; then, for $E(Y)=0$ its probability density is given by the formula (2.2.10), which exhibits its $(\mu+\nu)$-dimensionality.

According to theorem 2.3.1 we have $B_Y = AB_ZA^T = AA^T$. By virtue of (2.3.30) and the rules of multiplication of partitioned matrices

$$AA^T = \begin{Vmatrix} A_5 \\ \cdots \\ A_6 \end{Vmatrix} \cdot \| A_5^T \vdots A_6^T \| = \begin{Vmatrix} A_5A_5^T & A_5A_6^T \\ A_6A_5^T & A_6A_6^T \end{Vmatrix}.$$

From (2.3.28) we have $A_5A_6^T = 0$; transforming this relationship, we find $A_6A_5^T = 0$. whence

$$AA^T = \begin{Vmatrix} A_5A_5^T & 0 \\ 0 & A_6A_6^T \end{Vmatrix}. \qquad (2.3.31)$$

Here $A_5A_5^T$ and $A_6A_6^T$ are symetrical matrices of types $(\mu \times \mu)$ and $(y \times y)$ respectively. We will prove that they are non-singular. On the basis of theorem 1.3.1., in view of the fact that $\mu \leqslant n$ and rank $(A_5) = \mu$, we obtain det $(A_6A_6^T) > 0$. By analogy, det $(A_5A_5^T) > 0$. Thus,

$$\det(AA^T) = \det(A_5A_5^T)\det(A_6A_6^T) > 0,$$

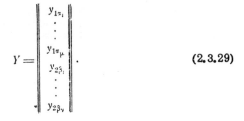

so that $B_{Y'} = AA^T$ is a non-singular matrix and Y is a $(\mu+\nu)$-dimensional normal vector. To prove the independence of Y_1' and Y_2', we construct the expression for the density function of Y corresponding to formula (2.2.19)

$$B_{Y}^{-1} = (AA^T)^{-1} = \left\| \begin{array}{c:c} (A_5A_5^T)^{-1} & 0 \\ \hdashline 0 & (A_6A_6^T)^{-1} \end{array} \right\|. \tag{2.3.32}$$

Further, we have

$$B_{Y_1'} = A_5A_5^T; \quad B_{Y_2'} = A_6A_6^T, \tag{2.3.33}$$

so that

$$B_Y^{-1} = \left\| \begin{array}{c:c} B_{Y_1'}^{-1} & 0 \\ \hdashline 0 & B_{Y_2'}^{-1} \end{array} \right\|. \tag{2.3.34}$$

Constructing the density function of Y according to (2.2.19) and remembering that

$$Y = Y_{\mu+\nu,\,1} = \left\| \begin{array}{c} Y_1' \\ \hdashline Y_2' \end{array} \right\|$$

and

$$Y^T B_Y^{-1} Y = \| (Y_1')^T \,\vdots\, (Y_2')^T \| \cdot \left\| \begin{array}{c:c} B_{Y_1'}^{-1} & 0 \\ \hdashline 0 & B_{Y_2'}^{-1} \end{array} \right\| \cdot \left\| \begin{array}{c} Y_1' \\ \hdashline Y_2' \end{array} \right\| =$$

$$= (Y_1')^T B_{Y_1'}^{-1} Y_1' + (Y_2')^T B_{Y_2'}^{-1} Y_2',$$

we find, for the probability density of Y the expression

$$\frac{1}{(2\pi)^{\frac{\mu}{2}} \left(\det \left(B_{Y_1'}\right)\right)^{\frac{1}{2}}} \exp\left[-\frac{1}{2}(Y_1')^T B_{Y_1'} Y_1'\right] \frac{1}{(2\pi)^{\frac{\nu}{2}} \left(\det \left(B_{Y_2'}\right)\right)^{\frac{1}{2}}} \times$$

$$\times \exp - \frac{1}{2}(Y_2')^T B_{Y_2'} Y_2'.$$

We see that the probability density of Y splits up into the product of probability densities of Y_1' and Y_2', which proves their independence. With this, theorem 2.3.3 is finally proved.

4. Reduction of Normal Vector to Simpler Form. Correlation Ellipsoid and Ellipsoid of Constant Variance

We will consider an n-dimensional normal vector $X_{n1}=X$ together with its correlation matrix B_X. The vector of means, $E(X)$, we will consider to be a zero vector, so that on changing X to $X-E(X)$ we have the same correlation matrix B_X. We know that an orthogonal matrix $F_{nn}=F$, can be selected such that, putting $Y=FX$, we get

$$B_Y=FB_XF^T=D, \tag{2.4.1}$$

where D is a diagonal non-singular matrix with positive diagonal elements:

$$D=\begin{Vmatrix} d_1 & 0 & \dots & 0 \\ 0 & d_2 & \dots & 0 \\ \cdot & \cdot & \cdot & \cdot \\ 0 & 0 & \dots & d_n \end{Vmatrix} \tag{2.4.2}$$

Therefore the probability density function of the normal vector Y is of the form

$$f(y_1, \dots, y_n)=\frac{1}{(2\pi)^{\frac{n}{2}}(d_1 \dots d_n)^{\frac{1}{2}}}\exp-\frac{1}{2}\left(\frac{y_1^2}{d_1}+\dots+\frac{y_n^2}{d_n}\right).$$

We see that the vector Y has independent components y_i, and also

$$E(y_i)=0; \quad D(y_i)=d_i. \tag{2.4.3}$$

If we introduce, further, the transformation $Z=D^{-\frac{1}{2}}Y$, then we obtain

$$E(Z)=0; \quad B_Z=D^{-\frac{1}{2}}DD^{-\frac{1}{2}}=E. \tag{2.4.4}$$

The probability density function of the vector Z is of the form (2.4.2), where all $d_i=1$. Z is a normal vector, components of which are independently distributed as $N(0, 1)$ Such a vector we can call a standard normal vector.

We will consider a n-dimensional vector $X=\begin{Vmatrix} x_1 \\ \vdots \\ x_n \end{Vmatrix}$; we will treat the x_i's as rectangular co-ordinates. Let

$$E(X)=M=\begin{Vmatrix} m_1 \\ \vdots \\ m_n \end{Vmatrix}; \quad B_X=\|b_{rs}\|.$$

We introduce the normal vector

$$X - M = Z = \begin{Vmatrix} z_1 \\ \vdots \\ z_n \end{Vmatrix}$$

(The vector of deviations from the mean).

Let $a = A_{1n} = \|a_1, \ldots, a_n\|$ be a unit vector $(a_1^2 + \ldots + a_n^2 = 1)$; We form the scalar product

$$[aZ] = \sum_{i=1}^{n} a_i Z_i = AZ.$$

This is a normal variate with zero mean and variance equal to $D(AZ) = E(AZZ^T A^T) = AB_X A^T$ (see theorem 2.3.1). And so, in the direction defined by the unit vector $(a_1, \ldots, a_n)$, there is obtained a random projection with variance $AB_X A^T$. Now we will consider a surface obtained by laying off the corresponding standard deviation $\sqrt{AB_X A^T}$. in the direction $(a_1 \ldots, a_n)$ We will call it the correlation surface of the n-dimensional normal vector X.

Theorem 2.4.1.

The correlation surface of a normal n-dimensional vector X is an ellipsoid with the equation

$$(X - M)^T B_X^{-1} (X - M) = 1. \qquad (2.4.5)$$

Hence, as we see from (2.2.19), the probability density function is constant on this surface.

To prove this we introduce the quadratic form $U^T B_X U$, where

$$U = U_{n1} = \begin{Vmatrix} u_1 \\ \vdots \\ u_n \end{Vmatrix}.$$ If $u_i = a_i$ $(i = 1, 2, \ldots, n)$ and $A = A_{1n} = \|a_1, \ldots, a_n\|$, then $U^T B_X U = AB_X A^T$. We make an orthogonal transformation $U = FV$, $FF^T = E$, such that

$$F^T B_X F = \begin{Vmatrix} \sigma_1^2 & 0 & \ldots & 0 \\ 0 & \sigma_2^2 & \ldots & 0 \\ \cdot & \cdot & \cdot & \cdot \\ 0 & 0 & \ldots & \sigma_n^2 \end{Vmatrix} = D,$$

where D is a diagonal matrix.

To the unit vector $\|a_1, \ldots, a_n\|$ in the old system of co-ordinates there corresponds another unit vector $\|b_1, \ldots, b_n\|$ in the new system of co-ordinates and in its (the vector $(\|b_1, \ldots, b_n\|)$ direction is laid off the standard deviation $\sqrt{\sum_{i=1}^{n}\sigma_i^2 b_i^2}$. Thus, we obtain the correlation surface.

We transform this surface, putting $b_i = \frac{v_i}{\sigma_i}$ $(i = 1, 2, \ldots, n)$. In the new surface in the direction $(b_1, \ldots, b_n)$ is laid off the distance $\sqrt{\sum_{i=1}^{n} b_i^2} = 1$, so that a sphere with unit radius is obtained. This means, that the previous surface was an ellipsoid with semi-axes $\sigma_1, \ldots, \sigma_n$ and equation

$$V^T D^{-1} V = \sum_{i=1}^{n} \frac{v_i^2}{\sigma_i^2} = 1.$$

In the old co-ordinates its equation, since $V = F^T U$ has the form

$$U^T F D^{-1} F^T U = U^T B_X^{-1} U = 1,$$

because $F^T B_X F = D$; $B_X = FDF^{-1}$; $B_X^{-1} = FD^{-1}F^{-1} = FD^{-1}F^T$. And so, for the correlation surface we have the equation

$$U^T B_X^{-1} U = 1, \qquad (2.4.6)$$

which, on putting $U = X - M$ (where X is understood as the ordinary vector $= \left\| \begin{matrix} x_1 \\ \vdots \\ x_n \end{matrix} \right\|$), leads to (2.4.5).

We will consider the special cases $n = 1$ and $n = 2$. For $n = 1$ we have a random variable; $M = m$; $B_X = \sigma^2$, and (2.4.5) converts into

$$|x - m| = \sigma; \quad x = m \pm \sigma \qquad (2.4.7)$$

(a correlation segment).

For $n = 2$, from (2.2.20) we have

$$\frac{1}{\sigma_1^2}(x_1 - m_1)^2 - \frac{2\rho}{\sigma_1 \sigma_2}(x_1 - m_1)(x_2 - m_2) + \frac{1}{\sigma_2^2}(x_2 - m_2)^2 = 1 \qquad (2.4.8)$$

(a correlation ellipse).

If we stretch the correlation ellipsoid (2.4.5) $\sqrt{n+2}$ times, then we obtain the ellipsoid

$$(X-M)^T B_X^{-1}(X-M)=n+2,$$

which is called the ellipsoid of dispersion or ellipsoid of concentration (see Cramer [25], p. 331). The probability density of the vector X, is also, of course, constant on this ellipsoid.

The probabilistic meaning of the ellipsoid of concentration is as follows: if, given a normal vector X, we look for a random vector R, which is uniformly distributed over some ellipsoid having a constant probability density inside it, and zero probability density outside it, and for which $E(X)=E(R)$, $B_X=B_R$ (i.e. for which the vector of means and the correlation matrix coincide with the corresponding values for X), then that ellipsoid is uniquely defined by the equation (2.4.9).

The proof of this assertion for $n=2$ may be found in Cramér's book [25], (pp. 312-4); it can also be proved very easily in the general case using matrix methods, but we will stop here, because such an approach is not necessary in the theory of the method of least squares.

We consider a n-dimensional normal vector X with $E(X)=M$ and with given correlation matrix B_X. Let the vector

$$Z=Z_{n1}=\begin{Vmatrix} z_1 \\ \vdots \\ z_n \end{Vmatrix}$$

be given.

We construct the scalar product $\sum (z_i-m_i)(x_i-m_i)=$ $=[Z-M, \quad X-M]$. The variance of this product is $(Z-M)^T B_X(Z-M)$. The set of points $(z_1, \ldots, z_n)$, where this variance is equal to 1, is given by the equation

$$(Z-M)^T B_X(Z-M)=1. \tag{2.4.10}$$

For every vector in the direction $Z-M$, the ellipsoid (2.4.10) gives a length, for which the variance of the corresponding projection is equal to 1.

We see that on the left hand sides of the equations (2.4.5) and (2.4.10) there are mutually reciprocal quadratic forms.

Theorem 2.4.2.*

If, for two n-dimensional normal vectors X and Y with the

---

* It is not known to the author, if this theorem is new.

common vector of means $M=E(X)=E(Y)$ the correlation ellipsoid Y lies inside the correlation ellipsoid X, then the ellipsoid of constant variance of X lies inside the ellipsoid of constant variance of Y, and conversely.

5. Comparison of Different Normal Distributions

Suppose that we make a measurement of some physical quantity m, where the observations are accompanied by random errors ξ without systematic error, so that the result of an observation may be expressed by the random variable $X=m+\xi$. We will assume that X is normal with parameters m, σ:

$$X \in N(m, \sigma).$$

If another method of measuring of the same quantity (or another observer) gives results expressed by the random variable $X_1=m+$ $+\xi_1 \in N(m, \sigma_1)$, where $\sigma_1<\sigma$, then it is natural to regard these results as being "more precise" than the previous results, because the quantity ξ_1 is "more concentrated" near zero than ξ. The exact meaning of this concept is as follows: for any arbitrarily chosen number $\varepsilon>0$, deviations of observations from m greater than ε will be more probable in the first case than in the second, i.e.

$$P\{|X_1-m|>\varepsilon\}<P\{|X-m|>\varepsilon\}. \tag{2.5.1}$$

In fact, we have

$$P\{|X_1-m|>\varepsilon\}=\frac{2}{\sqrt{2\pi}\,\sigma_1}\int_{\varepsilon}^{\infty} e^{-\frac{t^2}{2\sigma_1^2}}\,dt=\frac{2}{\sqrt{2\pi}}\int_{\varepsilon/\sigma_1}^{\infty} e^{-u^2/2}\,du$$

and by analogy

$$P\{|X-m|>\varepsilon\}=\frac{2}{\sqrt{2\pi}}\int_{\varepsilon/\sigma}^{\infty} e^{-u^2/2}\,du.$$

If $\sigma_1<\sigma$, then $\frac{\varepsilon}{\sigma_1}>\frac{\varepsilon}{\sigma}$, and the first interval is less than the second, which proves (2.5.1).

We can describe this in the following way: the second measurements are more accurate than the first, if the correlation segment of the second measurements $[m-\sigma_1,\ m+\sigma_1]$ lies inside the correlation segment of the first measurements $[m-\sigma,\ m+\sigma]$, or the normal variate ξ_1 is "better" than ξ, if $E(\xi_1)=E(\xi)$ and the correlation segment of ξ_1 lies inside the correlation segment of ξ. We try to transfer these considerations to the case of an n-dimensional normal vector. Let n physical quantities $m_1, \ldots, m_n$ be measured, without systematic errors, but with errors $\xi_1, \ldots, \xi_n$, so that the result of the measurements is expressed by the random vector

$$X = \begin{Vmatrix} x_1 \\ \vdots \\ x_n \end{Vmatrix} = \begin{Vmatrix} m_1 + \xi_1 \\ \vdots \\ m_n + \xi_n \end{Vmatrix}.$$

In many problems, the random errors ξ_i (and consequently also the quantities x_i) are independent, but sometimes we have statistically dependent (correlated) errors. Later, we will meet such cases, for example, in the theory of non-direct (indirect) observations.

Thus, in the general case X is an n-dimensional normal vector of general type. Let

$$E(X) = \begin{Vmatrix} m_1 \\ \vdots \\ m_n \end{Vmatrix}; \quad B_X = E[(X-M)(X-M)^T] = \|b_{rs}\|.$$

Suppose that another method of measuring (or another observer) leads to results expressed by the n-dimensional normal vector $Y = \begin{Vmatrix} y_1 \\ \vdots \\ y_n \end{Vmatrix}$ with the same mean vector $E(Y) = \begin{Vmatrix} m_1 \\ \vdots \\ m_n \end{Vmatrix}$, but with a different correlation matrix $B_Y = \|c_{rs}\|$.

We construct the equations of the correlation ellipsoids in the same system of co-ordinates $(x_1, \ldots, x_n)$:

$$(X-M)^T B_X^{-1} (X-M) = 1, \tag{2.5.2}$$

$$(X-M)^T B_Y^{-1} (X-M) = 1. \tag{2.5.3}$$

Suppose the ellipsoid (2.5.3) is entirely inside ellipsoid (2.5.2). Can it be considered, as in the one-dimensional case, that the normal vector Y is, in some sense, "better" than the normal vector X ? In this respect it is not difficult to prove the following assertion.

Theorem 2.5.1.

Let $\alpha = (\alpha_1, \ldots, \alpha_n)$ be any vector. We form the scalar products of vectors $X - M$ and $Y - M$ with the vector α:

$$\xi = \sum_{i=1}^{n} \alpha_i (x_i - m_i); \quad \eta = \sum_{i=1}^{n} \alpha_i (y_i - m_i). \tag{2.5.4}$$

The quantities ξ and η are normal and $D(\eta) < D(\xi)$, so that, as was explained above, we have

$$P(|\eta| > \varepsilon) < P(|\xi| > \varepsilon). \tag{2.5.5}$$

for any given $\varepsilon > 0$

Proof. We have $E(\xi) = E(\eta) = 0$. On the basis stated above, putting $A = \|\alpha_1; \ldots, \alpha_n\|$, we find that

$$D(\xi) = A^T B_X A > A^T B_Y A = D(\eta),$$

which is what it was required to prove.

In particular, putting $\alpha_i = 1; 0$, we have $D(y_i - m_i) < D(x_i - m_i)$ $(i = 1, 2, \ldots, n)$.

The theorem proved above may be slightly paraphrased. The condition $\left|\sum \alpha_i (x_i - m_i)\right| \leqslant \varepsilon$ defines a plane slab in n-dimensional space with centre of symetry at $(m_1, \ldots, m_n)$. For any $\varepsilon > 0$ the probability of falling in this slab is greater for vector Y than for vector X.

The above statement helps us to clarify the real meaning of the method of least squares.

6. Distributions of Random Variables Connected with the Normal Distribution Which are Encountered in Mathematical Statistics

χ^2-distribution. In many branches of mathematical statistics the squares of normal random variables play an important part. In the method of least squares we have very often to consider the sums of squares of independent random errors (without systematic bias), which are very well described by normal random variables with zero mathematical expectations. In view of this the random variable

$$\chi_n^2 = x_1^2 + \ldots + x_n^2, \tag{2.6.1}$$

where $x_1, \ldots, x_n$ are independent unit normal random variables $(x_i \in N(0, 1))$. has great importance. This variate is called "Chi-squared with n degrees of freedom"; n may be equal to 1, 2, 3,.... For $n = 2$ and $n = 3$ the variate χ_n^2 has a clear geometrical meaning; it is the square of the distance of the point with normal random components $x_i \in N(0, 1)$. from the origin of the co-ordinates.

We will evaluate the probability density $k_n(x)$ of the variate χ_n^2. We have

$$P\{x \leqslant \chi_n^2 < x + dx\} \approx k_n(x)\, dx. \tag{2.6.2}$$

Since χ_n^2 is non-negative we have $k_n(x) = 0$ for $x < 0$. For $n = 1$, $k_1(x)$ is calculated immediately. We have, for $x > 0$

$$P\{x \leqslant \chi_1^2 < x+dx\} = P\left\{x^{\frac{1}{2}} \leqslant x_1 < (x+dx)^{\frac{1}{2}}\right\} +$$
$$+ P\left\{-(x+dx)^{\frac{1}{2}} \leqslant x_1 < -x^{\frac{1}{2}}\right\} = 2P\left\{x^{\frac{1}{2}} \leqslant x_1 < (x+dx)^{\frac{1}{2}}\right\}.$$

Further,

$$(x+dx)^{\frac{1}{2}} = x^{\frac{1}{2}} + \frac{dx}{2x^{\frac{1}{2}}} + \dots,$$

so that

$$2P\left\{x^{\frac{1}{2}} \leqslant x_1 < (x+dx)^{\frac{1}{2}}\right\} \approx 2P\left\{x^{\frac{1}{2}} \leqslant x_1 < x^{\frac{1}{2}} + \frac{dx}{2x^{\frac{1}{2}}}\right\} \approx$$
$$\approx \frac{2}{\sqrt{2\pi}} e^{-\frac{x}{2}} \frac{dx}{2x^{\frac{1}{2}}} = \frac{1}{\sqrt{2\pi x}} e^{-\frac{x}{2}} dx,$$

whence

$$k_1(x) = \frac{1}{\sqrt{2\pi x}} e^{-\frac{x}{2}} \qquad (x > 0).$$

Now we will prove the general result:

$$k_n(x) = \frac{1}{2^{\frac{n}{2}}\Gamma\left(\frac{n}{2}\right)} x^{\frac{n}{2}-1} e^{-\frac{x}{2}} \text{ for } x \geqslant 0;\ k_n(x) = 0 \text{ for } x < 0 \qquad (2.6.3)$$

Here $\Gamma\left(\frac{n}{2}\right)$ is Euler's Γ function, defined for $s > 0$ by the integral

$$\Gamma(s) = \int_0^\infty x^{s-1} e^{-x}\, dx.$$

We have proved that $k_1(x) = \frac{1}{\sqrt{2\pi x}} e^{-\frac{x}{2}}$. This agrees with formula (2.6.3) for $n = 1$, in view of the well known equality $\Gamma\left(\frac{1}{2}\right) = \sqrt{\pi}$, which is very easy to prove from the obvious identity

$$1 = \int_0^\infty k_1(x)\, dx = \frac{1}{\sqrt{2\pi}} \int_0^\infty x^{-\frac{1}{2}} e^{-\frac{x}{2}} dx =$$
$$= \frac{1}{\sqrt{\pi}} \int_0^\infty y^{\frac{1}{2}-1} e^{-y} dy = \frac{1}{\sqrt{\pi}} \Gamma\left(\frac{1}{2}\right).$$

We will prove (2.6.3) by induction. We suppose that the formula is true for indices $1, 2, 3, \ldots, n$ and we will prove it for index $n+1$.

The function $k_{n+1}(x)$ is the probability density function of the random variable $\chi^2_{n+1} = \chi^2_n + \chi^2_1$, where the summands χ^2_n and χ^2_1 are independent random variables with probability densities $k_n(x)$ and $k_1(x)$ respectively. Therefore, for the probability density $k_{n+1}(x)$ we have

$$k_{n+1}(x) = \int_0^x k_n(y)\, k_1(x-y)\, dy = C_n \int_0^x y^{\frac{n}{2}-1} (x-y)^{-\frac{1}{2}} e^{-\frac{x}{2}} dy$$

according to the principle of induction; C_n is a certain constant depending only on n. Hence we have

$$k_{n+1}(x) = C_n e^{-\frac{x}{2}} \int_0^x y^{\frac{n}{2}-1} (x-y)^{-\frac{1}{2}} dy =$$

$$= C_n e^{-\frac{x}{2}} x^{\frac{n-1}{2}} \int_0^x \left(\frac{y}{x}\right)^{\frac{n}{2}-1} \left(1 - \frac{y}{x}\right)^{-\frac{1}{2}} \frac{dy}{x} =$$

$$= C_n e^{-\frac{x}{2}} x^{\frac{n-1}{2}} \int_0^1 z^{\frac{n}{2}-1} (1-z)^{-\frac{1}{2}} dz = C'_n x^{\frac{n-1}{2}} e^{-\frac{x}{2}},$$

where $C'_n = C_n \int_0^1 z^{\frac{n}{2}-1} (1-z)^{-\frac{1}{2}} dz$ is a new constant, depending only on n. We notice that, for calculating C'_n we must have

$$\int_0^\infty k_{n+1}(x)\, dx = C'_n \int_0^\infty x^{\frac{n-1}{2}} e^{-\frac{x}{2}} dx = 1.$$

Putting $\frac{x}{2} = y$, we obtain

$$C'_n 2^{\frac{n-1}{2}} \int_0^\infty y^{\frac{n+1}{2}-1} e^{-y} dy = 1,$$

or, by definition of Γ-function, $C'_n \cdot 2^{\frac{n+1}{2}} \Gamma\left(\frac{n+1}{2}\right) = 1$, so that

$$C'_n = \frac{1}{2^{\frac{n+1}{2}} \Gamma\left(\frac{n+1}{2}\right)}$$

and

$$k_{n+1}(x) = \frac{1}{2^{\frac{n+1}{2}} \Gamma\left(\frac{n+1}{2}\right)} x^{\frac{n+1}{2}-1} e^{-\frac{x}{2}} \quad (x > 0),$$

which is what it was required to prove. Thus, formula (2.6.3) is true for all positive integral n.

In statistical calculations we have to use not $k_n(x)$, but

$$K_n(x)=\int_0^x k_n(t)\,dt=P\{\chi_n^2<x\};$$

this function (removing the multiplier $\frac{1}{2^{\frac{n}{2}}\Gamma\left(\frac{n}{2}\right)}$) is sometimes called an incomplete Γ-function. There exist for it double-entry tables against degrees of freedom n and argument x.

We note some properties of the random variable χ_n^2. By the definition, $\chi_n^2=x_1^2+\ldots+x_n^2$, where the x_i are independent. In view of this we have $\chi_n^2=\chi_p^2+\chi_q^2$, if p and q are arbitrary integral numbers, $p+q=n$, and χ_p^2 and χ_q^2 are independent. Therefore we must have

$$k_n(x)=\int_0^x k_p(y)\,k_q(x-y)\,dy;\quad p+q=n. \tag{2.6.4}$$

This equality is called the law of composition of densities.

We often meet distributions directly connected with χ_n^2. If $X=y_1^2+\ldots+y_n^2$, where the random variables $\frac{y_i}{\sigma}\in N(0,1)$ and are independent, then $\frac{X}{\sigma^2}=\left(\frac{y_1}{\sigma}\right)^2+\ldots+\left(\frac{y_n}{\sigma}\right)^2$, where $\frac{y_i}{\sigma}\in N(0,1)$ and independent. Hence $X/\sigma^2=\chi_n^2$, or $X=\sigma^2\chi_n^2$.

Variables of the form $\frac{1}{n}X=\frac{1}{n}(y_1^2+\ldots+y_n^2)$; (the mean value of y_i's),

$\sqrt{X}=\sqrt{y_1^2+\ldots+y_n^2}$; $\sqrt{\frac{X}{n}}=\sqrt{\frac{1}{n}(y_1^2+\ldots+y_n^2)}$ are also encountered. They have probability densities directly connected with $k_n(x)$ and easily evaluated by formula (2.4.5) from (2.6.3). We give a summary of expressions for such densities (see Cramér [25]).

Variate	Probability density function
$X=\sum_{i=1}^{n} y_i^2$	$\frac{1}{\sigma^2}k_n\left(\frac{y}{\sigma^2}\right)=\frac{1}{2^{\frac{n}{2}}\Gamma\left(\frac{n}{2}\right)\sigma^n}\,y^{\frac{n}{2}-1}e^{-\frac{y}{2\sigma^2}}$

$$\frac{1}{n}X=\frac{1}{n}\sum_{i=1}^{n}y_i^2 \qquad \frac{n}{\sigma^2}k_n\left(\frac{ny}{\sigma^2}\right)=\frac{\left(\frac{n}{2}\right)^{\frac{n}{2}}}{\Gamma\left(\frac{n}{2}\right)\sigma^n}y^{\frac{n}{2}-1}e^{-\frac{ny}{2\sigma^2}}$$

$$\sqrt{X}=\sqrt{\sum_{i=1}^{n}y_i^2} \qquad \frac{2y}{\sigma^2}k_n\left(\frac{y^2}{\sigma^2}\right)=\frac{2}{2^{\frac{n}{2}}\sigma^n\Gamma\left(\frac{n}{2}\right)}y^{n-1}e^{-\frac{y^2}{2\sigma^2}}$$

$$\sqrt{\frac{X}{n}}=\sqrt{\frac{1}{n}\sum_{i=1}^{n}y_i^2} \qquad \frac{2ny}{\sigma^2}k_n\left(\frac{ny^2}{\sigma^2}\right)=\frac{2\left(\frac{n}{2}\right)^{\frac{n}{2}}}{\sigma^n\Gamma\left(\frac{n}{2}\right)}y^{n-1}e^{-\frac{n}{2\sigma^2}y^2}$$

Visual representation is obtainable for $n=2$ and $n=3$. If the horizontal and vertical deviations of a point of impact from the centre of a target, y_1 and y_2 respectively, are independent and $y_i \in N(0, \sigma)$, then the distance $r=\sqrt{y_1^2+y_2^2}$ of the point of impact from the centre of the target has the probability density function

$$\frac{2y}{\sigma^2}k_2\left(\frac{y^2}{\sigma^2}\right)=\frac{y}{\sigma^2}e^{-\frac{y^2}{2\sigma^2}}.$$

If $y_i \in N(0, \sigma)$ are statistically independent components of the velocity of motion of a molecule in rectangular co-ordinates, then the distance $r=\sqrt{y_1^2+y_2^2+y_3^2}$ has the probability density function

$$\frac{2y}{\sigma^2}k_3\left(\frac{y^2}{\sigma^2}\right)=\sqrt{\frac{2}{\pi}}\frac{y^2}{\sigma^3}e^{-\frac{y^2}{2\sigma^2}}.$$

Student's distribution. This distribution plays an important part in statistical calculations connected with the normal law $N(a, \sigma)$, where σ is unknown and estimated on the basis of experimental data; for example, in the statistical analysis of observations with unknown accuracy. Let y; $y_1, y_2, \ldots, y_n$ be independent normal variates with zero mean and common variance σ^2. The non-dimensional quantity

$$t=\frac{y}{\sqrt{\frac{1}{n}\sum_{i=1}^{n}y_i^2}} \qquad (2.6.5)$$

is called Student's* ratio. We see that its distribution is independent of σ by virtue of the non-dimensionality of t, so that, without loss of generality, we can assume $\sigma=1$; y, $y_i \in N(0, 1)$. The number

* Student - pseudonym of the English statistician W. Gosset

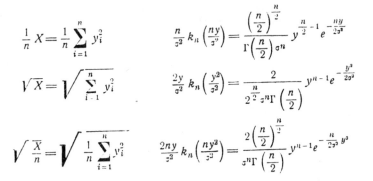

n is called the number of degrees of freedom of t. The probability density function of t has the expression

$$s_n(x) = \frac{1}{\sqrt{\pi n}} \frac{\Gamma\left(\frac{n+1}{2}\right)}{\Gamma\left(\frac{n}{2}\right)} \left(1 + \frac{x^2}{n}\right)^{-\frac{n+1}{2}}. \tag{2.6.6.}$$

We will prove this formula. First we calculate

$$S_n(x) = \int_{-\infty}^{x} s_n(t)\, dt = P(t < x)$$

(this function is useful in calculations and it is tabulated in double-entry tables for n and x).

We have $t = \dfrac{y}{\sqrt{\frac{1}{n} X}}$ in the notation of the table on page 67; we put $\sigma = 1$. The joint probability density function of y and $\sqrt{\frac{X}{n}}$ at the point (u, v) is equal to

$$c_n v^{n-1} \exp -\left(\frac{u^2 + nv^2}{2}\right). \tag{2.6.7}$$

where

$$c_n = \sqrt{\frac{2}{\pi}} \frac{n^{\frac{n}{2}} 2^{-\frac{n}{2}}}{\Gamma\left(\frac{n}{2}\right)}. \tag{2.6.8}$$

We have

$$S_n(x) = P\left(\frac{y}{\sqrt{\frac{1}{n} X}} < x\right) = c_n \int\int_{\Omega} v^{n-1} \exp -\frac{u^2 + nv^2}{2}\, du\, dv,$$

where Ω is the region $\{v > 0,\ u \leqslant vx\}$. To calculate the double integral we introduce the new variables $\frac{u}{v} = \alpha$, $v = \beta$. Then, we obtain

$$J = \frac{\partial(u, v)}{\partial(\alpha, \beta)} = \begin{vmatrix} v & 0 \\ 0 & 1 \end{vmatrix} = v = \beta > 0,$$

whence

$$S_n(x) = c_n \int_0^x d\alpha \int_0^\infty \beta^n \exp -\left(\frac{n + \alpha^2}{2} \beta^2\right) d\beta.$$

Further, we make the substitution $\beta = z^{\frac{1}{2}}$, $d\beta = \frac{1}{2} z^{-\frac{1}{2}} dz$, so that

$$\int_0^\infty \beta^n \exp -\left(\frac{n+\alpha^2}{2}\beta^2\right) d\beta = \frac{1}{2}\int_0^\infty z^{\frac{n+1}{2}-1} \exp -\left(\frac{n+\alpha^2}{2} z\right) dz =$$

$$= 2^{\frac{n-1}{2}} \Gamma\left(\frac{n+1}{2}\right) \frac{1}{(n+\alpha^2)^{\frac{n+1}{2}}},$$

whence

$$S_n(x) = 2^{\frac{n-1}{2}} \Gamma\left(\frac{n+1}{2}\right) c_n \int_{-\infty}^{x} \frac{d\alpha}{(n+\alpha^2)^{\frac{n+1}{2}}}.$$

Substituting the value of c_n from (2.6.8) we find

$$S_n(x) = \frac{1}{\sqrt{\pi n}} \frac{\Gamma\left(\frac{n+1}{2}\right)}{\Gamma\left(\frac{n}{2}\right)} \int_{-\infty}^{x} \frac{d\alpha}{\left(1+\frac{\alpha^2}{n}\right)^{\frac{n+1}{2}}},$$

whence formula (2.6.7) is obtained by differentiation with respect to x. For large values of n, and x bounded, the variate $\left(1+\frac{x^2}{n}\right)^{-\frac{n+1}{2}}$ in the formula (2.6.6) is approximated by $e^{-\frac{x^2}{2}}$, and the multiplicand $\frac{1}{\sqrt{\pi n}} \frac{\Gamma\left(\frac{n+1}{2}\right)}{\Gamma\left(\frac{n}{2}\right)}$ is approximated by $\frac{1}{\sqrt{2\pi}}$, therefore, Student's distribution is approximated by the normal distribution $N(0, 1)$, which in fact was used for the tabulation of $S_n(x)$ for larger numbers of degrees of freedom. This property of $S_n(x)$ can also been seen without difficulty from the definition of the ratio t.

The table of Student's distribution $S_n(x)$ (Table I of the Appendix) has two entries - the number of degrees of freedom n and the probability (confidence coefficient), p_0. According to these two entries Table I gives a number γ such that

$$P\{|t_n| \leqslant \gamma\} = p_0,$$

where t_n is Student's ratio with n degrees of freedom.

Fisher's distribution. This distribution is encountered in problems of comparison and estimation of unknown variances of normal distributions, on the basis of experimental data about them. Let the variates $x_1, \ldots, x_m; \ y_1, \ldots, y_n$ be independent and normal $N(0, \sigma)$. We form the non-dimensional ratio

$$\varkappa = \frac{\sum_{i=1}^{m} x_i^2}{\sum_{i=1}^{n} y_i^2}. \tag{2.6.9}$$

We see that the distribution of the ratio $\varkappa$, by virtue of its non-dimensionality, is independent of σ, and we can assume $\sigma = 1$. Let $F_{mn}(x) = P(\varkappa < x)$ and $f_{mn}(x) = F'_{mn}(x)$. Evidently $f_{mn}(x) = 0$ for $x < 0$. We will prove that

$$f_{mn}(x) = \frac{\Gamma\left(\frac{m+n}{2}\right)}{\Gamma\left(\frac{m}{2}\right)\Gamma\left(\frac{n}{2}\right)} \frac{x^{\frac{m}{2}-1}}{(x+1)^{\frac{m+n}{2}}} \ (x > 0). \tag{2.6.10}$$

We can write

$$\varkappa = \frac{\chi_m^2}{\chi_n^2}, \tag{2.6.11}$$

where χ_m^2 and χ_n^2 are independent. Further calculations are carried out in the same way as in the case of Student's distribution. The joint probability density function of the variables χ_m^2 and χ_n^2 (at the point (u, v)) is of the form

$$c_{mn} u^{\frac{m}{2}-1} v^{\frac{n}{2}-1} e^{-\frac{u+v}{2}}, \tag{2.6.12}$$

where

$$c_{mn} = \frac{1}{2^{\frac{m+n}{2}} \Gamma\left(\frac{m}{2}\right)\Gamma\left(\frac{n}{2}\right)}.$$

Firstly $P(\varkappa < x)$, is calculated, so that the region of integration is Ω: $\{v > 0, \ u \leqslant vx\}$ $(x > 0)$. Introducing the same substitutions α, β, for u, v as before, we find

$$F_{mn}(x) = P(\varkappa < x) = c_{mn} \int_0^x \alpha^{\frac{m}{2}-1} d\alpha \cdot \int_0^1 \beta^{\frac{m+n}{2}-1} e^{-\frac{\alpha+1}{2}\beta} d\beta.$$

Calculation, exactly analogous to the previous calculation, gives

$$F_{mn}(x) = \frac{\Gamma\left(\frac{m+n}{2}\right)}{\Gamma\left(\frac{m}{2}\right)\Gamma\left(\frac{n}{2}\right)} \int_0^x \frac{a^{\frac{m}{2}-1}}{(a+1)^{\frac{m+n}{2}}} da. \qquad (2.6.13)$$

Differentiation with respect to x leads to the required formula (2.6.10). At the end of this book a table of Fisher's distribution (quantiles) is given for a particular case of values m, n used in chapters XI. and XIV.

7. Approximately Normal Distributions and their Rôle in the Theory of Probability

In section 1 of this chapter we have already cited some examples, from which it was clear that the empirical distribution of errors of observations was approximately normal (see Table 6). Many similar examples of approximate normality of empirical distributions have been collected by statisticians; the frequent appearance of approximate normality explains the name of 'normal law'. An important class of cases, in which we deal with approximately normal distributions, is that in which the observed quantitive characters can be described as the resultant effect of a great number of independent causes. This happens in the errors of physical or astronomical measurements, according to the 'hypothesis of elementary errors' by Huygens and Bessel and also in reality. We can assume the approximate normality of distributions in many cases and, almost always, in those cases where we usually apply the method of least squares. A similar situation is encountered in anthropometry, when studying the distributions of growth and sizes of separate organs of people of the same sex and age. This distribution is described with very good approximation by the normal law. Many examples of the approximate normal distribution of characters may be found in national economy; such as the linear dimensions of items of the same type in mass production, the total consumption of electric energy from a given electrical station as the sum of the quantities of energy consumed by each customer, etc.

Naturally, we are speaking only about approximate normality; for instance, many measured characters are essentially positive, while the normal random variable is distributed over the whole axis $(-\infty, \infty)$. Further, we also often have cases, in which some empirical distributions are non-normal. This happens, for example, in heterogeneous populations. Suppose we consider the distribution of measurements of different characters, etc., then we obtain 'multimodal', non-normal distributions (which, however, we can often represent as a 'mixture' of normal distributions).

Often, also, distributions are encountered which are connected with a normal distribution. For instance, the logarithmic-normal distribution of a positive quantity X, i.e. that, for which $\log X$ is normal approximates very well to such empirical distributions as the weight of grains of sand in a single aggregate, the weight of nuggets of natural gold, the weight of small stones from a stonecrusher (see the paper by Kolmogorov [21]).

Zimovnov, in a pamphlet [17], has considered a combination of the normal law with the uniform law on some segments of distribution as a one of many possible laws of distribution for errors in geodesy.

A theoretical basis for explaining the appearance of normality, in a model of 'additive effects of a great number of independent causes' is given by the central limit theorem of Liapunov (see Gnedenko [11]). We cite it here without proof.

Theorem 2.7.1. (Liapunov).
Let $S_n = Y_1 + \ldots + Y_n$ be the sum of n independent random variables with expected values $E(Y_i) = a_i$, variances $D(Y_i) = b_i$ and absolute third moments $\gamma_i = E|Y_i - a_i|^3$ respectively.

We consider the standardized deviation of the sum S_n, i.e. the variate

$$Z_n = \frac{S_n - E(S_n)}{\sqrt{D(S_n)}}; \quad \text{let} \quad F_n(z) = P(Z_n < z).$$

We construct 'Liapunov's ratio' $L_n = \dfrac{\sum_{i=1}^{n} \gamma_i}{[D(S_n)]^{\frac{3}{2}}}$. If $L_n \to 0$ for $n \to \infty$, then for any given number z

$$F_n(z) \to \frac{1}{\sqrt{2\pi}} \int_{-\infty}^{z} e^{-\frac{t^2}{2}} dt \tag{2.7.1}$$

uniformly with respect to z.

We can express the relationship (2.7.1) verbally: Z_n is asymptotically normal $N(0, 1)$, and S_n is asymptotically normal $N(E(S_n), \sqrt{D(S_n)})$.

The condition $L_n \to 0$, expresses quantitively the requirement that none of the summands in S_n dominates the others, i.e. the requirement of 'negligibility in the limit' of the summands.

In the particular case, when all the summands Y_i are identically distributed, the existence of the variance alone is sufficient for (2.7.1) to hold.

The central limit theorem explains very well the appearance of approximate normality in the model of sums of independent, 'negligible in limit' factors. However, it often happens that the separate factors are not independent.

For special types of 'weak dependence' it is also possible to demonstrate approximate normality (see Bernstein [4] and Loeve [31]).

We note also a situation, which is important for us, arising in the analysis of observations, when the functions $\Phi(x_1, \ldots, x_n)$ of 'equal likelihood' of errors of observations are constructed. (See more details about this in chapters III and IV), which should express approximately some measurable factors - such functions as, for example $\frac{1}{n}\sum_{i=1}^{n} x_i^2 - \left(\frac{1}{n}\sum_{i=1}^{n} x_i\right)^2$ and others. These functions, in most cases, are symmetrical (which means equality of accuracy of the measurements). It is found that, for a wide class of such symmetrical functions, it is possible to define approximate normality theoretically. We now cite (without proof) the following theorem of Hoeffding [49].

Theorem 2.7.2. (W. Hoeffding*).

Let $x_1, \ldots, x_n$ be a mutually independent set of random variables, let $\Phi(x_1, \ldots, x_m)$ (m is fixed) be a measurable function such that $E\Phi^2(x_1, \ldots, x_n)$ exists (and consequently, $E\Phi(x_1, \ldots, x_m) = \theta$ exists). We construct the symmetrical function

$$U = \frac{1}{n(n-1)\ldots(n-m+1)} \sum_{(\alpha_1, \ldots, \alpha_m)} \Phi(x_{\alpha_1}, \ldots, x_{\alpha_m}),$$

where summation is over all combinations $(\alpha_1, \ldots, \alpha_m)$ from n different numbers. Then for $n \to \infty$, the distribution of the random variable $\sqrt{n}(U - \theta)$ tends to the normal distribution.

Law of Large Numbers

To understand the real meaning of probabilistic calculations it is often sufficient to apply the law of large numbers in the form of Chebyshev. This theorem is less exact than the central limit theorem, but is proved for less strict conditions.

Theorem 2.7.3.

(Law of large numbers in Chebyshev's form). Let $Y_1, \ldots, Y_n$ be pair-wise independent random variables with expected values $E(Y_i) = a_i$ and variances $D(Y_i) \leqslant L$, where L is the same for $i = 1, 2, \ldots, n$. Let $S_n = Y_1 + \ldots + Y_n$; $A_n = a_1 + \ldots + a_n$. Then, for any arbitrary $\varepsilon > 0$

$$P\left\{\left|\frac{S_n}{n} - \frac{A_n}{n}\right| \leqslant \varepsilon\right\} > 1 - \frac{L}{n\varepsilon^2}. \tag{2.7.2}$$

---

* For simplicity of expression this is a little more stringent than Hoeffding's formulation.

Thus, for large n, and given ε, the ratio $\frac{S_n}{n}$ will lie, with probability as near to 1 as desired, not further from the ratio $\frac{A_n}{n}$ than the 'distance' ε.

CHAPTER III

NECESSARY KNOWLEDGE OF MATHEMATICAL STATISTICS

1. Sample. Statistic

A fundamental concept in mathematical statistics is a sample or a set of observations $X=(x_1, \ldots, x_n)$ of some quantitive character. If this character is a random variable, then the sample $X=(x_1, \ldots, x_n)$ is a random vector. The number n is called the size of sample. The sample is called repeated *) if components of the vector X are independent and identically distributed, so that $P(X_i < x)=F_0(x)$, $i=1, 2, \ldots, n$ ($F_0(x)$ is the distribution function of each component, and the sample is called non-repeated if this condition is not fulfilled.

Any function $g(x_1, \ldots, x_n)$ of the observations $(x_1, \ldots, x_n)$ is called a statistic; a statistic is some arbitrary characteristic of the observations. We will consider statistics of only two types: continuous and discrete (whole number) statistics (principally, the first).

Examples of Continuous Statistics and their Conventional Designations:

sample mean $\bar{x}=\frac{1}{n}\sum_{i=1}^{n} x_i$;

sample variance $s^2=\frac{1}{n}\sum_{i=1}^{n}(x_i-\bar{x})^2$;

sample third central moment $m_3=\frac{1}{n}\sum(x_i-\bar{x})^3$;

sample coefficient of variation $v=\frac{s}{\bar{x}}$;

---

* In English statistical terminology this is a definition of simple sample (translator's remark)

the greatest element in the sample x_{max};

the least element in the sample x_{min}.

An Example of Discrete Statistics (W.N. Gosteb's statistics).
Let the sample $x_1, x_2 \ldots, x_n$ give measurements of diameters of rolling-pins from the current production of a lathe, which have to pass two gauges of width equal to u_1 and u_2, $(u_1 < u_2)$, respectively. Let n^- be the number of rolling-pins passing by the first gauge, n^0 - the number of rolling-pins not passing by the first gauge, but passing by the second gauge, and n^+, the remaining number of rolling-pins $(n^- + n^0 + n^+ = n)$. The quantities n^- and n^+ are discrete statistics characterizing the sample distribution of measurements of rolling-pins.

2. Estimation of Parameters

It is most natural, for our purposes, to approach problems of estimation of parameters from the point of view of the theory of observation errors. We will consider the simpler case of n independent measurements of a physical quantity m, from which is obtained a repeated sample $(x_1, x_2, \ldots, x_n)$ of observations $x_i = m + \Delta_i$, where Δ_i are independent normal errors with zero mean and variance σ_0^2, i.e. $\Delta_i \in N(0, \sigma_0)$. (These errors are called unbiased errors with known equal accuracy). The observations are $x_i \in N(m, \sigma_0)$, so that the probability density function of the observations is

$$f(x, m) = \frac{1}{\sqrt{2\pi}\,\sigma_0} \exp - \frac{(x-m)^2}{2\sigma_0^2}. \tag{3.2.1}$$

In the given case we know the quantity σ_0, and do not know m.

The probability density function of the random vector $X = (x_1, \ldots, x_n)$ (of a repeated sample) is of the form

$$L(x_1, \ldots, x_n, m) = \frac{1}{(2\pi)^{\frac{n}{2}} \sigma_0^n} \exp - \frac{1}{2} \sum_{i=1}^{n} \frac{(x_i - m)^2}{\sigma_0^2}. \tag{3.2.2}$$

With respect to this probability density, the unknown quantity m appears as a parameter of the distribution. We want to obtain the value of the unknown parameter m on the basis of the observations $x_1, \ldots, x_n$ (in the sample). This task is called the problem of estimation of parameter by means of sample values. We see that in a given case it is a problem of measuring a physical quantity in the presence of random errors of observations. The general statement of the problem is as follows. Suppose we have a sample $x_1, \ldots, x_n$, repeated or non-repeated with probability density

$$L(x_1, \ldots, x_n; \quad \alpha_1, \alpha_2, \ldots, \alpha_s), \tag{3.2.3}$$

dependent on s parameters $\alpha_1, \ldots, \alpha_s$. The probability density of the sample has a special name in mathematical statistics - the likelihood function of the sample. From the sample $(x_1, \ldots, x_n)$ we have to construct 'approximations' to the parameter values $\alpha_1, \ldots, \alpha_s$ (to estimate the parameters $\alpha_1, \ldots, \alpha_s$). For this we construct and calculate functions $g_1(x_1, \ldots, x_n)$, $g_2(x_1, \ldots, x_n)$, $\ldots, g_s(x_1, \ldots, x_n)$ of the observations (s 'statistics') chosen in a special way. These statistics are called estimators *) of $\alpha_1, \ldots, \alpha_s$ respectively; the estimator $g_i(x_1, \ldots, x_n)$ of the parameter α_i is a random variable giving, in some sense, a 'good' approximation to the parameter α_i (later, we will use a more informative way of estimation by means of so called conficence intervals, but we will use it in connexion with the method of least squares). In the case of a one-dimensional physical quantity with likelihood function (3.2.2) the 'good' and, in some sense, the 'best' estimator of m is the statistic $\bar{x} = \frac{1}{n}\sum_{i=1}^{n} x_i$. We note that it possesses the following properties:

$$E(\bar{x}) = \frac{1}{n}\sum_{i=1}^{n} E(x_i) = m; \quad D(\bar{x}) = \frac{1}{n^2}\sum_{i=1}^{n} D(x_i) = \frac{\sigma^2}{n}. \tag{3.2.4}$$

In the case of a repeated sample the likelihood function is of the form

$$L(x_1, \ldots, x_n; \alpha_1, \ldots, \alpha_s) = \prod_{i=1}^{n} f(x_i; \alpha_1, \ldots, \alpha_s) \tag{3.2.5}$$

where $f(x; \alpha_1, \ldots, \alpha_s)$ is the probability density function of x_i.

In the case of a repeated sample the observations $x_1, x_2, \ldots, x_n$ appear completely 'equally possible' and therefore, it is natural to use as the statistics $g_1 = g_1(x_1, \ldots, x_n), \ldots, g_s = g_s(x_1, \ldots, x_n)$ for estimating the parameters $\alpha_1, \ldots, \alpha_s$, the symmetrical functions of observations. For the larger size of sample these n functions are, in general, approximately normal (see theorem of Hoeffding 2.7.2).

The random vector $G = \begin{Vmatrix} g_1 \\ \vdots \\ g_n \end{Vmatrix}$, constructed from these statistics is also, in sufficiently general cases, approximately (asymptotically) normal. Asymptotically normal statistics play an important role in

---

* We will call the value of an estimator in any particular case an estimate; in Russian for 'estimator' and 'estimate' the same term 'otsenka' is used (translator's remark).

the theory of estimation of parameters. Besides, the most used methods of estimation: the method of maximum likelihood and the method of moments, which we will discuss later, lead to asymptotically normal estimators which also confirms the importance of these estimators. Thus, in most cases of estimation of parameters, we will deal, for large samples, with asymptotically normal estimators.

We will also introduce the important concept of unbiased and asymptotically unbiased estimators of parameters.

In the problem of estimation of a physical quantity by the sample mean $\bar{x}$, we have had, in the situation there considered, the relationship

$$E(\bar{x}) = a,$$

where a is a measurable physical quantity; we can call $\bar{x}$ an <u>unbiased estimator of a</u>, or estimator without systematic errors.

In the general case we call the vector $G = \begin{Vmatrix} g_1 \\ \vdots \\ g_s \end{Vmatrix}$; $g_i = g_i(x_1, \ldots, \ldots, x_n)$,

a vector of unbiased estimators of parameters $\alpha_1, \ldots, \alpha_s$, or a vector without constant errors, if

$$E(g_i) = \alpha_i \quad (i = 1, 2, \ldots, s). \tag{3.2.6}$$

Why do we want to get unbiased estimators for the measurable parameters $\alpha_1, \alpha_2, \ldots, \alpha_s$? We already have seen that, generally, for large samples, we are concerned with asymptotically normal estimators; according to formula (2.1.3) we also have

$$P\{E(g_i) - 1{,}96\sigma(g_i) \leqslant g_i \leqslant E(g_i) + 1{,}96\sigma(g_i)\} \approx 0.95$$

for large samples. For precise measurements (i.e. for small $\sigma(g_i)$), if $E(g_i) \neq \alpha_i$, then g_i falls often in the neighbourhood of $E(g_i)$ and not of α_i, and this way measures the parameter α_i with systematic error equal to $E(g_i) - \alpha_i$, which is impossible.

However, as well as unbiased estimators g_i of parameters α_i we often apply asymptotically unbiased estimators, e.g. such that $E(g_i) - \alpha_i \to 0$ with increase of sample size for chosen statistics g_i measuring α_i. We cite an example. Suppose we want an estimator of σ^2 from a repeated sample $(x_1, x_2, \ldots, x_n)$ of normal observations $x_i \in N(a, \sigma)$. If we form the sample variance

$$s^2 = \frac{1}{n} \sum_{i=1}^{n} (x_i - \bar{x})^2 = \frac{1}{n} \sum_{i=1}^{n} x_i^2 - \bar{x}^2,$$

then we obtain

$$E(s^2) = \frac{1}{n}\sum_{i=1}^{n} E(x_i^2) - E(\bar{x}^2) = \left(1 - \frac{1}{n}\right)\sigma^2, \qquad (3.2.7)$$

by direct calculation. Thus, this estimator of σ^2 is biased and σ^2 is underestimated. Further, it is clear that an unbiased estimator of σ^2 is

$$s_1^2 = \frac{n}{n-1}s^2 = \frac{1}{n-1}\sum_{i=1}^{n}(x_i - \bar{x})^2,$$

because

$$E(s_1^2) = \frac{n}{n-1}E(s^2) = \sigma^2.$$

However, for large sample sizes, s^2 will be an asymptotically unbiased estimator of σ^2, since $E(s^2) - \sigma^2 = -\frac{\sigma^2}{n} \to 0$ for $n \to \infty$.

3. Accuracy of Estimation of Parameters for a Given Number of Observations

Rao - Cramér *) Inequality

Dealing with unbiased or asymptotically unbiased and approximately normal estimators g_i of parameters α_i, we will regard the variances of the estimators, $D(g_i)$, as a characteristic of their accuracy. If we have two estimators, g and h, with $D(g) = \sigma^2$, $D(h) = \rho^2$, $\rho > \sigma$, then, by virtue of (2.5.1) and (2.1.3), we obtain for any given $\varepsilon > 0$, and in large samples, the relationships

$$P\{|g - \alpha| < \varepsilon\} > P\{|h - \alpha| < \varepsilon\}, \qquad (3.3.1)$$

$$P\{|g - \alpha| \leqslant 1{,}96\sigma(g)\} \approx 0{,}95;\ P\{|h - \alpha| \leqslant 1{,}96\sigma(h)\} \approx 0{,}95. \qquad (3.3.2)$$

From these relationships is clear that a natural measure of accuracy is the quantity $\frac{1}{\sigma(g_i)} = \frac{1}{\sqrt{D(g_i)}}$, which may be called the weight of the estimator g_i.

If the estimator g_i is not approximately normal, then the relationships (3.3.1) and (3.3.2) do not, in general, exist. However, by virtue of Chebyshev's inequality (2.1.9) we obtain for unbiased esti-

* C. Radhakrishna Rao (born 1921) - Indian statistician and mathematician; H. Cramér (born 1893) - Swedish mathematician

mators g_i

$$P\{|g_i-\alpha|\leqslant t\sigma_i\}\geqslant 1-\frac{1}{t^2} \qquad (3.3.3)$$

for any arbitrary $t>0$, which justifies, in a precise way the use of $\frac{1}{\sigma_i}=\frac{1}{\sqrt{D(g_i)}}$ as a measure of accuracy in the general case.

There arises the question, how accurately, in the sense indicated, can the parameters be estimated for a given number of observations (whether there is a lower limit for the variance of the estimator of a parameter for a given size of sample)?

This problem was put forward and solved by Rao [43] and Cramer [24], independently of each other. Here will be presented two Rao-Cramer theorems, the first for estimators of one, the second for a number of parameters. We follow the elegant presentation of Rao [42]*) restricting ourselves to cases of unbiased estimators.

We turn to the case of one parameter.

Let the likelihood function of the sample depend on a parameter α, so that it has the form $L(x_1, \ldots, x_n, \alpha)$, and let $t(x_1, \ldots, x_n)$ be an unbiased estimator for α. We have then

$$\int\limits_R\cdots\int L(x_1, \ldots, x_n, \alpha)\,dx_1, \ldots, dx_n=1. \qquad (3.3.4)$$

Here R is the whole 'sample space', i.e. the set of all points $(x_1, \ldots, x_n)$. Further, we assume that differentiation with respect to the parameter, under the integral sign, is justifiable. We have

$$\int\limits_R\cdots\int \frac{\partial L}{\partial\alpha}\,dx_1\ldots dx_n=0. \qquad (3.3.5)$$

Further, since $Et(x_1, \ldots, x_n)=\alpha$, we have

$$\int\limits_R\cdots\int tL\,dx_1\ldots dx_n=\alpha,$$

whence

$$\int\limits_R\cdots\int t\frac{\partial L}{\partial\alpha}\,dx_1\ldots dx_n=1, \qquad (3.3.6)$$

---

* Filling out some small lacunae in his presentation

or by virtue of (3.3.5)

$$\int_R \cdots \int [t(x_1, \ldots, x_n) - \alpha] \frac{\partial}{\partial \alpha} L(x_1, \ldots, x_n, \alpha)\, dx_1 \ldots dx_n = 1. \quad (3.3.7)$$

To abbreviate the writing we omit the arguments and write (3.3.7) in the form

$$\int_R \cdots \int (t - \alpha)\left(\frac{1}{L}\frac{\partial L}{\partial \alpha}\right) \cdot L\, dx_1 \ldots dx_n = 1. \quad (3.3.8)$$

If $L = L(x_1, \ldots, x_n, \alpha)$ can be equal to zero at some points, then we assume $\frac{\partial}{\partial \alpha} L = \frac{1}{L}\frac{\partial L}{\partial \alpha} \cdot L$, so that the integral is defined. Now, we can write (3.3.8) as:

$$E(t - \alpha)\left(\frac{1}{L}\frac{\partial L}{\partial \alpha}\right) = 1. \quad (3.3.9)$$

It is important to note that here $L = L(x_1, \ldots, x_n, \alpha)$ is considered as a random variable; it is a function of the random vector $(x_1, \ldots, x_n)$.

Putting $t - \alpha = X$; $\frac{1}{L}\frac{\partial L}{\partial \alpha} = Y$, we find

$$E(XY) = 1. \quad (3.3.10)$$

Further, from the inequality (2.1.16) we have

$$EX^2 \cdot EY^2 \geqslant (E(XY))^2.$$

Hence, and from (3.3.10), we obtain

$$E(t - \alpha)^2 \cdot E\left(\frac{1}{L}\frac{\partial L}{\partial \alpha}\right)^2 \geqslant 1, \quad (3.3.11)$$

provided only that the quantities on the left hand side exist as separate integrals.

We will also make a small transformation of the expression $E\left(\frac{1}{L}\frac{\partial L}{\partial \alpha}\right)^2$. We have (for $L \neq 0$)

$$\frac{\partial \ln L}{\partial \alpha} = \frac{1}{L}\frac{\partial L}{\partial \alpha};$$

$$\frac{\partial^2 \ln L}{\partial \alpha^2} = -\frac{1}{L^2}\left(\frac{\partial L}{\partial \alpha}\right)^2 + \frac{1}{L}\frac{\partial^2 L}{\partial \alpha^2}. \quad (3.3.12)$$

If we multiply (3.3.12) by L and integrate over the whole region R, we obtain the expected values of these quantities. Further

$$E\left(\frac{1}{L}\frac{\partial^2 L}{\partial \alpha^2}\right) = \int \dots \int_R L\left(\frac{\partial^2 L}{\partial \alpha^2}\right) dx_1 \dots dx_n = 0,$$

therefore

$$= \int \dots \int \frac{\partial^2 L}{\partial \alpha} dx \dots d\alpha_n = \frac{\partial}{\partial \alpha}\left\{\int \dots \int \frac{\partial L}{\partial \alpha} d\alpha_1 \dots d\alpha_n\right\} = \frac{\partial}{\partial \alpha}$$

$$= 0$$

$$E\left(\frac{1}{L^2}\frac{\partial^2 L}{\partial \alpha^2}\right) = -E\frac{\partial^2 \ln L}{\partial \alpha^2}.$$

Consequently, (3.3.11) can be written as:

$$D(t) = E(t-\alpha)^2 \geqslant \frac{1}{E\left(-\dfrac{\partial^2 \ln L}{\partial \alpha^2}\right)}. \qquad (3.3.13)$$

The quantity

$$E\left(-\frac{\partial^2 \ln L}{\partial \alpha^2}\right) = -\int \dots \int_R \frac{\partial^2 \ln L}{\partial \alpha^2} dx_1 \dots dx_n$$

(of course, we assume the convergency of the integral by which it is expressed) is called <u>Fisher's amount of information</u>; Fisher was the first to consider this problem. This quantity does not depend on the method of estimation, i.e. on the statistic t, and gives the lower limit of accuracy of any arbitrary estimator.

We arrive at the following conclusion: for a given size of sample, the accuracy of an unbiased estimator of parameter is bounded from below. We will consider some important special cases. Let the sample of observations be repeated, so that

$$L(x_1, \dots, x_n, \alpha) = f(x_1, \alpha) \dots f(x_n, \alpha) \text{ and } f(x_i, \alpha) \neq 0.$$

Then

$$\frac{\partial^2 \ln L}{\partial \alpha^2} = \sum_{i=1}^{n} \frac{\partial^2 \ln f(x_i, \alpha)}{\partial \alpha^2}$$

and

$$E\frac{\partial^2 \ln L}{\partial \alpha^2} = \sum_{i=1}^{n} E\frac{\partial^2 \ln f(x_i, \alpha)}{\partial \alpha^2} = nE\frac{\partial^2 \ln f(x_1, \alpha)}{\partial \alpha^2},$$

because, evidently, the quantities

$$E\frac{\partial^2 \ln f(x_i, \alpha)}{\partial \alpha^2} \qquad (i = 1, 2, \ldots n)$$

are all equal. Hence

$$D(t) \geqslant \frac{1}{nE\left(-\frac{\partial^2 \ln f(x_1, \alpha)}{\partial \alpha^2}\right)}, \tag{3.3.14}$$

so that

$$\frac{1}{\sqrt{D(t)}} \leqslant \sqrt{nE\left(-\frac{\partial^2 \ln f(x_1, \alpha)}{\partial \alpha^2}\right)}.$$

We reach the conclusion: in a very wide class of unbiased estimators, the weight of the estimator from a repeated sample cannot be greater than a quantity proportional to the square root of the number of observations.

An estimator t, for which equality is attained in (3.3.14) is called efficient.

We now return to the case of measurements of a physical quantity $\alpha = m$, with normal distribution of errors, which was considered in section 2 of this chapter.

Here we have

$$L = \prod_{i=1}^{n} f(x_i, m); \quad f(x_i, m) = \frac{1}{\sqrt{2\pi}\,\sigma} \exp - \frac{(x_i - m)^2}{2\sigma^2};$$

$$\ln f(x_1, m) = \ln\left(\sqrt{2\pi}\,\sigma\right) - \frac{(x_1 - m)^2}{2\sigma^2};$$

$$\frac{\partial^2 \ln f(x_1, m)}{\partial m^2} = -\frac{1}{\sigma^2};$$

$$E\left(-\frac{\partial^2 \ln f(x_1, m)}{\partial m^2}\right) = E\left(\frac{1}{\sigma^2}\right) = \frac{1}{\sigma^2},$$

whence

$$D(t) \geqslant \frac{\sigma^2}{n}. \tag{3.3.15}$$

For the special estimator $t = \bar{x}$, we have

$$D(\bar{x}) = \frac{\sigma^2}{n}, \tag{3.3.16}$$

i.e. this estimator has the maximum possible accuracy. Because of this, we can explain the real meaning of this property of an estimator for a very wide class of asymptotically unbiased and asymptotically normal estimators t, for from section 6, chapter II (see formula (2.5.1)) we have

$$P\{|\bar{x}-m|>\varepsilon\} \leqslant P\{|t-m|>\varepsilon\} \quad (3.3.17)$$

for sufficiently large samples, and any given ε.

Now, we will consider the problem of joint estimation of a set of parameters $\alpha_1, \ldots, \alpha_s$. Here the likelihood function of the sample is of the form

$$L=L(x_1, \ldots, x_n;\ \alpha_1, \ldots, \alpha_s).$$

Let

$$t_1=t_1(x_1, \ldots, x_n), \ldots, t_s=t_s(x_1, \ldots, x_n) \quad (3.3.18)$$

be unbiased estimators of the parameters $\alpha_1, \ldots, \alpha_s$ respectively. We form the quantities

$$L_{ij}=-\frac{\partial^2 \ln L}{\partial \alpha_i \partial \alpha_j}, \quad (3.3.19)$$

which are random variables, because they are dependent on a random sample. Then, we consider the expected values of these variates

$$I_{ij}=E(L_{ij}); \qquad i, j=1, 2, \ldots, s, \quad (3.3.20)$$

and from these quantities we construct the matrix

$$I=I_{(ss)}=\|I_{ij}\|, \quad (3.3.21)$$

which is called Fisher's information matrix. We note that for $X=\begin{Vmatrix} x_1 \\ \vdots \\ x_n \end{Vmatrix}$ the quadratic form $X^T I X$ is positive definite or semi-definite. It is so, because

$$E\left(-\frac{\partial^2 \ln L}{\partial \alpha_i \partial \alpha_j}\right)=E\left(\frac{1}{L}\frac{\partial L}{\partial \alpha_i}\cdot\frac{1}{L}\frac{\partial L}{\partial \alpha_j}\right), \quad (3.3.22)$$

so that I is the correlation matrix of the random vector

$$\left(\frac{1}{L}\frac{\partial L}{\partial \alpha_1}, \ldots, \frac{1}{L}\frac{\partial L}{\partial \alpha_s}\right) \quad (3.3.23)$$

which has zero mean vector.

We now prove (3.3.22). We have

$$\frac{\partial \ln L}{\partial \alpha_i}=\frac{1}{L}\frac{\partial L}{\partial \alpha_i}; \quad \frac{\partial^2 \ln L}{\partial \alpha_i \partial \alpha_j}=\frac{1}{L}\frac{\partial^2 L}{\partial \alpha_i \partial \alpha_j}-\frac{1}{L^2}\frac{\partial L}{\partial \alpha_i}\frac{\partial L}{\partial \alpha_j},$$

whence, as before, we find

$$E\left(-\frac{\partial^2 \ln L}{\partial\alpha_i \partial\alpha_j}\right) = E\left(\frac{1}{L}\frac{\partial L}{\partial\alpha_i}\cdot\frac{1}{L}\frac{\partial L}{\partial\alpha_j}\right),$$

which is what it was required to prove.

Now, we consider Fisher's information matrix I, which is non-singular: $\det(I) \neq 0$, so that I^{-1} exists. The correlation ellipsoid of the random vector (3.3.23) is of the form

$$X^T I^{-1} X = 1 \qquad (3.3.24)$$

(see formula (2.4.5)).

Now we consider a set of unbiased estimators $t_1, \ldots t_s$ and parallel to (3.3.18), we construct the random vector of deviations

$$(t_1 - \alpha_1,\ t_2 - \alpha_2,\ \ldots,\ t_s - \alpha_s), \qquad (3.3.25)$$

which has zero mean vector, correlation matrix

$$B_t = \|b_{ij}\| = \|E(t_i - \alpha_i)(t_j - \alpha_j)\|,\quad i, j = 1, 2, \ldots, s \qquad (3.3.26)$$

and the correlation quadratic form

$$Z^T B_t Z;\quad Z = \begin{Vmatrix} z_1 \\ \vdots \\ z_s \end{Vmatrix}. \qquad (3.3.27)$$

There is a theorem generalizing inequality (3.3.13).

Theorem 3.3.1 (Rao-Cramér)

For conditions under which Fisher's information matrix $I = \left\| E\left(-\frac{\partial^2 \ln L}{\partial\alpha_i \partial\alpha_j}\right)\right\|$ exists, and is non-singular, and the quantities $E\left(t_j \frac{1}{L}\frac{\partial L}{\partial\alpha_i}\right)$ exist, we have for any arbitrary $Z = \begin{Vmatrix} z_1 \\ \vdots \\ z_s \end{Vmatrix}$

$$Z^T B_t Z \geqslant Z^T I^{-1} Z, \qquad (3.3.28)$$

where B_t is the correlation matrix of the statistics $t_1, \ldots, t_s$ *).

---

* In the proof we assume also permutability of the operations of integration and differentiation with respect to parameters

Proof. We must prove that, for all Z

$$Q = Z^T(B_t - I^{-1})Z \geqslant 0 \quad (3.3.29)$$

i.e. that the quadratic form Q is positive definite or semi-definite.

We make use of the kind of partially defined quadratic form described in section 4, chapter I. If $A = A_{ss}$ is any arbitrary quadratic form, then by $(A)_{kk}$ $(k \leqslant s)$ we will denote a square matrix cut out from the left upper corner of the given matrix, having k rows and k columns ('the main diagonal sub-matrix').

Let $F_{ss} = F$ be any orthogonal transformation. Evidently (see section 4, chapter I), the quadratic form Q is non-negative, if and only if the matrix

$$F(B_t - I^{-1})F^T = FB_tF^{-1} - FI^{-1}F^{-1} = B' - H^{-1}, \quad (3.3.30)$$

is non-negative.
Here

$$B' = FB_tF^{-1}; \; H^{-1} = FI^{-1}F^{-1}, \quad (3.3.31)$$

evidently, also

$$H = FIF^{-1} \quad (3.3.32)$$

Now we construct the correlation matrix of the random vector

$$\left(t_1, \ldots, t_s, \; \frac{1}{L}\frac{\partial L}{\partial \alpha_1}, \ldots, \frac{1}{L}\frac{\partial L}{\partial \alpha_s}\right). \quad (3.3.33)$$

We have $E(t_i) = \alpha_i$, and

$$E\left(\frac{1}{L}\frac{\partial L}{\partial \alpha_i}\right) = \int_R \cdots \int \frac{\partial L}{\partial \alpha_i} dx_1 \ldots dx_n =$$

$$= \frac{\partial}{\partial \alpha_i} \int_R \cdots \int L dx_1 \ldots dx_n = \frac{\partial}{\partial \alpha_i} 1 = 0.$$

By virtue of (3.3.32) we have

$$E\left(\frac{1}{L}\frac{\partial L}{\partial \alpha_i} \cdot \frac{1}{L}\frac{\partial L}{\partial \alpha_j}\right) = \{I\}_{ij}. \quad (3.3.34)$$

Further,

$$E\left[(t_i - \alpha_i)\left(\frac{1}{L}\frac{\partial L}{\partial \alpha_j}\right)\right] = E\left(t_i \frac{1}{L}\frac{\partial L}{\partial \alpha_j}\right) - \alpha_i E\left(\frac{1}{L}\frac{\partial L}{\partial \alpha_j}\right) = E\left(t_i \frac{1}{L}\frac{\partial L}{\partial \alpha_j}\right). \quad (3.3.35)$$

$$E\left(t_i \frac{1}{L}\frac{\partial L}{\partial \alpha_j}\right) = \frac{\partial}{\partial \alpha_j} \int_R \cdots \int t_i L dx_1 \ldots dx_n = \frac{\partial}{\partial \alpha_j} E(t_i) = \frac{\partial \alpha_i}{\partial \alpha_j}. \quad (3.3.36)$$

The last expression, of course, is equal to zero, if $i \neq j$, and is equal to one, if $i = j$.

The relationships (3.3.34) - (3.3.36) allow us to write the correlation matrix of the vector (3.3.33) in the form

$$B_{2s,\,2s} = \left\| \begin{array}{c:c} B_{ss} & E_{ss} \\ \hdashline E_{ss} & I_{ss} \end{array} \right\| \tag{3.3.37}$$

Here the matrix B_{ss} is the correlation matrix of the vector $t = (t_1, \ldots, t_s)$; I_{ss} is the correlation matrix of the vector $l = \left(\frac{1}{L}\frac{\partial L}{\partial \alpha_1}, \ldots, \frac{1}{L}\frac{\partial L}{\partial \alpha_s}\right)$, and the unit matrix E_{ss} coincides with the matrix $E\left(tl^T\right)$. Let the vectors t and l now be subjected to the orthogonal transformation F, so that we obtain the vectors Ft and Fl Then, B_{ss} is transformed into B', I_{ss} into H and $E\left(tl^T\right)$ into $E\left(Ftl^T F^T\right) = E_{ss}$, i.e. into itself. Now we consider the first k components $(k \leqslant s)$ each of the vectors Ft and Fl, and construct the correlation matrix of the vector, with $2k$ components, so obtained. It is easy to note that we obtain the matrix

$$M_{2k,\,2k} = \left\| \begin{array}{c:c} (B')_{kk} & E_{kk} \\ \hdashline E_{kk} & (H)_{kk} \end{array} \right\|. \tag{3.3.38}$$

In fact, putting $F = \|f_{ij}\|$ we find

$$E\left(\sum_{j=1}^{s} f_{ij}t_j \sum_{n=1}^{s} f_{mn}l_n\right) = 0$$

for $i \neq m$ and

$$E\left(\sum_{j=1}^{s} f_{ij}t_j \sum_{n=1}^{s} f_{mn}l_n\right) = 1$$

for $i = m$ by virtue of (3.3.36). Thus, the matrix (3.3.38) is a correlation matrix and therefore non-negative (implying a definite or semi-definite quadratic form).

Now we choose F in (3.3.31) so that H is a diagonal matrix. Then, $(H)_{kk}$ is also a diagonal matrix and we have the simple, but for us important, property:

$$\left(H^{-1}\right)_{kk} = (H)_{kk}^{-1}. \tag{3.3.39}$$

Now we consider an auxiliary matrix

$$N_{2k,\,2k} = \left\| \begin{array}{c:c} E_{kk} & -(H)_{kk}^{-1} \\ \hdashline 0 & (H)_{kk}^{-1} \end{array} \right\|. \tag{3.3.40}$$

According to Laplace's theorem (section 2, chapter I) we have

$$\det(N_{2k,\,2k}) = [\det(H)_{kk}]^{-1} > 0 \qquad (k = 1,\ 2,\ \ldots,\ s). \qquad (3.3.41)$$

Remembering that

$$\det(M_{2k,\,2k}) \geqslant 0; \qquad (k = 1,\ 2,\ \ldots,\ s), \qquad (3.3.42)$$

we find

$$\det(N_{2k,\,2k} \cdot M_{2k,\,2k}) \geqslant 0; \quad (k = 1,\ 2,\ \ldots,\ s). \qquad (3.3.43)$$

But we have

$$N_{2k,\,2k} \cdot M_{2k,\,2k} = \left\| \begin{array}{c|c} E_{kk} & -(H)_{kk}^{-1} \\ \hline 0_{kk} & (H)_{kk}^{-1} \end{array} \right\| \cdot \left\| \begin{array}{c|c} (B')_{kk} & E_{kk} \\ \hline E_{kk} & (H)_{kk} \end{array} \right\| =$$

$$= \left\| \begin{array}{c|c} (B')_{kk} - (H)_{kk}^{-1} & 0_{kk} \\ \hline 0_{kk} & E_{kk} \end{array} \right\| = \left\| \begin{array}{c|c} (B')_{kk} - (H^{-1})_{kk} & 0_{kk} \\ \hline (H^{-1})_{kk} & E_{kk} \end{array} \right\|$$

by the rule for multiplying partitioned matrices (section 2, chapter I) and applying (3.3.9). Hence

$$\det[(B')_{kk} - (H^{-1})_{kk}] \geqslant 0; \quad k = 1,\ 2,\ \ldots,\ s. \qquad (3.3.44)$$

Exactly analogously we could take the components with indices $i_1, i_2, \ldots, i_k$ in the place of the first k components ($k \leqslant s$) of the vectors Ft and Fl. Then a relationship is obtained analogous to (3.3.34) in which, in the place of the principal diagonal minors, there are principal minors with column and row numbers $i_1, i_2, \ldots, i_k$. From this it follows that the matrix $B' - H^{-1}$ is non-negative. Then, by virtue of earlier work, the matrix $B_t - I^{-1}$ is also non-negative, which is what it was required to prove.

Let $Y = \left\| \begin{array}{c} y_1 \\ \cdot \\ \cdot \\ y_s \end{array} \right\|$ be a unit vector $\left(\sum_{i=1}^{s} y_i^2 = 1 \right)$; we project onto it the random vector $(t_1, \ldots, t_s)$; we obtain (see section 4, chapter II) a random variable with variance $Y^T B_t Y$ and

$$Y^T B_t Y \geqslant Y^T I^{-1} Y. \qquad (3.3.45)$$

This means that the correlation ellipsoid, $Y^T B_t^{-1} Y = 1$ of the random vector $(t_1, \ldots, t_s)$ contains the fixed ellipsoid $Y^T I Y = 1$ (see theorems of section 4, chapter II). In the case, when the correlation ellipsoid of the system of unbiased estimators $t_1^{(0)}, \ldots, t_s^{(0)}$ having the form $Y^T B_0^{-1} Y = 1$ coincides with the ellipsoid $Y^T I Y = 1$, all other systems of unbiased estimators have correlation ellipsoids containing the given ellipsoid. The system of estimators $t_1^{(0)}, \ldots, t_s^{(0)}$ is called in this case a system of jointly efficient estimators. A similar case is met with in the theory of the method of least squares, but much more often we meet systems of asymptotically unbiased and asymptotically jointly efficient estimators. By this we understand sequences of systems of estimators of parameters $\alpha_1, \ldots, \alpha_s$: $(t_{1\nu}, \ldots t_{s\nu})$, depending on the sample size n, asymptotically unbiased and having the correlation ellipsoid $Y^T(B^{(\nu)})^{-1}Y = 1$ such that for $n \to \infty$ it approaches asymptotically to the ellipsoid $Y^T IY = 1$ given by Fisher's information matrix.

4. Supplementary Knowledge of the Estimation of Parameters. Fundamental Methods of Estimation

We will consider the problem of the real meaning of jointly efficient estimators. Let $t_1, \ldots, t_s$ be any system of unbiased estimators of the parameters $\alpha_1, \ldots \alpha_s$, and let $t_1^{(0)}, \ldots t_s^{(0)}$ be a system of jointly efficient estimators. We construct the random vectors of deviations $(\Delta_1^{(0)}, \ldots, \Delta_s^{(0)})$, where $\Delta_i^{(0)} = t_i^{(0)} - \alpha_i$, and $(\Delta_1, \Delta_2, \ldots, \Delta_s)$, where $\Delta_i = t_i - \alpha_i$. The correlation ellipsoid of the vector $(\Delta_1^{(0)}, \ldots, \Delta_s^{(0)})$ lies inside the correlation ellipsoid of the vector $(\Delta_1, \ldots, \Delta_s)$. Now we can apply theorem 2.5.1. Let

$$\xi = \sum \beta_i \Delta_i; \quad \eta = \sum \beta_i \Delta_i^{(0)},$$

where β_i $(i = 1, 2, \ldots, s)$ are any fixed numbers. Then, for any arbitrary fixed $\varepsilon > 0$

$$P\{|\eta| > \varepsilon\} < P\{|\xi| > \varepsilon\}, \tag{3.4.1}$$

i.e. for any given linear combination of deviations of estimators from the true values of parameters, the probability of a deviation greater than ε is less for the system of jointly efficient estimators than for other estimators of a very wide class of unbiased estimators. In particular, we can take, in (3.4.1) $\xi = \Delta_i$, $\eta = \Delta_i^{(0)}$ $(i = 1, 2, \ldots, s)$.

For a sequence of asymptotically unbiased and asymptotically jointly efficient estimators the assertion (3.4.1) is fulfilled for sufficiently large samples and with accuracy up to a term which tends to zero.

We will consider fundamental methods of estimation of parameters. The fundamental methods of estimation of parameters in mathematical statistics are the method of maximum likelihood and the method of moments. The method of moments was introduced by Pearson *).

Suppose we have a repeated sample $x_1, \ldots, x_n$ with the likeli-

---

* Pearson (1857-1936) - English statistician

hood function

$$L(x_1, \ldots, x_n; \alpha_1, \ldots, \alpha_s) = \prod_{i=1}^{n} f(x_i; \alpha_1, \ldots, \alpha_s). \quad (3.4.2)$$

We construct s sample moments

$$a_\nu = \frac{x_1^\nu + \ldots + x_n^\nu}{n}; \qquad \nu = 1, 2, \ldots, s. \qquad (3.4.3)$$

If $Ex_i^{2\nu} = \alpha'_{2\nu}$, exists, then for $n \to \infty$ the law of large numbers is valid (see section 7, chapter II), so that

$$P\{|a_\nu - \alpha'_\nu| > \varepsilon\} \to 0 \quad \text{for} \quad n \to \infty,$$

i.e. for large size of sample the estimate a_ν is near α'_ν with high probability. Therefore it is natural to construct the equation

$$\alpha'_\nu = \int_{-\infty}^{\infty} x^\nu f(x_1, \alpha_1, \ldots, \alpha_s)\, dx = a_\nu \qquad (\nu = 1, 2, \ldots, s), \quad (3.4.4)$$

from which we find estimators of the parameters $\alpha_1, \ldots, \alpha_s$. For $n \to \infty$ these estimators are asymptotically unbiased and asymptotically normal with variances of order $\frac{1}{n}$. We will not pause to give examples, because this method, although used sometimes for its comparative simplicity, is not theoretically the best. For us it is important, since it leads to asymptotically normal estimators.

The method of maximum likelihood was derived by Bernoulli *) (1776) and Gauss, but systematically worked out by Fisher (1912). In this method we choose those estimators of the parameters $\alpha_1, \ldots, \alpha_s$, which give the maximum value for the likelihood function $L(x_1, \ldots, x_n; \alpha_1, \ldots, \alpha_s)$, if we substitute them in place of $\alpha_1, \ldots, \alpha_s$.

We note that, in this way, we obtain the maximum of the sample probability density but not 'the most probable values' as is said in old text-books. Generally, distributions having probability density functions do not have 'most probable values', because the probability of any particular value is equal to zero.

In the case of a repeated sample, when the likelihood function is of the form (3.22.5) and we assume the necessary differentiations are possible, the likelihood equations take the form

$$\frac{\partial \ln L}{\partial \alpha_i} = \sum_{j=1}^{n} \frac{\partial \ln f(x_j; \alpha_1, \ldots, \alpha_s)}{\partial \alpha_i} = 0; \qquad i = 1, 2, \ldots, s. \quad (3.4.5)$$

The estimators obtained by the method of maximum likelihood are usually denoted by $\alpha_1, \ldots, \alpha_s$. They possess a series of remarkable properties, which will be presented here, without proofs, for the case of a single parameter α.

---

* Akad. V.I. Smirnov called my attention to this

Let $f(x, \alpha)$ be the probability density of x so that $L = \prod_{i=1}^{n} f(x_i, \alpha)$ is the likelihood function of a repeated sample, and assume that

1) $\frac{\partial \ln L}{\partial \alpha}$ and $\frac{\partial^2 \ln L}{\partial \alpha^2}$ exist and are continuous for all $(x_1, \ldots, x_n)$ and for α in an interval including the value α_0 of the parameter α, which is being estimated. Further, the inequalities:

$$\left|\frac{\partial \ln L}{\partial \alpha}\right| < F_1(x_1, \ldots, x_n); \quad \left|\frac{\partial^2 \ln L}{\partial \alpha^2}\right| < F_2(x_1, \ldots x_n),$$

should be satisfied, where the integrals $\int \ldots \int_R F_1\, dx_1 \ldots dx_n$ and $\int \ldots \int_R F_2\, dx_1 \ldots dx_n$ are convergent;

2) $\frac{\partial^3 \ln L}{\partial \alpha^3}$ exists; $\left|\frac{\partial^3 \ln L}{\partial \alpha^3}\right| < M(x_1, \ldots, x_n)$,

$$|E\{M(x_1, \ldots x_n)\}| < \text{const};$$

3) $E\left(-\frac{\partial^2 \ln L}{\partial \alpha^2}\right) = I(\alpha)$ exists and is not equal to zero.

Then we have the theorems:

Theorem 1.

As $n \to \infty$ the likelihood equation $\frac{\partial \ln L}{\partial \alpha} = 0$ has the solution $\hat{\alpha}$ with probability tending to one and also

$$P\{|\hat{\alpha} - \alpha_0| > \varepsilon\} \to 0 \tag{3.4.6}$$

for $n \to \infty$ and given $\varepsilon > 0$. (Dugué, 1937 [16]).

Theorem 2.

Any solution, $\hat{\alpha}$, of the likelihood equations with the property (3.4.6) gives the maximum of the likelihood function L, with probability tending to one for $n \to \infty$ (Huzurbazar [13]).

Theorem 3.

The solution, $\hat{\alpha}$, of the likelihood equation with the property (3.4.6) is asymptotically normal with mean value α_0. Cramér (1948) [25].

Theorem 4.

The solution, $\hat{\alpha}$, which was considered in the theorems given above, is asymptotically efficient, Cramér (1948) [25].

Most important for us now are the properties of asymptotic unbiasedness, asymptotic normality and asymptotic efficiency of estimators $\hat{\alpha}$ obtained by the method of maximum likelihood. These properties distinguish this method from other methods (such as, for example, the method of moments).

We also give one theorem which will be important later (see Cramér [25], p. 543).

Theorem 5.

If there exist jointly efficient estimators $a_1, \ldots, a_s$ of the parameters $\alpha_1, \alpha_2, \ldots \alpha_s$ and the conditions analogous to 1), 2) and 3) are fulfilled, then the equations of maximum likelihood have a unique solution $(a_1, \ldots, a_s)$.

Examples of the application of maximum likelihood will be given concurrently with the presentation of the method of least squares.

CHAPTER IV

DIRECT MEASUREMENTS OF EQUAL ACCURACY

1. Point Estimation of a Measurable Quantity

Let measurements of a physical quantity a have values $x_2, \ldots, x_n$. We will suppose that these values are the sums of a and random errors

$$\Delta_i = x_i - a \qquad (i = 1, \ldots, n), \tag{4.1.1}$$

where the errors Δ_i are mutually independent and normally distributed. Further, we will suppose that

$$E(\Delta_i) = 0; \quad E(\Delta_i^2) = \sigma^2 \tag{4.1.2}$$

(i.e. $\Delta_i \in N(0, \sigma)$).

The equation $E(\Delta_i) = 0$ means that the measurements are unbiased (without systematic error). If the number σ, which we do not know, is the same for all values of i, we have equally accurate measurements.

It is required to find an approximation to the value of the physical quantity a, on the basis of the observations $x_1, \ldots, x_n$. As we have seen, this is a problem of estimating a parameter a from a repeated sample. We will use for the solution of this problem the method of maximum likelihood (section 4, chapter III). The likelihood function has the form

$$L(x_1, \ldots, x_n, a) = \prod_{i=1}^{n} f(x_i, a),$$

where

$$f(x_i, a) = \frac{1}{\sqrt{2\pi}\,\sigma} \exp - \frac{(x_i - a)^2}{2\sigma^2}.$$

Thus,

$$L(x_1, \ldots, x_n, a) = (2\pi)^{-\frac{n}{2}} \sigma^{-n} \exp - \frac{1}{2\sigma^2} \sum_{i=1}^{n} (x_i - a)^2. \tag{4.1.3}$$

The method of maximum likelihood, for any given σ, leads us to choose $a = \hat{a}$ such that we have

$$L(x_1, \ldots, x_n, a) = \max. \tag{4.1.4}$$

From (4.1.3), it is clear that this is equivalent to

$$Q = \sum_{i=1}^{n} (x_i - a)^2 = \min, \tag{4.1.5}$$

which is also the least squares condition.

Introducing the sample mean

$$\bar{x} = \frac{1}{n} \sum_{i=1}^{n} x_i, \tag{4.1.6}$$

we find

$$Q = \sum_{i=1}^{n} (x_i - a)^2 = \sum_{i=1}^{n} (x_i - \bar{x})^2 + n(a - \bar{x})^2, \tag{4.1.7}$$

whence it can be seen that $\min Q$ is attained if and only if a is replaced by $\bar{x}$, i.e.

$$a = \bar{x}. \tag{4.1.8}$$

Thus, in the present case, estimation by the method of least squares gives $\hat{a} = \bar{x}$ as an approximation to the quantity a. We will now explain the true meaning of this approximation.

We have

$$E(\bar{x}) = a; \quad D(\bar{x}) = \frac{\sigma^2}{n}.$$

Since $\bar{x}$ is a normal random variable, we have

$$\bar{x} \in N\left(a, \frac{\sigma}{\sqrt{n}}\right).$$

This means that $\bar{x}$ is normally distributed with mean equal to the measurable physical quantity a, and with standard deviation equal to $\frac{\sigma}{\sqrt{n}}$. In particular we have

$$P\left\{ |\bar{x} - a| > \frac{1{,}96\sigma}{\sqrt{n}} \right\} = 0{,}05. \tag{4.1.9}$$

For a large number, n, of observations we have, when working with the estimate $\bar{x}$, almost certainly approximation of order $\frac{2\sigma}{\sqrt{n}}$ to the measurable quantity a. Rarely (with probability $< 0{,}05$) is it possible to have larger deviations. Deviations greater than $\frac{3\sigma}{\sqrt{n}}$ have already a probability of about only 0.003. Further, $\bar{x}$ is an efficient estimator of a, since from (3.3.13) we have, for an extremely wide class of other unbiased estimators t of the parameter a, the inequality

$$D(t) \geqslant \frac{\sigma^2}{n} = D(\bar{x}).$$

Thus, on the basis of the discussion in section 5 of chapter II, the true meaning of the estimator $\bar{x}$, obtained by the method of least squares, is this: for an extremely wide class of asymptotically unbiased and asymptotically normally distributed estimators, t, we have, for any arbitrarily small $\varepsilon > 0$

$$P\{|\bar{x} - a| > \varepsilon\} \leqslant P\{|t - a| > \varepsilon\}, \tag{4.1.10}$$

with possibly a few exceptions which disappear as the size of sample increases. This serves to justify the choice of the method of least squares in preference to any other.

2. Estimation by Confidence Intervals

Although we know, that the point estimator $\bar{x}$, obtained in section 1, is preferable with respect to a wide class of other point estimators, it is not possible to say that it is certain to coincide with the measurable quantity a: also, to define its accuracy, it is necessary to know the variance of a single observation. The latter question requires a separate solution. Now we will put forward a new, more perfect method of estimation - the method of confidence intervals, for which we are indebted to the American statistician Neyman [38]. We will not consider this method in its full generality, but only in its application to the method of least squares.

As well as the sample mean $\bar{x}$ we introduce the sample variance $s^2 = \frac{1}{n}\sum_{i=1}^{n}(x_i - \bar{x})^2$. We prove the following theorem.

Theorem 4.2.1.
s^2 is a random variable, statistically independent of $\bar{x}$, and distributed as the variable

$$\frac{\sigma^2}{n}\chi^2_{n-1}. \tag{4.2.1}$$

For the proof of independence of s^2 and $\bar{x}$ we prove first that $\bar{x}$ is independent of the normal random vector $(x_1 - \bar{x}, \ldots, x_n - \bar{x})$ (degenerate, since the sum of its components is equal to zero).

We consider the n-dimensional random normal vector

$$(x_1 - \bar{x}, \ldots, x_{n-1} - \bar{x}, \bar{x}). \tag{4.2.2}$$

The component $\bar{x}$ is uncorrelated with the other components. In fact,

$$E(x_i - \bar{x}) = 0,$$

$$E(x_i - \bar{x})(\bar{x} - a) = E[(x_i - a) - (\bar{x} - a)](\bar{x} - a) =$$

$$= \frac{1}{n}E(x_i - a)^2 - E(\bar{x} - a)^2 = \frac{\sigma^2}{n} - \frac{\sigma^2}{n} = 0.$$

In view of the normality of the probability density function of (4.2.2) this means that $\bar{x}$ and $x_i - \bar{x}$ $(i = 1, 2, \ldots, n-1)$ are mutually independent, therefore $\bar{x}$ does not depend on any continuous function $f(x_1 - \bar{x}, \ldots, x_{n-1} - \bar{x})$. Consequently, $\bar{x}$ does not depend on $x_n - \bar{x} = -\sum_{i=1}^{n-1}(x_i - \bar{x})$, on the set $(x_1 - \bar{x}, \ldots, x_n - \bar{x})$ or on any continuous function $f(x_1 - \bar{x}, \ldots, x_n - \bar{x})$; or, in particular, on $s^2 = \frac{1}{n}\sum(x_i - \bar{x})^2$. It remains to show that s^2 is distributed as $\frac{\sigma^2}{n}\chi^2_{n-1}$. We consider the quantity $\frac{ns^2}{\sigma^2}$ and put $y_i = \frac{x_i - a}{\sigma}$, so that $y_i \in N(0, 1)$.

Then

$$\frac{ns^2}{\sigma^2} = \sum_{i=1}^{n} y_i^2 - n\bar{y}^2.$$

We consider the orthogonal transformation

$$\begin{aligned} z_1 &= \sqrt{n}\,\bar{y} = \frac{1}{\sqrt{n}}y_1 + \ldots + \frac{1}{\sqrt{n}}y_n \\ z_2 &= c_{21}y_1 + \ldots + c_{2n}y_n \\ &\ldots\ldots\ldots\ldots \\ z_n &= c_{n1}y_1 + \ldots + c_{nn}y_n \end{aligned}$$

with the first line given $\sqrt{n}\,\bar{y}$ and the other lines chosen suitably.

From Fisher's theorem (theorem 2.3.2), $(z_1, \ldots, z_n)$ will be a normal vector like $(y_1, \ldots, y_n)$, i.e. $z_i \in N(0, 1)$ and z_i's are mutually independent $(i = 1, 2, \ldots, n)$. Further,

$$\sum y_i^2 = \sum z_i^2, \quad \frac{ns^2}{\sigma^2} = \sum y_i^2 - n\bar{y}^2 = \sum_{i=1}^{n} z_i^2 - z_1^2 = \sum_{i=2}^{n} z_i^2.$$

Thus, the quantity $\frac{ns^2}{\sigma^2}$ is distributed as χ^2 with $n-1$ degrees of freedom (χ^2_{n-1}). From this follows the important theorem.

<u>Theorem 4.2.2.</u>
The ratio

$$t_{n-1} = \frac{\bar{x} - a}{s}\sqrt{n-1} \qquad (4.2.3)$$

is distributed according to Student's law with $n-1$ degrees of freedom.

For the proof we note that $t_{n-1} = \frac{\xi}{\sqrt{(n-1)^{-1}(\eta_1^2 + \ldots + \eta_{n-1}^2)}}$, where $\xi, \eta_1, \ldots, \eta_{n-1}$ are mutually independent normal $N(0, 1)$ variables.

According to results given above, the quantity $\sqrt{\frac{ns^2}{\sigma^2(n-1)}}$ is distributed as $\sqrt{\frac{\chi^2_{n-1}}{n-1}}$, while the quantity $\frac{(\bar{x}-a)\sqrt{n}}{\sigma}$ is independent of it and distributed normally as $N(0, 1)$. Therefore the quantity

$$t_{n-1}=\frac{\bar{x}-a}{s}\sqrt{n-1}=\frac{\bar{x}-a}{\sigma}\sqrt{n}\left(\frac{s\sqrt{n}}{\sigma\sqrt{n-1}}\right)^{-1}$$

is, in fact, distributed according to Student's law with probability density function $s_{n-1}(x)$ (see (2.6.6)), i.e. with $n-1$ degrees of freedom.

The theorem proved provides a way to estimate a by the method of confidence intervals. For the given number, $n-1$, of degrees of freedom we select from Table 1 a value, γ, such that

$$P\{|t_{n-1}|\leqslant\gamma\}=0{,}95. \tag{4.2.4}$$

This means that

$$P\left\{\left|\frac{\bar{x}-a}{s}\right|\sqrt{n-1}\leqslant\gamma\right\}=0{,}95, \tag{4.2.5}$$

or

$$P\left\{\bar{x}-\frac{\gamma s}{\sqrt{n-1}}\leqslant a\leqslant\bar{x}+\frac{\gamma s}{\sqrt{n-1}}\right\}=0{,}95. \tag{4.2.6}$$

In other words, the probability, that the interval with random end-points

$$I=\left[\bar{x}-\frac{\gamma s}{\sqrt{n-1}},\quad \bar{x}+\frac{\gamma s}{\sqrt{n-1}}\right] \tag{4.2.7}$$

covers the unknown value a, is 0,95.

Such an interval I, with random end-points, is called a confidence interval and this method of approach is called the method of estimation by confidence intervals. In comparison with the method of point estimation, this method requires little supplementary computation.

The quantity 0.95, in the present case, is called the confidence coefficient of the confidence interval, and the mathematical expectation of the length of the interval, i.e.

$$E\left(\frac{2\gamma s}{\sqrt{n-1}}\right), \tag{4.2.8}$$

is called the precision of the estimate.

The confidence coefficient can be made equal not only to 0.95, but to 0.99, 0.999 or to any required value, by performing the necessary interpolation in the tables. For a given confidence coefficient the precision is reciprocal to $\sqrt{n-1}$ and for a given number of observations an increase in reliability implies an increase in γ, but a reduction in precision.

We now proceed to the question of the true meaning of the method of confidence intervals. We will assume that the observer obtains a large number N of sets of equally accurate direct measurements of the different quantities $a_1, a_2, \ldots, a_N$, calculating confidence intervals in each case with the same confidence coefficient 0.95, say.

We can then affirm that in a large number N of series of measurements, about $0.95N$ of the confidence intervals I_i constructed from the observations will cover the measured quantity a_i.

To show this, we introduce a random variable ξ_i taking the value one, if the confidence interval I_i covers a_i and zero, if it does not cover a_i. Then $\Xi_N = \xi_1 + \ldots + \xi_N$ is the number of successful observed measurements. Here the variables $\xi_1, \ldots, \xi_N$ are independent and

$$E(\xi_i) = 1 \times 0{,}95 + 0 \times 0{,}05 = 0{,}95,$$
$$D(\xi_i) = 0{,}95 \times 0{,}05 < 0{,}05.$$

Hence, by the law of large numbers (theorem 2.7.3)

$$P\left\{\left|\frac{\Xi_N}{N} - 0{,}95\right| > \varepsilon\right\} \to 0$$

as $N \to \infty$ and for any arbitrarily $\varepsilon > 0$, which proves what we require.

There arises the question - why should we use the confidence interval (4.2.7) and not some other? We note that the mid-point of the confidence interval (4.2.7), the estimator x, found by the method of least squares, which is the point estimator of a, is optimal in a certain sense (see (4.1.10)). It appears that the confidence interval (4.2.7) is also, in a certain sense, optimal, but we will not stop at this point because the matter needs the more advanced theory of the so-called sufficient statistics.

We have seen that $D(\bar{x}) = \frac{\sigma^2}{n}$. Evidently an unbiased estimator of $\frac{\sigma^2}{n}$ will be given by

$$\frac{s_1^2}{n} = \frac{1}{n(n-1)} \sum_{i=1}^{n} (x_i - \bar{x})^2. \tag{4.2.9}$$

For the analysis of observations of the type described a terminology and notations which were also used by Gauss is usually employed. The quantities $\Delta_i = x_i - a$ (in general, unknown to us) are called <u>true errors.</u>

The quantities $v_i = x_i - \bar{x}$ are called apparent errors. Sums of the type $\sum_{i=1}^{n} a_i$ will be denoted by the symbol $[a]$ and sums of the type $\sum_{i=1}^{n} b_i^2$ by the symbol $[bb]$.

Rules for Standard Analysis of Direct, Equally Accurate Observations

a) Point estimation. We find

$$\bar{x} = \frac{1}{n}[x]; \quad s_1^2 = \frac{1}{n-1}[vv]; \quad \frac{s_1^2}{n} = \frac{1}{n(n-1)}[vv].$$

Calculations are facilitated by using a suitably chosen number β and the obvious equations

$$\bar{x} = \frac{1}{n}[x-\beta] + \beta, \tag{4.2.10}$$

$$[vv] = \frac{1}{n}[x-\beta,\ x-\beta] - (x-\beta)^2. \tag{4.2.11}$$

To check the calculation of $\bar{x}$ we use the equation $[v] = 0$.

b) Estimation by the method of confidence intervals. We calculate the quantities $\bar{x}$ and $s = \sqrt{\frac{1}{n}[vv]}$; we select an appropriate value for the confidence coefficient, p_0; this is the first entry in Table I of the Appendix. The second entry is the number of degrees of freedom $n-1=k$. These two entries determine a tabled value γ. The confidence interval

$$I = \left[\bar{x} - \frac{\gamma s}{\sqrt{n-1}},\ \bar{x} + \frac{\gamma s}{\sqrt{n-1}}\right] \text{*)}$$

covers the measured quantity a with the assigned confidence coefficient p_0. If we use the unbiased estimator s_1^2 for σ^2, then the confidence interval for a is of the form

*) Translator's Note:
Despite the definitions: $\sum_{i=1}^{n} a_i = [a]$; $\sum_{i=1}^{n} b_i^2 = [bb]$, so that, in (4.2.11) for example, $[x-\beta,\ x-\beta] = \sum_{i=1}^{n}(x_i-\beta)^2$, the author continues to use the notation $\left[\bar{x} - \frac{\gamma s}{\sqrt{n-1}},\ \bar{x} + \frac{\gamma s}{\sqrt{n-1}}\right]$ to denote confidence intervals, and not quantities like $\sum_{i=1}^{n} \left(\bar{x}_i - \frac{\gamma s_i}{\sqrt{n-1}}\right)\left(\bar{x}_i + \frac{\gamma s_i}{\sqrt{n-1}}\right)$. This should not cause confusion if the context is clearly understood.

$$I=\left[\bar{x}-\frac{\gamma s_1}{\sqrt{n}},\ \bar{x}+\frac{\gamma s_1}{\sqrt{n}}\right].$$

Estimation of the accuracy of measurements using confidence intervals will be described below.

3. Estimation of the Accuracy of Equally Accurate Measurements

The method of confidence intervals has led us to make some inferences about the measured quantity on the basis of a repeated sample with observations $x_1, x_2, \ldots, x_n$, each distributed with probability density

$$\varphi(x)=\frac{1}{\sigma\sqrt{2\pi}}\exp-\frac{(x-a)^2}{2\sigma^2}. \tag{4.3.1}$$

In this method of estimation a knowledge of the value of the variance of the observations, $\sigma^2=E(x_i-a)^2$, which characterizes their accuracy, was not necessary. However, it will often be necessary to study the standard deviation σ on its own account. Such a problem arises in studying the accuracy of the work of measuring instruments, the mechanics of production, the distribution of shells for a given artillery system, etc.

From the point of view of mathematical statistics (see section 2, chapter III), this is a problem of estimating the parameter σ on the basis of the observations $(x_1, x_2, \ldots, x_n)$ in a repeated sample.

As we know (see section 2 of this chapter), the statistic

$$s_1^2=\frac{1}{n-1}\sum_{i=1}^{n}(x_i-\bar{x})^2 \tag{4.3.2}$$

is an unbiased estimator of σ^2, i.e.

$$E\left(s_1^2\right)=\sigma^2. \tag{4.3.3}$$

Study of the statistic (4.3.2), (for example, using W.Hoeffding's theorem 2.7.2), shows that, for any given $\varepsilon>0$

$$P\left\{\left|s_1^2-\sigma^2\right|>\varepsilon\right\}\to 0, \tag{4.3.4}$$

as $n\to\infty$
It is also possible to assess the speed of this convergence. For large samples we can, therefore, take $\sigma^2\approx s_1^2$; $\sigma\approx s_1$ ($\approx$ is a sign of approximate equality). Thus, we obtain approximate point estimators of σ^2 and σ.

We can however, obtain greater exactness by estimating by the method of confidence intervals. This will be based on the result, proved in section 2 (theorem 4.2.1) that the quantity $u=\frac{ns^2}{\sigma^2}$ is distributed as χ^2_{n-1}. We construct the confidence interval

$$I_s = [\gamma_1 s^2, \gamma_2 s^2]. \tag{4.3.5}$$

The probability that this interval, I_s, covers σ^2 is equal to

$$P\{\gamma_1 s^2 \leqslant \sigma^2 \leqslant \gamma_2 s^2\} = P\left\{\frac{n}{\gamma_2} \leqslant \frac{ns^2}{\sigma^2} \leqslant \frac{n}{\gamma_1}\right\} = P\left\{\frac{n}{\gamma_2} \leqslant \chi^2_{n-1} \leqslant \frac{n}{\gamma_1}\right\}.$$

We will denote the probability density function of χ^2_{n-1} by $k_{n-1}(x)$ (see section 6, chapter II).

The confidence coefficient, of covering χ^2_{n-1} by the interval I_s is equal to

$$\int_{\frac{n}{\gamma_2}}^{\frac{n}{\gamma_1}} k_{n-1}(x)\,dx = K_{n-1}\left(\frac{n}{\gamma_1}\right) - K_{n-1}\left(\frac{n}{\gamma_2}\right).$$

Thus, in order to obtain a required confidence coefficient, given $\frac{\gamma_2}{\gamma_1}$, we need tables of the incomplete gamma function $K_{n-1}(x)$. We can use the tables of Slutsky [45]. We will now consider whether this method of estimation is optimal in a certain sense.

To simplify the task we can choose (see Kolmogorov [22]) γ_1 and γ_2, so that

$$K_{n-1}\left(\frac{n}{\gamma_2}\right) = \frac{1-\omega}{2} = P_1; \quad K_{n-1}\left(\frac{n}{\gamma_1}\right) = \frac{1+\omega}{2} = P_2,$$

where ω is the specified confidence coefficient. The corresponding tables are given by Kolmogorov [22].

4. Examples

Example 1.

In determining the amount of charge on an electron, equal to $e_0 \cdot 10^{-10}$ $CGSE$ units, Millikan obtained 58 values for the quantity e_0 (denoted in Table 7 by x_i').

We will estimate the true value a of the amount of charge and the standard error (standard deviation) of the observations σ.

Point estimation of the parameters. We first estimate the true value a and the standard error σ of measurements of e_0. Then the estimators $\bar{x}$ and s_1 for a and σ respectively, are obtained by multiplying the estimators of e_0 by 10^{-10}. We will denote the estimators for e_0 by corresponding letters with dashes.

TABLE 7

x_i'	$x_i'-\beta$	$(x_i'-\beta)^2$	x_i'	$x_i'-\beta$	$(x_i'-\beta)^2$
4,781	0,081	0,00656	4,771	0,071	0,00504
4,795	0,095	0,00903	4,809	0,109	0,01188
4,769	0,069	0,00476	4,790	0,090	0,00810
4,792	0,092	0,00846	4,779	0,079	0,00624
4,779	0,079	0,00624	4,788	0,088	0,00774
4,775	0,075	0,00563	4,772	0,072	0,00518
4,772	0,072	0,00518	4,791	0,091	0,00828
4,791	0,091	0,00828	4,788	0,088	0,00774
4,782	0,082	0,00672	4,783	0,083	0,00689
4,767	0,067	0,00449	4,740	0,040	0,00160
4,764	0,064	0,00410	4,775	0,075	0,00563
4,776	0,076	0,00578	4,761	0,061	0,00372
4,771	0,071	0,00504	4,792	0,092	0,00846
4,789	0,089	0,00792	4,758	0,058	0,00336
4,772	0,072	0,00518	4,764	0,064	0,00410
4,789	0,089	0,00792	4,810	0,110	0,01210
4,764	0,064	0,00410	4,799	0,099	0,00980
4,774	0,074	0,00548	4,799	0,099	0,00980
4,778	0,078	0,00608	4,797	0,097	0,00941
4,791	0,091	0,00828	4,790	0,090	0,00810
4,777	0,077	0,00593	4,747	0,047	0,00221
4,765	0,065	0,00423	4,769	0,069	0,00476
4,785	0,085	0,00723	4,806	0,106	0,01124
4,805	0,105	0,01103	4,779	0,079	0,00624
4,768	0,068	0,00462	4,785	0,085	0,00723
4,801	0,101	0,01020	4,790	0,090	0,00810
4,785	0,085	0,00723	4,777	0,077	0,00593
4,783	0,083	0,00689	4,749	0,049	0,00240
4,808	0,108	0,01166	4,781	0,081	0,00656
			Sum . . .	4,687	0,39209

Thus

$$\overline{x'} = \frac{1}{n}[x' - \beta] + \beta.$$

We take $\beta = 4{,}7$. In Table 7 are given the values of $x_i' - \beta$ and $(x_i' - \beta)^2$ *). We have $[x' - \beta] = 4{,}687$ and $\overline{x'} = \frac{4{,}687}{58} + 4{,}7 = 4{,}78081$ **).

* The intermediate columns can be omitted if the calculations are carried out on a calculating machine with storage facilities

** In the calculation of mean values, when dividing the sum by an integral number we retain in the result more significant figures, recognizing the possibility of losing significant figures in the subsequent calculations. (For example, later, in the calculation of $[vv]$, three significant figures are lost).

This means that the estimate of the amount of charge is $\bar{x} = 4{,}78081 \times 10^{-10}$ units.

The estimate, s_1', of the standard error of measurements of the quantity e_0 is obtained from the formula

$$s_1' = \sqrt{\frac{1}{n-1}[vv]},$$

where

$$[vv] = [x' - \beta,\ x' - \beta] - n(\bar{x'} - \beta)^2.$$

We compute $[vv] = 0{,}39209 - 0{,}37876 = 0{,}01333$. Hence $s_1' = 0{,}0153$. Consequently the estimate for σ is $s_1 = 0{,}0153 \times 10^{10}$ units.

Estimation of parameters using confidence intervals. We will estimate the values of a and σ using confidence intervals, i.e. we will find an interval such that, with a specified probability p_0 (confidence probability, confidence coefficient) we can assert that it covers the value of the estimated parameter.

The confidence interval for the value of a is the interval

$$I = \left[\bar{x} - \frac{\gamma s_1}{\sqrt{n}},\ \bar{x} + \frac{\gamma s_1}{\sqrt{n}}\right];$$

here γ is determined in the table of Student's t-distribution by the condition $P\{|t_{n-1}| \leqslant \gamma\} = p_0$, where p_0 is the specified confidence coefficient, and by the number of degrees of freedom, which is equal to $n - 1 = k$.

We take $p_0 = 0{,}95$. From tables of the t-distribution *), for $k = n - 1 = 57$ and $p_0 = 0{,}95$ we find the value $\gamma = 2{,}02$. Hence $\frac{\gamma s_1}{\sqrt{n}} = 0{,}00406 \times 10^{-10}$, and we have the confidence interval

$$4{,}776 \times 10^{-10} \leqslant a \leqslant 4{,}785 \times 10^{-10}.$$

As was shown in section 3 of the present chapter, the confidence interval for σ^2, constructed on the basis of the χ^2-distribution (with $n - 1$ degrees of freedom) is given by the interval $I' = [\gamma_1'^2 s^2,\ \gamma_2'^2 s^2]$. It corresponds to the probability

$$P\{\gamma_1'^2 s^2 \leqslant \sigma^2 \leqslant \gamma_2'^2 s^2\} = P_2 - P_1 = p.$$

The confidence interval for the standard deviation σ is then the interval

$$I'' = \left[\sqrt{\frac{n}{\chi^2_{P_1}}}\, s,\ \sqrt{\frac{n}{\chi^2_{P_2}}}\, s\right].$$

---

* See Table 1 of the Appendix

We will use the unbiased estimator, s_1^2, of σ^2 so that, using the the equation $ns^2=(n-1)s_1^2$, we write the confidence interval for σ in the form

$$I=\left[\sqrt{\frac{n-1}{\chi^2_{P_1}}}s_1, \sqrt{\frac{n-1}{\chi^2_{P_2}}}s_1\right].$$

The coefficients $\sqrt{\frac{n-1}{\chi^2_{P_1}}}=\gamma_1$ and $\sqrt{\frac{n-1}{\chi^2_{P_2}}}=\gamma_2$ for a series of values of n and p have been tabulated *)

We take $p_1=0{,}90$ $(P_1=0{,}05;\ P_2=0{,}95)$. Then for $k=n-1=57$ we find, from Table III, the values $\gamma_1\approx 0{,}868$, $\gamma_2\approx 1{,}186$; whence $P\{0{,}868\,s_1\leqslant\sigma\leqslant 1{,}186\,s_1\}=0{,}90$. The confidence interval for σ is

$$0{,}0132\times 10^{-10}\leqslant\sigma\leqslant 0{,}0182\times 10^{-10}.$$

We take also, for the same example, $p_1=0{,}95$ $(P_1=0{,}025;\ P_2=0{,}975)$. Then $\gamma_1\approx 0{,}845$, $\gamma_2\approx 1{,}225$, and for the confidence coefficient 0, 95 we obtain the inequality

$$0{,}0129\times 10^{-10}\leqslant\sigma\leqslant 0{,}0188\times 10^{-10}$$

Thus, for a reasonably large confidence coefficient and the given number of observations we find that the estimate of accuracy of the observations is rather coarse, which corresponds to the reality of the situation. It is impossible, in any known way, to make it better.

Example 2.

The English physicist Cavendish published, in 1789, the results of 29 measurements of the density of soil (see the first and fourth columns of Table 8).

It is required to estimate the measurable quantity a and the standard error σ.

We first make a point estimation of the parameters. We put $\beta=5$. An estimate of a is $\bar{x}=\frac{13{,}99}{29}+5=5{,}482$. We now estimate σ. We calculate $[vv]=7{,}948-6{,}749=1{,}199$. The estimate s_1 of σ is $s_1=\sqrt{\frac{1}{28}1{,}199}=0{,}207$.

---

* See Table III of the Appendix

TABLE 8

x_i	$x_i - \beta$	$(x_i - \beta)^2$	x_i	$x_i - \beta$	$(x_i - \beta)^2$
5,50	0,50	0,250	5,34	0,34	0,116
5,61	0,61	0,372	5,79	0,79	0,624
5,88	0,88	0,774	5,10	0,10	0,010
5,07	0,07	0,005	5,27	0,27	0,073
5,26	0,26	0,068	5,39	0,39	0,152
5,55	0,55	0,303	5,42	0,42	0,176
5,36	0,36	0,130	5,47	0,47	0,221
5,29	0,29	0,084	5,63	0,63	0,397
5,58	0,58	0,336	5,34	0,34	0,116
5,65	0,65	0,423	5,46	0,46	0,212
5,57	0,57	0,325	5,30	0,30	0,090
5,53	0,53	0,281	5,75	0,75	0,563
5,62	0,62	0,384	5,68	0,68	0,462
5,29	0,29	0,084	5,85	0,85	0,723
5,44	0,44	0,194			
			Sum . .	13,99	7,948

We now find a confidence interval for a. We take $p_0 = 0{,}90$. The number of degrees of freedom is $k = n - 1 = 28$. From the tables of the t-distribution we find for $k = 28$ and $p_0 = 0{,}90$ the value $\gamma = 1{,}701$. Then $\frac{\gamma s_1}{\sqrt{n}} = \frac{1{,}701 \times 0{,}207}{5{,}385} = 0{,}065$. Thus, for the confidence coefficient 0.90 we obtain the confidence interval

$$5{,}41 < a < 5{,}55.$$

We will estimate the accuracy of the observations with the same confidence coefficient, $p_0 = 0{,}90$. For this confidence coefficient and $k = n - 1 = 28$ we find, from Table III, the values $\gamma_1 = 0{,}823$, $\gamma_2 = 1{,}286$. Consequently, with confidence coefficient 0.90 we have the inequality $0{,}823\, s_1 < \sigma < 1{,}286\, s_1$, or

$$0{,}170 < \sigma < 0{,}267.$$

Example 3.

We take as data some observations of azimuth of Helsinki from basis Elshank-Blagodatao *) (Table 9) in 1926.

We will find a point estimate of the measurable quantity a and of the standard error σ, and we will construct confidence intervals for a and σ.

* Data are taken from a book by A.S.Chebotaryov [51]

TABLE 9

Date	No. of observation	Azimuth x_i	$x_i - \beta$	$(x_i - \beta)^2$
16/IX	1	62°01′11″,46	1″,46	2,132
	2	11,01	1,01	1,020
	3	12,29	2,29	5,244
	4	13,47	3,47	12,041
	5	14,07	4,07	16,565
	6	10,60	0,60	0,360
17/IX	7	10,76	0,76	0,578
	8	14,13	4,13	17,057
	9	12,98	2,98	8,880
	10	10,46	0,46	0,212
	11	11,25	1,25	1,563
18/IX	12	12,02	2,02	4,080
		Sum . . .	24,50	69,732

We put $\beta = 62°01'10''$. The estimate of the measured azimuth a is

$$\bar{x} = \frac{24'',50}{12} + 62°01'10'' = 62°01'12'',04.$$

We now estimate σ. We calculate

$$[vv] = [x - \beta, x - \beta] - n(\bar{x} - \beta)^2 = 69,73 - 49,94 = 19,79.$$

Hence the estimate s_1 of σ is

$$s_1 = \sqrt{\frac{1}{11} 19,79} = 1'',34.$$

We now find a confidence interval for a with confidence coefficient $p_0 = 0,90$. The number of degrees of freedom is $k = 11$. For these values of p_0 and k we have $\gamma = 1,796$. Hence

$$\frac{\gamma s_1}{\sqrt{n}} = \frac{1,796 \times 1,34}{3,464} = 0,69.$$

We obtain the confidence interval

$$62°01'11'',35 < a < 62°01'12'',73.$$

We will estimate σ by a confidence interval. For $k = n - 1 = 11$ and $p = 0,90$, we have, from Table III, $\gamma_1 = 0,748$, $\gamma_2 = 1,550$. Hence, for confidence coefficient 0.90, we obtain the confidence interval $0,748\, s_1 < \sigma < 1,550\, s_1$, or $1'',00 < \sigma < 2'',08$.

Example 4.

There are given the measurements of an angle a in Table 10.

TABLE 10

No. of observ.	Measured value of angle, x_i	$x_i - \beta$	$(x_i - \beta)^2$
1	72°13′38″,3	8″,3	68,89
2	44,6	14,6	213,16
3	33,7	3,7	13,69
4	41,1	11,1	123,21
5	43,0	13,0	169,00
6	36,2	6,2	38,44
7	39,6	9,6	92,16
8	37,8	7,8	60,84
9	40,3	10,3	106,09
	Sum . . .	84,6	885,48

We will find a point estimate of the measurable quantity a, the standard error of measurements, σ, and construct confidence intervals for them.

We put $\beta = 72°13'30''$. Then the estimate of the mean is

$$\bar{x} = \frac{84'',6}{9} + 72°13'30'' = 72°13'39'',4.$$

We now estimate σ. We calculate

$$[vv] = 885,48 - 795,24 = 90,24.$$

Hence the estimate of σ is

$$s_1 = \sqrt{\frac{1}{8}\,90,24} = 3'',36.$$

We now find confidence limits for a. Let the confidence coefficient be $p_0' = 0,90$. The number of degrees of freedom is $k = n - 1 = 8$. From the tables of the t-distribution we find $\gamma = 1,860$, whence

$$\frac{\gamma s_1}{\sqrt{n}} = \frac{1,860 \times 3,36}{3} = 2'',08.$$

For confidence coefficient 0,90 we have the confidence interval

$$72°13'37'',3 < a < 72°13'41'',5,$$

We estimate by confidence intervals. Let $p_0 = 0,90$. Then from

Table III, for $k=n-1=8$ we find $\gamma_1=0,718$, $\gamma_2=1,711$. Hence a confidence interval for σ is $0,718 s_1<\sigma<1,711 s_1$, or $2'',41<\sigma<5'',75$.

5. Outlying Observations

The foregoing methods were applied in situations where the observations $x_1, x_2, \ldots, x_n$ were obtained by repeated sampling from a normal population: $x_i \in N(a, \sigma)$. Sometimes, however, in series of observations there occur figures which, by eye, are sharply distinct from the others. This could be a random occurence, since in a long series of observations it is theoretically possible that there will be values of x_i differing violently from a on both sides, but it could also be ascribed to some special occurrence disturbing the usual mode of formation of random errors, or caused by a gross mistake of an observer.

Consider, for example, the maximum value x_{max} in a series of observations $x_1, x_2, \ldots, x_n$. Following Grubbs [12] we will study the non-dimensional ratio 'of Student's type'

$$v=\frac{x_{max}-\bar{x}}{s}. \tag{4.5.1}$$

If it be supposed that the series of observations $x_1, \ldots, x_n$ are all taken from the same normal population $N(a, \sigma)$, then the distribution of the ratio v will depend on neither of the parameters a, σ, but only on the sample size n. In this case the distribution of v can be computed, and it has been tabled by Grubbs [12] for arguments n and p.

For a given sample size n and a given probability p a number ξ_n can be found such that

$$P\{v \geqslant \xi_n\}=p. \tag{4.5.2}$$

Values of ξ_n are given in Table IV of the Appendix *) for $p=0,10$; $0,05$; $0,025$; $0,01$. We can use the following rule (criterion).

Rule.

To solve this problem it is necessary to select the observation, x_{max} as a gross error, to take a value for p (0.05, say), find ξ_n from Table IV, for the number n of observations and the probability p, and form the ratio

$$v=\frac{x_{max}-\bar{x}}{s}.$$

If $v>\xi_n$, then x_{max} should be rejected as an observation containing a gross error, but if $v \leqslant \xi_n$, then x_{max} can be retained. If we suspect that the observation, x_{min}, deviating on the left hand, is a mistake, then the observations $x_1, \ldots, x_n$ can be changed to $(-x_1), \ldots,$

* Table IV is taken from the paper [12], p. 29.

$(-x_n)$; and $x_{min} = (-x)_{max}$. In this case the same rule can be applied, with v replaced by

$$v_1 = -\frac{x_{min} - \bar{x}}{s} = \frac{\bar{x} - x_{min}}{s}.$$

We will not discuss here in what way this criterion is optimal.

Example.

In Clarke's book 'Geodesy' there are given the results of 20 micro-measurements of marks on a scale:

3,68	5,08	2,81	4,43
3,11	2,95	4,65	3,43
4,76	6,35	3,27	3,26
2,75	3,78	4,08	2,48
4,15	4,49	4,51	4,84

Assuming that the measurements are of equal accuracy, mutually independent and each taken from the same normal population with unknown a and σ, we will judge, whether to treat the value $x_{max} = 6{,}35$ as a coarse error measurement or not.

We form the ratio

$$v = \frac{x_{max} - \bar{x}}{s}.$$

We have

$$\bar{x} = \frac{\sum_{i=1}^{20} x_i}{20} = \frac{78{,}86}{20} = 3{,}943,$$

$$s = \sqrt{\frac{1}{n}\left[\sum_{i=1}^{n}(x_i - \bar{x})^2\right]} = \sqrt{0{,}8892} = 0{,}943.$$

Hence

$$v = \frac{6{,}35 - 3{,}943}{0{,}943} = 2{,}552.$$

From Table IV of the Appendix we find that with $n = 20$, the value of ξ_n for 5 per cent level of significance is equal to 2.623. Since the value of v, 2.552, is less than ξ_n, $x_{max} = 6{,}35$ can be treated as a member of the given series of observations.

6. Improvement of Abbé's Criterion

Abbé's criterion is for testing the hypothesis of the absence of a systematic trend in the observations $x_1, x_2, \ldots, x$ i.e. the hypothesis that

$$E(x_i) = a \qquad (i = 1, 2, \ldots, n). \tag{4.6.1}$$

It would be more natural to study the general question of testing the hypothesis that all x_i's belong to the normal population $N(a, \sigma)$. Testing such a hypothesis is a problem of mathematical statistics. However, since the question of Abbé's criterion (Abbé [1], 1863) is presented in some old text-books (see, for example, Helmert), we shall study it. Abbe's criterion compares the (mean) sum of squares of errors (deviations from the mean) with the (mean) sum of squares of differences between successive observations, which is less sensitive to a systematic trend in the mathematical expectations.

We will express it in a more precise way. We introduce the statistics

$$q^2 = \frac{1}{2(n-1)} \sum_{i=1}^{n-1} (x_{i+1} - x_i)^2,$$

$$s_1^2 = \frac{1}{n-1} \sum_{i=1}^{n} (x_i - \bar{x})^2.$$

We form the ratio

$$r = \frac{q^2}{s_1^2}. \tag{4.6.2}$$

It can be shown (Hald [48]) that, for the case $x_i \in N(a, \sigma)$, we have

$$E(r) = 1, \quad D(r) = \frac{1}{n+1}\left(1 - \frac{1}{n+1}\right).$$

It is also known that, for $n \geqslant 20$, the quantity r is distributed approximately normally with parameters $\left(1;\ \left(\frac{1}{n+1}\left(1 - \frac{1}{n-1}\right)\right)^{\frac{1}{2}}\right)$.

If we have a systematic trend in $E(x_i)$, it is to be expected that s_1^2 will be much greater than q^2. In Table V of the Appendix, for different values of n, there are given numbers r_p such that the probability $P\{r \leqslant r_p\} = p$ $(p = 0{,}001;\ 0{,}01;\ 0{,}05)$. If it happens that, for the observed values $x_1, \ldots, x_n$, $r < r_p$, the probability of such an event would be less than p, if the hypothesis (4.6.1) were true, and therefore we would regard the hypothesis as rejected.

We get the following rule: in order to test for the absence of a systematic trend in the errors of observations $x_1, x_2, \ldots, x_n$, we calculate the quantities

$$q^2 = \frac{1}{2(n-1)} \sum_{i=1}^{n-1} (x_{i+1} - x_i)^2,$$

$$s_1^2 = \frac{1}{n-1} \sum_{i=1}^{n} (x_i - \bar{x})^2,$$

and their ratio $r = \frac{q^2}{s_1^2}$.

Then, from Table V, we find the appropriate number r_p.

If $r \geqslant r_p$, it may be assumed that our observations do not indicate a systematic trend in the mathematical expectations; if $r < r_p$, then we conclude that such a trend exists.

Example.

In the first column of Table 11 are given values (less 400) of the compression resistance in kg/cm^2 for standard cubes. The values were obtained in trials in a production process over 45 days *).

It must be decided, whether we can assume that the mean compression resistance is not subject to systematic variability with time, or, on the other hand there may perhaps take place, in the process of production, periodic changes in the general mean.

We will test the hypothesis of absence of systematic bias in the mean, using the criterion of mean square of successive differences. From the given sample we evaluate the quantities

$$q^2 = \frac{1}{2(n-1)} \sum_{i=1}^{n-1} (x_{i+1} - x_i)^2,$$

$$s_1^2 = \frac{1}{n-1} \sum_{i=1}^{n} (x_i - \bar{x})^2$$

and their ratio

$$r = \frac{q^2}{s_1^2}.$$

Small values of r indicate significance, i.e. for small r the hypothesis is rejected. In Table V of the Appendix are given values of the quantiles of the distribution of the quantity r for $P = 0{,}001$; 0.01; 0.05 and n from 4 to 60.

We give the calculations for our example. The values of the differences, squares of differences and also the sums of squares are given in Table 11 (the mean is $\bar{x} = \frac{3005}{45} = 66{,}778$). Hence

$$q^2 = \frac{1}{2 \times 44} \times 42\,819 = 486{,}6, \quad s_1^2 = \frac{1}{44} \times 37\,336 = 848{,}5.$$

* Data are taken from a book by Hald [48], p. 307-9

TABLE 11

x_i	$(x_i - \bar{x})$	$(x_i - \bar{x})^2$	$x_{i+1} - x_i$	$(x_{i+1} - x_i)^2$
40	— 26,778	717,1	— 7	49
33	— 33,778	1141,0	42	1764
75	8,222	67,6	— 57	3249
18	— 48,778	2379,3	44	1936
62	— 4,778	22,8	— 29	841
33	— 33,778	1141,0	5	25
38	— 28,778	828,2	31	961
69	2,222	4,9	— 4	16
65	— 1,778	3,2	35	1225
100	33,222	1103,7	24	576
124	57,222	3274,4	— 33	1089
91	24,222	586,7	— 12	144
79	12,222	149,4	— 37	1369
42	— 24,778	613,9	21	441
63	— 3,778	14,3	— 40	1600
23	— 43,778	1916,5	24	576
47	— 19,778	391,2	5	25
52	— 14,778	218,4	46	2116
98	31,222	974,8	— 1	1
97	30,222	913,4	— 24	576
73	6,222	38,7	12	144
85	18,222	332,0	3	9
88	21,222	450,4	— 48	2304
40	— 26,778	717,1	2	4
[illegible]	— 24,778	613,9	9	81
51	— 15,778	248,9	— 28	784
23	— 43,778	1916,5	52	2704
75	8,222	67,6	— 23	529
52	— 14,778	218,4	74	5476
126	59,222	3507,2	— 36	1296
90	23,222	539,3	21	441
111	44,222	1955,6	— 19	361
92	25,222	636,1	17	289
109	42,222	1782,7	— 37	1369
72	5,222	27,3	— 44	1936
28	— 38,778	1503,7	28	784
56	— 10,778	116,2	— 39	1521
17	— 49,778	2477,8	35	1225
52	— 14,778	218,4	16	256
68	1,222	1,5	7	49
75	8,222	67,6	27	729
102	35,222	1240,6	5	25
107	40,222	1617,8	— 30	900
77	10,222	104,5	— 32	1024
45	— 21,778	474,3		
Sum . . . 3005		37335,9		42819

We find the ratio

$$r = \frac{q^2}{s_1^2} = \frac{486{,}6}{848{,}5} = 0{,}573.$$

We will compare this with the 5 - level of significance for our criterion, i.e. we will regard an observed r as significant (we reject the hypothesis), if it does not exceed the quantile r_P with $P = 0{,}05$. From Table V of the Appendix we find, for $n = 45$ and $P = 0{,}05$, the value $r_p = 0{,}760$. We see that the observed value of r (equal to 0.573) is less than the 5 per cent quantile (or even the 1 per cent quantile, which is 0.666). Hence the hypothesis of absence of systematic bias in the mean is then rejected.

We note that the quantity r, for large n, is distributed approximately normally with mean equal to 1 and variance $\sigma^2 = \frac{n-2}{(n-1)(n+1)}$. Therefore the quantile r_P of the distribution of r, for $n > 60$, can be computed from the formula

$$r_P \approx 1 + u_P \sqrt{\frac{n-2}{(n-1)(n+1)}}$$

(or with sufficient practical accuracy

$$r_P \approx 1 + \frac{u_P}{\sqrt{n+1}},$$

where u_P is the P-percentage quantile of the normal distribution with parameters (0, 1)).

7. Grouped Direct Measurements of Equal Accuracy

Sometimes cases are encountered in which there are equally accurate measurements of whole groups of physical quantities $a_1, a_2, \ldots, a_r$. The quantity a_i has n_i measurements

$$x_{i1}, x_{i2}, \ldots, x_{in_i} \qquad (i = 1, 2, \ldots, r), \qquad (4.7.1)$$

with the x_{ij} normally distributed, i.e. $x_{ij} \in N(a_i, \sigma)$ and mutually independent. Here the quantity $D(x_{ij}) = \sigma^2$ is the same for all observations x_{ij}.

Taking advantage of the equal accuracy of the measurements, and using all the observations x_{ij} $(i = 1, 2, \ldots, r;\ j = 1, 2, \ldots, n_i)$, simultaneously it is possible to obtain more 'precise' confidence intervals for the quantities $a_1, a_2, \ldots, a_r$ than if the measurements x_{ij} $(j = 1, 2, \ldots, n_i)$ only are used for each quantity a_i.

For each system of measurements (4.7.1) we consider the sample mean $\bar{x}_i$ and the sample variance s_i^2. We have

$$\bar{x}_i = \frac{1}{n_i}\sum_{j=1}^{n_i} x_{ij}; \quad s_i^2 = \frac{1}{n_i}\sum_{j=1}^{n_i}(x_{ij} - \bar{x}_i)^2. \tag{4.7.2}$$

As is known from previous work, (see theorem 4.2.1), the quantity $\frac{n_i s_i^2}{\sigma^2}$ is distributed as $\chi^2_{n_i - 1}$ so that for the sum of the independent quantities $\frac{n_i s_i^2}{\sigma^2}$ we have

$$\frac{1}{\sigma^2}\sum_{i=1}^{r} n_i s_i^2 = \chi^2_{n-r}, \tag{4.7.3}$$

where

$$n = n_1 + n_2 + \ldots + n_r. \tag{4.7.4}$$

We now put $S^2 = \sum_{i=1}^{r} n_i s_i^2$.

The random variable $\frac{(\bar{x}_i - a_i)\sqrt{n_i}}{\sigma}$ is normally $N(0, 1)$ distributed and independent of S^2. Therefore the quantity

$$t_i = \frac{\bar{x}_i - a_i}{S}\sqrt{n_i(n-r)} = \frac{\frac{(\bar{x}_i - a_i)}{\sigma}\sqrt{n_i}}{\sqrt{\frac{\chi^2_{n-r}}{n-r}}}$$

is distributed according to Student's law with $n-r$ degrees of freedom.

For the construction of confidence intervals with specified confidence coefficient p, we find from Table 1, with $n-r$ degrees of freedom, the abscissa γ_p such that

$$P\{|t_i| \leqslant \gamma_p\} = p.$$

Then the confidence interval

$$I_i = \left[\bar{x}_i - \frac{\gamma_p S}{\sqrt{n_i(n-r)}}, \ \bar{x}_i + \frac{\gamma_p S}{\sqrt{n_i(n-r)}}\right] \tag{4.7.5}$$

will cover the measured quantity a_i with probability p. This will be true for $i = 1, 2, \ldots, r$, separately, but the probability that all the a_i's will be simultaneously covered by the corresponding I_i's is not equal to p^r, since the component events, consisting of the covering of a_i by the interval I_i, are dependent.

We will consider the special case $n_1 = n_2 = \ldots = n_r = 2$, which is encountered in practice. Here

$$n = 2r, \ n - r = r, \ \bar{x}_i = \frac{1}{2}(x_{i1} + x_{i2}),$$

$$s_i^2 = \frac{1}{4}(x_{i1} - x_{i2})^2, \quad S^2 = \frac{1}{2}\sum_{i=1}^{r}(x_{i1} - x_{i2})^2.$$

The confidence intervals take the form

$$I_i = \left[\bar{x}_i - \frac{1}{2}\gamma_p\sqrt{\frac{1}{r}\sum_{i=1}^{r}(x_{i1} - x_{i2})^2}, \ \bar{x}_i + \frac{1}{2}\gamma_p\sqrt{\frac{1}{r}\sum_{i=1}^{r}(x_{i1} - x_{i2})^2}\right], \tag{4.7.6}$$

where γ_p must be found for r degrees of freedom. We compare the confidence intervals so obtained with those which would be obtained if, in estimating a_i, only the observations x_{i1} and x_{i2} are used. The confidence interval I_i' constructed according to the rule of section 4 of this chapter, has the form

$$I_i' = \left[\bar{x}_i - \frac{1}{2}\gamma_p'|x_{i1} - x_{i2}|, \ \bar{x}_i + \frac{1}{2}\gamma_p'|x_{i1} - x_{i2}|\right]. \tag{4.7.7}$$

Here γ_p' is based on $2 - 1 = 1$ degree of freedom; from Table 1 it can be seen that γ_p' decreases as the number of degrees of freedom increases, and a brief calculation shows that consequently the interval I_i will be shorter, on the average, than the interval I_i' for large n.

We arrive at the rule:

Rule for analysing groups of equally accurate measurements by the method of confidence intervals. We form

$$\bar{x}_i = \frac{1}{n_i}\sum_{j=1}^{n_i} x_{ij}; \quad s_i^2 = \frac{1}{n_i}\sum_{j=1}^{n_i}(x_{ij} - \bar{x}_i)^2;$$

$$n = \sum_{i=1}^{r} n_i; \qquad S^2 = \sum_{i=1}^{r} n_i s_i^2.$$

We choose a confidence coefficient p, and from Table 1 of Student's distribution, with $n - r$ degrees of freedom, we select a number γ_p and construct the confidence intervals

$$I_i = \left[\bar{x}_i - \frac{\gamma_p S}{\sqrt{n_i(n-r)}}, \quad \bar{x}_i + \frac{\gamma_p S}{\sqrt{n_i(n-r)}}\right].$$

We pause to consider the question of estimating the accuracy of observations in groups.

We first derive a point estimator of σ^2 by the method of maximum likelihood. The likelihood function of the sample (4.7.1) has the form

$$L(x_{ij}, a_i, \sigma) = (2\pi)^{-\frac{n}{2}} \sigma^{-n} \exp\left\{-\frac{1}{2\sigma^2} \sum_{i=1}^{r} \sum_{j=1}^{n_i} (x_{ij} - a_i)^2\right\}.$$

We have

$$\ln L = -\frac{n}{2} \ln 2\pi - \frac{n}{2} \ln \sigma^2 - \frac{1}{2} \sum_{i=1}^{r} \frac{1}{\sigma^2} \sum_{j=1}^{n_i} (x_{ij} - a_i)^2.$$

The maximum likelihood equations are:

$$\frac{\partial \ln L}{\partial \sigma^2} = 0; \tag{4.7.8}$$

$$\frac{\partial \ln L}{\partial a_i} = 0, \qquad i = 1, 2, \ldots, r. \tag{4.7.9}$$

The last r equations are equivalent to the least squares requirement

$$Q = \sum_{i=1}^{r} \sum_{j=1}^{n_i} (x_{ij} - a_i)^2 = \min$$

and have the simple solutions

$$\hat{a}_i = \frac{1}{n_i} \sum_{j=1}^{n_i} x_{ij} = \bar{x}_i.$$

From this the first equation gives

$$-\frac{n}{2\sigma^2} + \frac{1}{2\sigma^4} \sum_{i=1}^{r} \sum_{j=1}^{n_i} (x_{ij} - \bar{x}_i)^2 = 0.$$

Hence

$$\hat{\sigma}^2 = \frac{1}{n} \sum_{i=1}^{r} \sum_{j=1}^{n_i} (x_{ij} - \bar{x}_i)^2 = \frac{1}{n} S^2 = \frac{1}{n} \sum_{i=1}^{r} n_i s_i^2.$$

We note that the estimator obtained for σ^2 is biased since

$$E\hat{\sigma}^2 = \frac{1}{n} \sum_{i=1}^{r} (n_i - 1)\sigma^2 = \left(1 - \frac{r}{n}\right)\sigma^2.$$

An unbiased estimator of σ^2 is obtained from this by the formula

$$\tilde{\sigma}^2 = \frac{1}{n-r} S^2.$$

It is also possible to construct a confidence interval for σ^2 using

$$\frac{1}{\sigma^2} S^2 = \chi^2_{n-r}.$$

In fact, proceeding as in section 3 of this chapter, we get the following result, for given values γ_1', γ_2' and confidence interval

$$I_s = [S^2\gamma_1', S^2\gamma_2'],$$

we have

$$P\{S^2\gamma_1' \leqslant \sigma^2 \leqslant S^2\gamma_2'\} = P\left\{\frac{n}{\gamma_2'} \leqslant \chi^2_{n-r} \leqslant \frac{n}{\gamma_1'}\right\} =$$

$$= K_{n-r}\left(\frac{n}{\gamma_2'}\right) - K_{n-r}\left(\frac{n}{\gamma_1'}\right), \tag{4.7.10}$$

where $K_{n-r}(x)$ is the integral of the χ^2_{n-r} distribution. As before, for simplification, we will choose γ_1' and γ_2' so that

$$K_{n-r}\left(\frac{n}{\gamma_2'}\right) = \frac{1-p_0}{2}, \quad K_{n-r}\left(\frac{n}{\gamma_1'}\right) = \frac{1+p_0}{2},$$

where p_0 is the specified confidence coefficient (see Kolmogorov [22]).

8. Example *)

In Table 12 are given a series of pairs of measurements ($x_{i1} = \beta_i + x_{i1}', x_{i2} = \beta_i + x_{i2}'$) of the angle between coastal objects, obtained with the sextant. Each measurements is repeated twice. Using the whole set of observations we will estimate the values m_i for each group of two measurements.

We will find confidence intervals for m_i. In this case

$$n_1 = n_2 = \ldots = n_r = 2, \quad n = \sum_{i=1}^{r} n_i = 2r, \quad n - r = r,$$

and the formulae are simplified. We have

$$\bar{x}_i = \frac{1}{2}(x_{i1} + x_{i2}), \quad s_i^{2'} = \frac{1}{4}(x_{i1} - x_{i2})^2$$

and

$$S^2 = \frac{1}{2}\sum_{i=1}^{r}(x_{i1} - x_{i2})^2.$$

---

* Data are taken from a book by Yushchenko [53], p. 42.

TABLE 12

β_i	x'_{i1}	x'_{i2}	$x'_{i1} - x'_{i2}$	$(x'_{i1} - x'_{i2})^2$	$\overline{x}'_i = \frac{1}{2}(x'_{i1} + x'_{i2})$	$m_i^H = \beta_i + \overline{x}'_i - 6,87$	$m_i^B = \beta_i + \overline{x}'_i + 6,87$
60°18′	20″	30″	—10	100	25	60° 18′ 18″,13	60° 18′ 31″,87
112 16	10	10	0	0	10	112 16 3,13	112 16 16,87
47 2	20	15	5	25	17,5	47 2 10,63	47 2 24,37
83 37	30	40	—10	100	35	83 37 28,13	83 37 41,87
17 12	40	40	0	0	40	17 12 33,13	17 12 46,87
32 12	35	40	—5	25	37,5	32 12 30,63	32 12 44,37
8 10	20	30	—10	100	25	8 10 18,13	8 10 31,87
51 19	30	20	10	100	25	51 19 18,13	51 19 31,87
73 51	40	30	10	100	35	73 51 28,13	73 51 41,87
90 3	55	50	5	25	52,5	90 3 45,63	90 3 59,37
Sum . .				575			

consequently, the confidence interval for m_i is

$$I_i = \left[\bar{x}_i - \frac{\gamma_p S}{\sqrt{2r}},\ \bar{x}_i + \frac{\gamma_p S}{\sqrt{2r}}\right].$$

(In our case $\bar{x}_i = \beta_i + \bar{x}'_i$). The calculations are shown in Table 12. Evidently

$$S^2 = \frac{1}{2} \times 575 = 287{,}5; \quad S = 16{,}96$$

We choose a confidence coefficient $p = 0{,}90$. From tables of Student's distribution, with $p = 0{,}90$ and degrees of freedom equal to $n - r = r = 10$, we find $\gamma_p = 1{,}812$. Hence

$$\frac{\gamma_p s}{\sqrt{2r}} = \frac{1{,}812 \times 16{,}96}{4{,}472} = 6{,}87.$$

In the last two columns are shown the values of the lower and upper limits of confidence intervals for m_i.

CHAPTER V

DIRECT OBSERVATIONS OF UNEQUAL ACCURACY

1. Statement of Problem

In practical applications of the theory of the analysis of observations, in astronomy and geodesy, for example, we often meet a situation, in which, when measuring the same quantity, we obtain systems of several equally accurate observations, which are classified in groups and which may be considered as original observations.

As an example we will take data on the determination of the latitude of the town of Shcheglovsk by several measurements on the Pole star (Ursae minoris) and on stars of the constellations: - Andromedae, Trianguli, Cygni and Cephei (Table 13) - given in Chebotarev's book [51].

TABLE 13

No.	Date of observn.	Name of star	Observed latitude of town	Number of observations
1	21/IX	α Ursae minoris	55°21′13″.5	8
2		ζ Andromedae	12.2	4
3		α Trianguli	11.5	2
4	4/XI	α Ursae minoris	12.4	4
5		γ Cigni	11.3	8
6		η Cephei	12.4	4

In this table the sample means $\bar{x}_1 = 55°21'13''5$; $\bar{x}_2 = 55°21'12''.2$ etc., and the number of observations $n_i = 8, 4, 2, \ldots$ are given for the separate systems of observations of equal accuracy (No. 1, 2, 3, . . .). Later, (section 10, chapter VI) we will see how suitable is the representation of observations by their sample means in this case.

If $\sigma^2 = D(x_i)$ is the variance of a single observation, then $D(\bar{x}_i) = \frac{\sigma^2}{n_i}$. Thus, the variates $\bar{x}_1, \bar{x}_2, \ldots, \bar{x}_n$ are normal; $\bar{x}_i \in N\left(a, \frac{\sigma}{\sqrt{n_i}}\right)$ $(i = 1, 2, \ldots, k)$. We can assume that we must estimate the measured quantity a by the observations $\bar{x}_1, \bar{x}_2, \ldots, \bar{x}_k$ with variances $\frac{\sigma^2}{n_i}$; here n_i is an integer representing the number of corresponding observations of equal accuracy. We will consider a more general situation. There are direct observations of unequal accuracy $x_1, x_2, \ldots, x_n$, which are independent and normal

$$x_i \in N\left(a, \frac{\sigma}{\sqrt{p_i}}\right),$$

where σ is unknown, but the quantities p_i are known, and reciprocal to the variances of the observations, $D(x_i) = \frac{\sigma^2}{p_i}$ $(i = 1, 2, \ldots, n)$. These quantities are called the weights of the observations. It is natural to assume that they are determined exactly up to a proportionality coefficient λ, so that

$$D(x_i) = \frac{\lambda\sigma^2}{\lambda p_i} = \frac{\mu^2}{\lambda p_i} \qquad (i = 1, 2, \ldots, n);$$

In the calculations the weights themselves will not be used, but the ratios

$$\frac{p_i}{\sum_{i=1}^{n} p_i} = \frac{p_i}{[p]}.$$

In the previous example the weights were proportional to the numbers of observations, n_i. In many cases the weights have a different structure; we will encounter examples, where weights are naturally ascribed to observations which are linearly related with some results.

We will consider the problem of estimating a measured quantity a by n direct, independent observations $x_1, \ldots, x_n$, not of equal accuracy, but with weights $p_1 : p_2 : \ldots : p_n$, such that

$$D(x_i) = \frac{\sigma^2}{p_i},$$

where σ^2 is a unknown proportionality coefficient, which must be estimated as well as the quantity a.

We will start with the point estimation of a and σ^2 by the method of maximum likelihood and show that for the estimation of a this is equivalent to the method of least squares, taking into account the weights p_i, and we will consider the 'quality' of the estimators we have obtained. Then, we will construct confidence intervals.

2. Point Estimation of a and σ^2

The observations x_i have the probability density function

$$f(x_i, a, \sigma^2) = \frac{\sqrt{p_i}}{\sqrt{2\pi}\,\sigma} \exp -\frac{p_i}{2\sigma^2}(x_i - a)^2. \tag{5.2.1}$$

In view of this, and by virtue of the independence of the observations, the likelihood function of the sample $x_1, \ldots, x_n$ is of the form

$$L(x_1, \ldots, x_n, a, \sigma^2) =$$
$$= (p_1 p_2 \ldots p_n)^{\frac{1}{2}} (2\pi)^{-\frac{n}{2}} (\sigma^2)^{-\frac{n}{2}} \exp -\frac{1}{2\sigma^2} \sum_{i=1}^{n} p_i (x_i - a)^2.$$

For every $\sigma^2 > 0$ the maximum of $L(x_1, \ldots, x_n, a, \sigma^2)$ is given by the condition

$$Q = \sum_{i=1}^{n} p_i (x_i - a)^2 = \min, \tag{5.2.2}$$

i.e. by choosing a by the method of least squares taking into account the weights p_i.

To find the minimum of Q we have

$$\frac{\partial Q}{\partial a} = \sum_{i=1}^{n} 2p_i (x_i - a) = 0,$$

whence we find the unique solution

$$\hat{a} = \frac{p_1 x_1 + \ldots + p_n x_n}{p_1 + \ldots + p_n} = \frac{[px]}{[p]}. \tag{5.2.3}$$

It is easy to show that $\hat{a}$ gives the minimum of Q. We have

$$\sum p_i (x_i - \hat{a}) = \sum p_i x_i - \hat{a} \sum p_i = [px] - \hat{a}[p] = 0. \tag{5.2.4}$$

Therefore for any arbitrary a we obtain

$$Q = \sum p_i (x_i - a)^2 = \sum p_i (x_i - \hat{a} + \hat{a} - a)^2 =$$
$$= \sum p_i (x_i - \hat{a})^2 + (\hat{a} - a) \sum p_i (x_i - \hat{a}) + \sum p_i (\hat{a} - a)^2 =$$
$$= \sum p_i (x_i - \hat{a})^2 + (\hat{a} - a)^2 \sum p_i, \tag{5.2.5}$$

from which our assertion follows.

The estimator $\hat{a} = \frac{[px]}{[p]}$ of the parameter a we will denote by $\tilde{x}$ and call a weighted mean.

Theorem 5.2.1.
The weighted mean $\tilde{x}$ is an unbiased estimator of a, i.e.

$$E(\tilde{x}) = a, \tag{5.2.6}$$

and the variance is

$$D(\tilde{x}) = \frac{\sigma^2}{\sum_{i=1}^{n} p_i}, \tag{5.2.7}$$

so that the weight of the weighted mean is equal to the sum of weights of the observations.

Thus theorem 5.2.1 affirms that $\tilde{x} \in N\left(a, \frac{\sigma}{\sqrt{[p]}}\right)$. To prove this we note that $E(x_i) = a \quad (i = 1, 2, \ldots, n)$, and therefore

$$E\frac{[px]}{[p]} = \frac{1}{[p]} \sum p_i E(x_i) = \frac{a[p]}{[p]} = a.$$

Further,

$$D(\tilde{x}) = D\frac{1}{[p]}\left(\sum p_i x_i\right) = \frac{1}{[p]^2} \sum p_i^2 D(x_i) =$$

$$= \frac{1}{[p]^2} \sum p_i^2 \frac{\sigma^2}{p_i} = \sigma^2 \frac{[p]}{[p]^2} = \frac{\sigma^2}{[p]},$$

which proves (5.2.7).

We will show that the estimator $\tilde{x}$ is efficient. From (3.3.13) we have

$$D(t) = E(t-a)^2 \geqslant \frac{1}{E\left(-\frac{\partial^2 \ln L}{\partial a^2}\right)}. \tag{5.2.8}$$

for a very wide class of unbiased estimators of t. Here

$$\ln L = \ln (p_1 p_2 \ldots p_n)^{\frac{1}{2}} - \frac{n}{2} \ln 2\pi - \frac{n}{2} \ln \sigma^2 - \frac{1}{2\sigma^2} \sum_{i=1}^{n} p_i (x_i - a)^2;$$

$$\frac{\partial^2 \ln L}{\partial a^2} = -\frac{\sum p_i}{\sigma^2} = -\frac{[p]}{\sigma^2};$$

$$E\left(-\frac{\partial^2 \ln L}{\partial a^2}\right) = \frac{[p]}{\sigma^2}.$$

Thus

$$D(t) \geqslant \frac{\sigma^2}{[p]} = D(\tilde{x}),$$

which proves the efficiency of the estimator $\tilde{x}$.

The real meaning of estimation by $\tilde{x}$ is: for given $\varepsilon > 0$ and a sufficiently large sample size n, for a very wide class of asymptotically normal and asymptotically unbiased estimators, t, of a we have

$$P\{|\tilde{x}-a| \leqslant \varepsilon\} \geqslant P\{|t-a| \leqslant \varepsilon\} . \tag{5.2.9}$$

To estimate σ^2 we construct the equation

$$\frac{\partial \ln L}{\partial \sigma^2} = -\frac{n}{2\sigma^2} + \frac{1}{2\sigma^4} \sum_{i=1}^{n} p_i (x_i - a)^2 = 0.$$

Hence

$$\widehat{\sigma^2} = \frac{1}{n} \sum p_i (x_i - \hat{a})^2 = \frac{1}{n} \sum p_i (x_i - \tilde{x})^2. \tag{5.2.10}$$

We will find $E(\widehat{\sigma^2})$, in order to assess the amount of bias in the estimator $\hat{\sigma}^2$. We put $y_i = x_i - a$; then $\tilde{y} = \frac{[py]}{[p]} = \tilde{x} - a$, and

$$\widehat{\sigma^2} = \frac{1}{n} \sum_{i=1}^{n} p_i (x_i - \tilde{x})^2 = \frac{1}{n} \sum_{i=1}^{n} p_i (y_i - \tilde{y})^2.$$

Therefore

$$E(\widehat{\sigma^2}) = \frac{1}{n} \left[\sum_i p_i E y_i^2 - 2 \sum_i p_i E y_i \tilde{y} + \sum_i p_i E \tilde{y}^2 \right]. \tag{5.2.11}$$

Further we have

$$E(y_i^2) = \frac{\sigma^2}{p_i},$$

$$E(y_i \tilde{y}) = \frac{1}{[p]} \sum_j p_j E(y_i y_j).$$

We note that $E(y_i y_j) = 0$ for $i \neq j$, so that

$$E(y_i \tilde{y}) = \frac{1}{[p]} p_i \frac{\sigma^2}{p_i} = \frac{\sigma^2}{[p]}.$$

$$E(\tilde{y}^2) = \frac{\sigma^2}{[p]}.$$

Hence substituting into (5.2.11) we obtain

$$E(\widehat{\sigma^2}) = \frac{1}{n} [n\sigma^2 - 2\sigma^2 + \sigma^2] = \frac{n-1}{n} \sigma^2.$$

Thus, $\widehat{\sigma^2}$ is a biased estimator of σ^2, but is asymptotically unbiased for $n \to \infty$. The unbiased estimator of σ^2 is, of course, the quantity

$$\tilde{q}^2 = \frac{n}{n-1}\,\sigma^2 = \frac{1}{n-1}\sum p_i (x_i - \tilde{x})^2 = \frac{Q}{n-1}.$$

Next, we find an unbiased estimator of the variance of $\tilde{x}$. We have

$$D(\tilde{x}) = \frac{\sigma^2}{[p]},$$

so that an unbiased estimator of $D(\tilde{x})$ is obtained from $\tilde{q}^2$, if we take

$$u^2 = \frac{\tilde{q}^2}{[p]} = \frac{1}{[p](n-1)}\sum_{i=1}^{n} p_i (x_i - \tilde{x})^2. \qquad (5.2.12)$$

The formulae obtained above give the solutions of the problem of point estimation in the case of observations of unequal accuracy with known weights; the real meaning of this estimation is explained by formula (5.2.9). The particular case in which $p_1 = p_2 = \ldots = p_n = 1$ leads to the results already obtained for measurements of equal accuracy, (chapter IV).

We conclude with some simplifications of the calculations of $\tilde{x}$, u^2 and $\tilde{q}^2$. If β is any arbitrary number, then, as is easily seen immediately

$$\tilde{x} = \frac{1}{[p]}[px] = \frac{1}{[p]}[p(x-\beta)] + \beta. \qquad (5.2.13)$$

Substituting the value $\tilde{x}$ in the place of β, we find

$$\tilde{x} = \frac{1}{[p]}[p(x-\tilde{x})] + \tilde{x},$$

whence

$$\frac{1}{[p]}[p(x-\tilde{x})] = 0. \qquad (5.2.14)$$

This equation can be used as a check on the calculation of $\tilde{x}$. Further, according to (5.2.5), replacing $\hat{a}$ by $\tilde{x}$ and a by β, we have

$$\sum p_i (x_i - \tilde{x})^2 = \sum p_i (x_i - \beta)^2 - (\tilde{x} - \beta)^2 \cdot [p], \qquad (5.2.15)$$

which can also be used for simplifying the calculations.

3. Estimation of a and σ^2 by confidence Intervals

First we will prove the following theorem which is useful in the estimation of a and σ^2 by confidence intervals.

Theorem 5.3.1.

If $x_i \in N\left(a, \frac{\sigma}{\sqrt{p_i}}\right)$ then the quantities $\tilde{x}$ and

$$q^2 = \frac{1}{n-1}Q = \frac{1}{n-1}\sum_i p_i (x_i - \tilde{x})^2$$

are statistically independent and the quantity Q is distributed as $\sigma^2\chi^2_{n-1}$.

First we prove, as in section 2, chapter IV, that the normal vector $(x_1-\tilde{x},\ x_2-\tilde{x},\ \ldots,\ x_{n-1}-\tilde{x})$ is independent of $\tilde{x}$. For this it is sufficient to verify that

$$E[(x_i-\tilde{x})\tilde{x}]=0.$$

Putting $y_i=x_i-a,\ \tilde{y}=\tilde{x}-a$, as before, we have

$$E[(x_i-\tilde{x})\tilde{x}]=E[(y_i-\tilde{y})(\tilde{y}+a)]=E(y_i-\tilde{y})\tilde{y}=$$
$$=Ey_i\tilde{y}-E\tilde{y}^2=\frac{\sigma^2}{[p]}-\frac{\sigma^2}{[p]}=0.$$ (see section 2 of this chapter).

This means that the random vector $(x_1-\tilde{x},\ \ldots,\ x_{n-1}-\tilde{x})$ is independent of $\tilde{x}$. Further $x_n-\tilde{x}=-\sum_{i=1}^{n-1}(x_i-\tilde{x})$, so that any arbitrary continuous function $\varphi(x_1-\tilde{x},\ \ldots,\ x_n-\tilde{x})$ is independent of $\tilde{x}$; in particular $Q=\sum_{i=1}^{n} p_i(x_i-\tilde{x})^2$ is independent of $\tilde{x}$. We will now prove that the quantity

$$Q=\sum_{i=1}^{n} p_i(x_i-\tilde{x})^2 \tag{5.3.1}$$

is distributed as $\sigma^2\chi^2_{n-1}$. Putting $\beta=0$ in (5.2.13), we have

$$Q=\sum_{i=1}^{n} p_i(x_i-\tilde{x})^2=\sum_{i=1}^{n} p_i(y_i-\tilde{y})^2=\sum_{i=1}^{n} p_i y_i^2-[p]\,\tilde{y}^2.$$

The quantities y_i are here independent and normal; $y_i\in N\left(0,\ \frac{\sigma}{\sqrt{p_i}}\right)$. Therefore the quantities $u_i=y_i\sqrt{p_i}$ are also independent and normal $N(0,\ \sigma)$. We have

$$Q=\sum_{i=1}^{n} u_i^2-(\tilde{y}\sqrt{[p]})^2;$$

$$\tilde{y}\sqrt{[p]}=\sqrt{[p]}\,\frac{\sum p_i y_i}{[p]}=\frac{1}{\sqrt{[p]}}\sum_{i=1}^{n} u_i\sqrt{p_i}.$$

We introduce the orthogonal transformation

$$Z=FU,\ \text{where}\ U=\begin{Vmatrix} y_1\\ \vdots\\ y_n\end{Vmatrix},\quad Z=\begin{Vmatrix} z_1\\ z_2\\ \vdots\\ z_n\end{Vmatrix},$$

and the matrix $F=\|f_{rs}\|$ is orthogonal: $FF^T=E$ and the first row of F corresponds to the equation

$$z_1=\sum_{i=1}^{n} u_i \frac{\sqrt{p_i}}{\sqrt{[p]}}=\tilde{y}\sqrt{[p]} \qquad \left(f_{1s}=\frac{\sqrt{p_s}}{\sqrt{[p]}}\right).$$

According to Fisher's theorem (theorem 2.3.2) the random vector $(z_1, \ldots, z_n)$ is normal with independent components $z_i \in N(0, \sigma)$. We have

$$Q=\sum_{i=1}^{n} u_i^2-u_1^2=\sum_{i=2}^{n} u_i^2.$$

Therefore the quantity $\frac{Q}{\sigma^2}$ is distributed as χ^2_{n-1}. This completes the proof of theorem 5.3.1.

We now form a ratio, analogous to the ratio $\frac{\bar{x}-a}{s}$ in the case of observations of equal accuracy, and distributed according to Student's law.

The quantity $\bar{x}-a$ is normal $N\left(0, \frac{\sigma}{\sqrt{[p]}}\right)$ and independent of $\sqrt{Q}$; hence the quantity

$$t_{n-1}=\frac{(\bar{x}-a)\sqrt{[p]}\,\sigma^{-1}}{\sqrt{\frac{Q}{[p]}}\,\sigma^{-1}}=\frac{(\bar{x}-a)\sqrt{n-1}}{\tilde{s}}, \tag{5.3.2}$$

where

$$\tilde{s}=\sqrt{\frac{Q}{[p]}}=\left(\frac{1}{[p]}\sum p_i(x_i-\tilde{x})^2\right)^{\frac{1}{2}} \tag{5.3.3}$$

is distributed as a Student's ratio with $n-1$ degrees of freedom. Therefore the construction of confidence intervals is similar to the construction in the case of observations of equal accuracy (section 2, chapter IV); we choose a confidence coefficient p_0 and, with degrees of freedom equal to $n-1$, we find a number γ such that

$$P\{|t_{n-1}|\leqslant\gamma\}=p_0.$$

We see from (5.3.2) that the confidence interval

$$I_\gamma=\left[\tilde{x}-\frac{\gamma\tilde{s}}{\sqrt{n-1}}, \quad \tilde{x}+\frac{\gamma\tilde{s}}{\sqrt{n-1}}\right] \tag{5.3.4}$$

covers the measured quantity a with probability p_0. We now proceed to the estimation of accuracy by the method of confidence intervals. As in section 2, chapter IV we have

$$\frac{Q}{\sigma^2}=\frac{[p]\,\tilde{s}^2}{\sigma^2}=\chi^2_{n-1}.$$

We construct the confidence interval

$$I=[q^2\gamma_1^2,\ q^2\gamma_2^2].$$

It is known that the quantity $\frac{(n-1)\,q^2}{\sigma^2}$ is distributed as χ^2_{n-1}.

Thus

$$P\{q^2\gamma_1^2\leqslant\sigma^2\leqslant q^2\gamma_2^2\}=$$

$$=P\left\{\frac{n-1}{\gamma_2^2}\leqslant\frac{(n-1)\,q^2}{\sigma^2}\leqslant\frac{n-1}{\gamma_1^2}\right\}=P\left\{\frac{n-1}{\gamma_2^2}\leqslant\chi^2_{n-1}\leqslant\frac{n-1}{\gamma_1^2}\right\}=$$

$$=K_{n-1}\left(\frac{n-1}{\gamma_1^2}\right)-K_{n-1}\left(\frac{n-1}{\gamma_2^2}\right).$$

From this the confidence coefficient is established for given γ_1, γ_2 (or vice-versa) using the tables.

We can now state the following rules.

Rules for Estimation of a Measurable Quantity and of the Accuracy of Independent Observations with Known Weights

a) Point estimation. We find the weighted mean $\tilde{x}$, and also q^2 and u^2, from the formulae

$$\tilde{x}=\frac{\sum_{i=1}^{n}p_ix_i}{\sum p_i}=\frac{[px]}{[p]}$$ which is an unbiased estimator of the quantity a,

$$q^2=\frac{1}{n-1}\sum p_i(x_i-\tilde{x})^2=\frac{[p\tilde{v}\tilde{v}]}{n-1}$$ which is an unbiased estimator of

σ^2, where $v=x_i-\tilde{x}$ are 'apparent errors'.

$$u^2=\frac{q^2}{[p]}=\frac{[p\tilde{v}\tilde{v}]}{(n-1)\,[p]}$$ is an unbiased estimator of the variance of $\tilde{x}$,

$$D(\tilde{x})=\frac{\sigma^2}{[p]}.$$

To facilitate the calculations we choose an auxiliary number β suitably. We have

$$\tilde{x}=\frac{1}{[p]}[p(x-\beta)]+\beta;$$

the check relation is $[v]=0$. We have also

$$(n-1)\,q^2=\sum_{i=1}^{n}p_i(x_i-\beta)^2-(\tilde{x}-\beta)^2[p],$$

$$u^2=\frac{q^2}{[p]}.$$

In the special case, in which the weights p_i are proportional to the numbers of observations, n_i, in series of equally accurate observations, it may be assumed that $p_i = n_i$; then, in the place of x_i, we take the sample mean $\overline{x}_i$ of a series of n_i observations.

b) Estimation by confidence intervals. We find $\tilde{x}$ and

$\tilde{s} = \sqrt{\frac{[p\tilde{v}\tilde{v}]}{[p]}}$. We determine the confidence coefficient p_0 and

for given p_0 and with degrees of freedom equal to $n-1$ we find the number γ from the table of Student's distribution (Table 1). The confidence interval

$$I_\gamma = \left[\tilde{x} - \gamma \frac{\tilde{s}}{\sqrt{n-1}},\ \tilde{x} + \gamma \frac{\tilde{s}}{\sqrt{n-1}}\right]$$

covers a with probability p_0. To estimate σ^2 we determine the confidence coefficient p_0 and, from Table 3, with $n-1$ degrees of freedom, we find the numbers γ_1, and γ_2. The confidence interval

$$\dot{I}_{\gamma_1\gamma_2} = [q^2\gamma_1^2,\ q^2\gamma_2^2]$$

covers σ^2 with probability p_0.

It would be logical, of course, to consider also the case of observations of unequal accuracy with unknown weights, i.e. to consider the problem of estimation of the measured quantity a from a sample $x_1, x_2, \ldots, x_n$ of independent observations $x_i \in N(a, \sigma_i)$; where the σ_i's are different and unknown. This problem can be solved theoretically, but as yet its solution has not been given in a form which would be convenient for practical application. Therefore we will not deal with it.

4. Examples

Example 1*). In the first column of Table 14 are given the values of an angle α obtained from different number of replications for each measurement.

TABLE 14

α_i	No. of observ.	p_i	$\alpha_i' = \alpha_i - \beta$	$p_i\alpha_i'$	$\alpha_i - \tilde{\alpha}$	$(\alpha_i - \tilde{\alpha})^2$	$p_i(\alpha_i - \tilde{\alpha})^2$
46°10′12″	8	2	2″	4	−1″,75	3,063	6,126
14	4	1	4	4	0,25	0,063	0,063
12	12	3	2	6	−1,75	3,063	9,189
18	8	2	8	16	4,25	18,063	36,126
Sum . .		8		30			51,501

* Data taken from the book by Yushchenko [56], p. 51.

We will estimate the value of the angle α and the accuracy of its determination. We will assume that the weights of separate results of measurements are proportional to the number of replications.

A point estimator of α is

$$\tilde{\alpha}=\frac{[p\alpha]}{[p]}=\beta+\frac{[p\alpha']}{[p]}.$$

We calculate

$$\tilde{s}=\sqrt{\frac{[p\tilde{v}\tilde{v}]}{[p]}},\text{ where } \tilde{v}_i=\alpha_i-\tilde{\alpha};\quad [p\tilde{v}\tilde{v}]=\sum_{i=1}^{n}p_i(\alpha_i-\tilde{\alpha})^2.$$

σ can be estimated using the quantity

$$q=\sqrt{\frac{[p\tilde{v}\tilde{v}]}{n-1}}.$$

The calculations are given in Table 14. Here it has been assumed that $\beta=46°10'10''$. Then

$$\tilde{\alpha}=46°10'10''+\frac{30''}{8}=46°10'13'',75.$$

Evidently

$$\tilde{s}=\sqrt{\frac{51{,}504}{8}}=2{,}537,\quad q=\sqrt{\frac{51{,}504}{3}}=4{,}144.$$

We estimate α and σ by confidence intervals. The confidence interval for α is

$$I=\left[\tilde{x}-\frac{\gamma_p\tilde{s}}{\sqrt{n-1}},\quad \tilde{x}+\frac{\gamma_p\tilde{s}}{\sqrt{n-1}}\right],$$

where γ_p is determined from Student's table, for confidence coefficient p and degrees of freedom $k=n-1$. We will take the confidence coefficient $p=0{,}90$. We find $\gamma_p=2{,}353$ from Student's table for $n-1=3$. Whence

$$\frac{\gamma_p\times\tilde{s}}{\sqrt{n-1}}=\frac{2{,}353\times2{,}537}{1{,}732}=3'',45,$$

and we have the confidence interval

$$46°10'10'',30<\alpha<46°10'17'',20.$$

We obtain the confidence interval for σ, using the tables of χ^2-distribution, from the condition

$$P\left\{\sqrt{\frac{[p]}{\chi_1^2}}\,\tilde{s}<\sigma<\sqrt{\frac{[p]}{\chi_2^2}}\,\tilde{s}\right\}=P_2-P_1=p,$$

or from the condition

$$P\left\{\sqrt{\frac{n-1}{\chi_1^2}}\,q<\sigma<\sqrt{\frac{n-1}{\chi_2^2}}\,q\right\}=P_2-P_1=p.$$

Here χ_2^2 and χ_1^2 correspond to probabilities P_2, P_1 for $n-1$ degrees of freedom. It is more convenient to apply the second condition, since the coefficients $\sqrt{\frac{n-1}{\chi_1^2}}=\gamma_1$ and $\sqrt{\frac{n-1}{\chi_2^2}}=\gamma_2$ are tabulated for different p and $k=n-1$ (see Table 3 of the Appendix).

We will take $p=0{,}90$ ($P_1=0{,}05$; $P_2=0{,}95$). From Table 3, for $k=n-1=3$ and $p=0{,}90$ we find $\gamma_1=0{,}620$, $\gamma_2=2{,}92$. Then, the confidence interval for σ, for confidence coefficient $p=0{,}90$ is $0{,}620\,q<\sigma<2{,}92\,q$ or $2{,}56<\sigma<12{,}10$.

Example 2*). In the first column of Table 15 are given 7 values of the constant of solar parallax obtained by different observers and different methods. In the second column are given the weights.

TABLE 15

x_i	p_i	$x_i'=x_i-\beta$	$p_i x_i'$	$(x_i-\tilde{x})$	$(x_i-\tilde{x})^2$	$p_i(x_i-\tilde{x})^2$
8″,780	1,0	0,080	0,0800	—0,0259	0,000671	0,000671
8,794	0,8	0,094	0,0752	—0,0119	0,000142	0,000114
8,857	0,8	0,157	0,1256	0,0511	0,002611	0,002089
8,802	8,2	0,102	0,8364	—0,0039	0,000015	0,000123
8,806	0,2	0,106	0,0212	0,0001	0,000000	0,000000
8,806	11,1	0,106	1,1766	0,0001	0,000000	0,000000
8,807	25,0	0,107	2,6750	0,0011	0,000001	0,000025
Sum . .	47,1		4,9900			0,003022

We will estimate a, the constant of solar parallax, and also the accuracy σ of the measurements.

We find point estimators of a and σ. The calculations are given in Table 15. We put $\beta=8''{,}7$. Then

$$\tilde{x}=\frac{[px]}{[p]}=\beta+\frac{[px']}{[p]}=8''{,}7+\frac{4''{,}99}{47{,}1}=8''{,}8059.$$

* The data are taken from Edelson's book [18], p. 99

We calculate

$$\tilde{s}=\sqrt{\frac{0{,}003022}{47.1}}=0{,}00801, \quad q=\sqrt{\frac{0{,}003022}{6}}=0{,}0224.$$

We seek a confidence interval for a. We take $p=0{,}90$. Then, for $k=n-1=6$ degrees of freedom and $p=0{,}90$ we find, in the Table of Student's distribution, the value $\gamma_p=1{,}943$. We have

$$\frac{\gamma_p\tilde{s}}{\sqrt{n-1}}=\frac{1{,}943\times0{,}00801}{2{,}45}=0''{,}0064.$$

Consequently, the confidence interval is

$$8''{,}7995 < a < 8''{,}8123.$$

We will estimate the accuracy of the observations with the same confidence coefficient $p=0{,}90$. For $k=n-1=6$ and $p=0{,}90$ we find, in Table 3, the values $\gamma_1=0{,}690$, $\gamma_2=1{,}92$. Therefore, the confidence interval for σ is

$$0{,}690\,q<\sigma<1{,}92\,q \quad \text{or} \quad 0{,}015<\sigma<0{,}043.$$

Example 3*). The results of 5 measurements of height of a certain point are given. These results (h_i) in millimeters, and also the weights are given in the first two columns of Table 16.

TABLE 16

h_i	p_i	$h'_i=h_i-\beta$	$p_ih'_i$	$(h_i-\tilde{h})$	$(h_i-\tilde{h})^2$	$p_i(h_i-\tilde{h})^2$
12356	1,0	6	6,0	−0,64	0,410	0,410
12361	0,4	11	4,4	4,36	19,010	7,604
12357	3,0	7	21,0	0,36	0,130	0,390
12355	0,2	5	1,0	−1,64	2,690	0,538
12352	0,4	2	0,8	−4,64	21,530	8,612
Sum . . .	5,0		33,2			17,554

We will estimate the value of h and also the accuracy of the observations, σ.

First we find point estimators for h and σ. The calculations are given in Table 16. We put $\beta=12{,}350$ mm. Then

$$\tilde{x}=\beta+\frac{[ph']}{[p]}=12{,}350+\frac{33{,}2}{5}=12\,356{,}64 \text{ mm.}$$

* The data are taken from Edelson's book [19], p. 84

We calculate $\tilde{s}=\sqrt{\frac{17,554}{5,0}}=1,87,\ q=\sqrt{\frac{17,554}{4}}=2,09.$

We seek for a confidence interval for h. We take the confidence coefficient $p=0,90$. Then, with degrees of freedom $k=n-1=4$ and probability $p=0,90$ we find, in the Table of Student's distribution, the value $\gamma_p=2,132$. Thus

$$\frac{\gamma_p \tilde{s}}{\sqrt{n-1}}=\frac{2,132\times 1,87}{2}=1,99.$$

The confidence interval for h is the interval

$$12{,}354,6 < h < 12{,}358,6.$$

We estimate the accuracy of observations with the same confidence coefficient $p=0,90$ From Table III for $k=n-1=4$ we find $\gamma_1=0,649$, $\gamma_2=2,37$. Whence the confidence coefficient for σ is

$$0,649q < \sigma < 2,37q \quad \text{or} \quad 1,35 < \sigma < 4,96.$$

Example 4*). Table 17 gives data from the measurement of latitude of Shcheglovsk determined from different stars and with numbers n_i of observations. In the table are given the mean values x_i from n_i observations of any star. We assume that the measurements in each group are of equal accuracy.

TABLE 17

x_i	$p_i(n_i)$	$x_i'=x_i-\beta$	p_ix_i'	$x_i-\tilde{x}$	$(x_i-\tilde{x})^2$	$p_i(x_i-\tilde{x})^2$
55°21′13″,5	8	3″,5	28,0	1,187	1,409	11,272
12,2	4	2,2	8,8	−0,113	0,013	0,052
11,5	2	1,5	3,0	−0,813	0,661	1,322
12,4	4	2,4	9,6	0,087	0,008	0,032
11,3	8	1,3	10,4	−1,013	1,026	8,208
12,4	4	2,4	9,6	0,087	0,008	0,032
Sum . .	30		69,4			20,918

We will estimate the degree of latitude of Shcheglovsk, a, and the standard deviation σ of the observations.

We will find point estimates for a and σ. The calculations are given in Table 17. We put $\beta=55°21'10''$. Then, the estimate $\tilde{x}$ of a is equal to

* The data are borrowed from Chebotarev's book [51].

$$\tilde{x} = \beta + \frac{[px']}{[p]} = 55°21'10'' + \frac{69''.4}{30} = 55°21'12''.313.$$

We calculate the quantities

$$\tilde{s} = \sqrt{\frac{20{,}918}{30}} = 0{,}835 \text{ and } q = \sqrt{\frac{20{,}918}{5}} = 2{,}045.$$

We now construct the confidence interval for a. We take $p = 0{,}90$. Then, for degrees of freedom $k = n - 1 = 5$ and probability $p = 0{,}90$ we find, from the table of the t-distribution the value $\gamma_p = 2{,}015$. Whence

$$\frac{\gamma_p \tilde{s}}{\sqrt{n-1}} = \frac{2{,}015 \times 0{,}835}{2{,}236} = 0''.752.$$

And so we can affirm, with confidence coefficient $p = 0{,}90$, that the inequality

$$55°21'11''{,}56 < a < 55°21'13''{,}07.$$

holds.

We estimate σ with the same confidence coefficient $p = 0{,}90$. For $p = 0{,}90$ and $k = n - 1 = 5$ we find in Table III of Appendix the values $\gamma_1 = 0{,}67$ and $\gamma_2 = 2{,}09$. Consequently, the confidence interval for σ is the interval

$$0{,}67q < \sigma < 2{,}09q \quad \text{or} \quad 1{,}37 < \sigma < 4{,}28.$$

CHAPTER VI

INDIRECT UNCONDITIONAL MEASUREMENTS

1. Statement of the Problem

In the introduction (section 1, formulae (0.1.1), (0.1.21) and others) we have seen that many problems, in which the method of least squares is applied, concern the determination of coefficients $a_1, a_2, \ldots, a_n$ in an over-determined system of equations of the form

$$y_r = \sum_{j=1}^{n} a_j x_{rj} \qquad (r = 1, 2, \ldots, N, \quad N > n). \quad \textbf{(6.1.1)}$$

This over-determined system of equations in section 1 of the introduction has appeared in many different examples.

Later, we will also encounter some examples of similar situations, but first we shall state the problem more precisely.

Suppose, we wish to find n quantities $a_1, a_2, \ldots, a_n$ from the equations (6.1.1) connecting y_r, a_j, x_{rj}. Here we know, accurately, the quantities x_{rj}, and the quantities $y_1, y_2, \ldots, y_N$ are measured with errors $\Delta_1, \Delta_2, \ldots, \Delta_N$, so that we observe the quantities

$$l_r = y_r + \Delta_r \qquad (r = 1, 2, \ldots, N), \qquad (6.1.2)$$

which are affected by errors.

Further, we suppose, that in the case when $y_1, y_2, \ldots, y_N$ are accurately determined (in this case the equations (6.1.1) should be self-consistent) we can find from these equations the a_j's $(j = 1, 2, \ldots, n)$. This means that the rank of the matrix

$$X = X_{Nn} = \|x_{rj}\| \qquad (6.1.3)$$

is equal to n and, consequently, $N \geqslant n$ (in fact, we need N greater than n). For the given statement of the problem we can apply the method of least squares and calculate $a_1, \ldots, a_n$ uniquely by this method. The calculating technique consists in the application of well known devices for the solution of linear equations, simplified because of the special form (symmetry) of the derived equations (called 'normal equations').

We, however, introduce additional conditions concerning the character of the errors Δ_r. These conditions will be a good model for what is encountered in practice, and also they make it possible to obtain some idea of the precise mathematico-statistical meaning of the results obtained, from a theoretical point of view.

We agree that the errors $\Delta_1, \Delta_2, \ldots, \Delta_N$ are independent, unbiased and normal $\Delta_r \in N(0, \sigma_r)$. Also

$$\sigma_r^2 = \frac{\sigma^2}{p_r} \qquad (r = 1, 2, \ldots, N), \tag{6.1.4}$$

where the weights p_r, we assume, are known and σ^2 is unknown. On the basis of observations $l_1, l_2, \ldots, l_N$ we need to estimate the parameters $a_1, a_2, \ldots, a_n$ and σ. We note that the case under consideration, of errors of unequal accuracy, easily reduces to the case of equal accuracy. Namely, if we multiply the rth equation (6.1.1) by $\sqrt{p_r}$ and replace y_r by $\sqrt{p_r}\, y_r$ and l_r by $l_r\sqrt{p_r}$, Δ_r by $\Delta_r' = \sqrt{p_r}\,\Delta_r$, x_{rj} by $\sqrt{p_r}\, x_{rj}$ respectively, then we obtain the system

$$y_r\sqrt{p_r} = \sum_{j=1}^{n} a_j x_{rj}\sqrt{p_r}, \tag{6.1.5}$$

$$l_r\sqrt{p_r} = y_r\sqrt{p_r} + \Delta_r', \tag{6.1.6}$$

where

$$E(\Delta_r') = 0; \quad D(\Delta_r') = \sigma^2; \quad \Delta_r' \in N(0, \sigma), \tag{6.1.7}$$

and the Δ_r''s are mutually independent, so that the case of measurements of equal accuracy is obtained. Later, however, we will deal with cases of measurements of unequal accuracy directly, only reducing them to the cases of measurements of equal accuracy when this considerably simplifies the analysis.

2. Application of the Method of Least Squares

As before, we start by applying of the method of maximum likelihood. We construct the likelihood function of the sample of independent observations $l_1, l_2, \ldots, l_N$. We have

$$l_r = y_r + \Delta_r = \Delta_r + \sum_{j=1}^{n} a_j x_{rj}. \tag{6.2.1}$$

Here $\Delta_r \in N\left(0, \frac{\sigma}{\sqrt{p_r}}\right)$ is random, and the other term is constant and contains unknown parameters $a_1, \ldots, a_n$.

We have

$$E(\Delta_r) = 0; \quad E(l_r) = \sum_{j=1}^{n} a_j x_{rj}. \tag{6.2.2}$$

In view of this, l_r is normal and has the probability density function

$$f_r(l_r) = \frac{p_r^{\frac{1}{2}} (2\pi)^{-\frac{1}{2}}}{\sigma} \exp\left\{-\frac{p_r}{2\sigma^2}\left(l_r - \sum_{j=1}^{n} a_j x_{rj}\right)^2\right\}. \tag{6.2.3}$$

Thus, the likelihood function of the sample values $l_1, l_2, \ldots, l_N$ is of the form

$$L(l_1, \ldots, l_N) = (2\pi)^{-\frac{N}{2}} (\sigma^2)^{-\frac{N}{2}} (p_1 p_2 \ldots p_N)^{\frac{1}{2}} \times$$
$$\times \exp\left\{-\frac{1}{2\sigma^2} \sum_{r=1}^{N} p_r \left(l_r - \sum_{j=1}^{n} a_j x_{rj}\right)^2\right\}.$$

Further, the expression

$$\ln L(l_1, \ldots, l_N) = -\frac{N}{2} \ln 2\pi - \frac{N}{2} \ln \sigma^2 + \frac{1}{2} \ln(p_1 p_2 \ldots p_N) -$$
$$-\frac{1}{2\sigma^2} \sum_{r=1}^{N} p_r \left(l_r - \sum_{j=1}^{n} a_j x_{rj}\right)^2$$

should be at its maximum.

We see that, for every value of σ^2, the maximum of the likelihood function is reached by choosing $a_1, \ldots, a_n$, independently of σ^2, and such that

$$\sum_{r=1}^{N} p_r \left(l_r - \sum_{j=1}^{n} a_j x_{rj}\right)^2 = \min, \tag{6.2.4}$$

i.e. if we choose the a_j's using the method of least squares. To obtain an idea of the geometrical meaning of this method we will state the calculations, in the case of measurements of equal accuracy ($p_i = 1$) for the method of least squares, in terms of multi-dimensional geometry (Kolmogorov [22]). We introduce the N-dimensional vectors

$$l = (l_1, \ldots, l_N); \quad y = (y_1, \ldots, y_N); \quad \Delta = (\Delta_1, \Delta_2, \ldots, \Delta_N),$$
$$x_j = (x_{1j}, x_{2j}, \ldots, x_{Nj}).$$

The method of least squares in this case is of the form

$$\sum_{r=1}^{N}\left(l_r - \sum_{j=1}^{n} a_j x_{rj}\right)^2 = \min. \tag{6.2.5}$$

We denote the values $a_1, a_2, \ldots, a_n$ obtained from the condition (6.2.5) by $\tilde{a}_1, \tilde{a}_2, \ldots, \tilde{a}_n$, and introduce the vector

$$\tilde{l} = \sum_{j=1}^{n} \tilde{a}_j x_j. \tag{6.2.6}$$

We put

$$l - \tilde{l} = \varepsilon; \quad l = \tilde{l} + \varepsilon. \tag{6.2.7}$$

Here $\varepsilon = (l_1 - \tilde{l}_1, l_2 - \tilde{l}_2, \ldots, l_n - \tilde{l}_n)$ is the vector of differences.

If $a_1, a_2, \ldots, a_n$ can take any arbitrary values, then the set of vectors

$$m = \sum_{j=1}^{n} a_j x_j$$

defines the linear space constructed on $x_1, x_2, \ldots, x_n$, and $l = (l_1, \ldots, l_N)$ is a fixed vector. The condition (6.2.5) means that $\sum_{i=1}^{N} (l_i - \tilde{l}_i)^2 = \min$, i.e. that the scalar square of vector ε, equal to $[\varepsilon\varepsilon] = \sum_{i=1}^{N} \varepsilon_i^2$, should be minimum.

From the point of view of multi-dimensional geometry, $[\varepsilon\varepsilon]$ is the square of the distance from the end of the vector l to the end of variable vector $\tilde{l}$, lying in the linear space defined by the vectors $x_1, x_2, \ldots, x_n$. This distance is a minimum, if and only if the vector $l - \tilde{l}$ is perpendicular to this linear space, i.e. $l - \tilde{l} \perp x_i$ $(i = 1, 2, \ldots, n)$ or $\varepsilon \perp x_i$, $(i = 1, 2, \ldots, n)$ (see Fig. 4, where $N = 3$, $n = 2$).

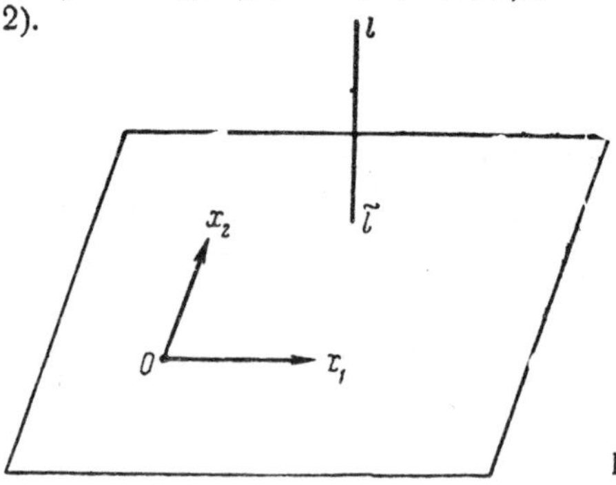

Fig. 4

This means that

$$[\varepsilon x_i] = \sum_{r=1}^{n} \varepsilon_r x_{ri} = 0 \qquad (i = 1, 2, \ldots, n). \tag{6.2.8}$$

We have, from (6.2.6) and (6.2.7)

$$\sum_{j=1}^{n} \tilde{a}_j x_j = l - \varepsilon. \tag{6.2.9}$$

Multiplying this equation by the scalars $x_i (i = 1, 2, \ldots, n)$ and taking into account (6.2.8) we find

$$\sum_{j=1}^{n} \tilde{a}_j [x_i x_j] = [x_i l], \quad i = 1, 2, \ldots, n. \tag{6.2.10}$$

The system of linear equations (6.2.10) for the coefficients $\tilde{a}_j$ is called the normal system. Its matrix $X = X_{nn} = \| [x_i \, x_j] \|$ is non-singular. Its determinant, $\det (X) = \det \| [x_i \, x_j] \|$ is the Gram's determinant of the system of vectors $x_1, x_2, \ldots, x_n$ (section 3, chapter I). Since rank $(X) = n$, then $\det (X) \neq 0$, and the system of equations is uniquely determined. The geometrical derivation of Kolmogorov in [22], corresponding to that given in section 1 of this chapter, is easy to generalize to the case of non-identical weights. However, in more complicated cases of conditional measurements and of estimation of linear combinations of parameters the geometrical reasoning becomes heavy. In these cases matrix derivations are preferred, which also permit a convenient and brief notation. We will use them systematically in all cases.

3. Matrix Derivation

We write the vectors introduced above in the form of one-column matrices

$$Y = Y_{N1} = \begin{Vmatrix} y_1 \\ y_2 \\ \vdots \\ y_N \end{Vmatrix}; \quad L = L_{N1} = \begin{Vmatrix} l_1 \\ l_2 \\ \vdots \\ l_N \end{Vmatrix}, \quad \tilde{L} = \tilde{L}_{N1} = \begin{Vmatrix} \tilde{l}_1 \\ \vdots \\ \tilde{l}_N \end{Vmatrix}, \quad \Delta = \begin{Vmatrix} \Delta_1 \\ \vdots \\ \Delta_N \end{Vmatrix},$$

$$A = \tilde{A}_{n1} = \begin{Vmatrix} \tilde{a}_1 \\ \tilde{a}_2 \\ \vdots \\ \tilde{a}_n \end{Vmatrix}.$$

The matrix A is the matrix of estimators obtained by the method of least squares.

We denote the matrix of the known quantities $\|x_{rj}\|$ $(r=1, 2, \ldots, N;$ $j=1, 2, \ldots, n)$ by $X=X_{Nn}=\|x_{rj}\|$, rank (X) is equal to n. We write the basic equations (6.1.1) in the form

$$Y=XA, \tag{6.3.1}$$

$$L=Y+\Delta,$$

$$XA-L=-\Delta. \tag{6.3.2}$$

If L_{N1} are fixed observations, then Δ_{N1} are fixed corrections unknown to us; however, if Δ_{N1} are random errors, then, evidently, the left hand side of (6.3.2) will also represent a random vector. The condition (6.2.5) of the method of least squares requires the matrix

$$\tilde{A}=\tilde{A}_{n1}=\begin{Vmatrix} \tilde{a}_1 \\ \tilde{a}_2 \\ \vdots \\ \tilde{a}_n \end{Vmatrix}$$

to be so chosen that, if we write

$$\tilde{V}=X\tilde{A}-L, \tag{6.3.3}$$

then

$$[p\tilde{v}\tilde{v}]=\sum_{r=1}^{N} p_r\tilde{v}_r^2=\min. \tag{6.3.4}$$

We will now introduce the diagonal matrix of weights

$$P=P_{NN}=\begin{Vmatrix} p_1 & 0 & \ldots & 0 \\ 0 & p_2 & \ldots & 0 \\ \cdot & \cdot & \cdot & \cdot \\ 0 & 0 & \ldots & p_N \end{Vmatrix}. \tag{6.3.5}$$

Then (see section 4, chapter I) we obtain

$$[p\tilde{v}\tilde{v}]=\sum_{r=1}^{N} p_r\tilde{v}_r^2=\tilde{V}^T P\tilde{V}, \tag{6.3.6}$$

so that the minimization condition, in terms of matrices, is

$$\tilde{V}^T P\tilde{V}=\min. \tag{6.3.7}$$

The necessary conditions for a minimum are of the form

$$\frac{\partial}{\partial \tilde{a}_i}[p\tilde{v}\tilde{v}] = 2\left[p\frac{\partial \tilde{v}}{\partial \tilde{a}_i}\cdot \tilde{v}\right] = 0 \qquad (i = 1, 2, \ldots, n). \tag{6.3.8}$$

From (6.3.3) we see that

$$\tilde{v}_r = x_{r1}\tilde{a}_1 + x_{r2}\tilde{a}_2 + \ldots + x_{rn}\tilde{a}_n - l_r, \tag{6.3.9}$$

$$\frac{\partial \tilde{v}_r}{\partial \tilde{a}_i} = x_{ri}. \tag{6.3.10}$$

We will show that the set of conditions (6.3.8) is equivalent to

$$X^T P\tilde{V} = 0, \tag{6.3.11}$$

We have

$$X = X_{Nn} = \begin{Vmatrix} x_{11} & x_{12} & \ldots & x_{1n} \\ x_{21} & x_{22} & \ldots & x_{2n} \\ \cdot & \cdot & \cdot & \cdot \\ x_{N1} & x_{N2} & \ldots & x_{Nn} \end{Vmatrix}; \quad (X_{Nn})^T = \begin{Vmatrix} x_{11} & x_{21} & \ldots & x_{N1} \\ x_{12} & x_{22} & \ldots & x_{N2} \\ \cdot & \cdot & \cdot & \cdot \\ x_{1n} & x_{2n} & \ldots & x_{Nn} \end{Vmatrix},$$

$$\left[p\frac{\partial \tilde{v}}{\partial \tilde{a}_i}\tilde{v}\right] = \sum_{r=1}^{N} x_{ri}p_r v_r; \tag{6.3.12}$$

$$\begin{Vmatrix} p_1 v_1 \\ \vdots \\ p_N v_N \end{Vmatrix} = PV. \tag{6.3.13}$$

Considering (6.3.12) and (6.3.13) we see that the condition (6.3.8) can be written

$$X^T P\tilde{V} = 0_{N1}, \tag{6.3.14}$$

which is what it was required to prove.

Theorem 6.3.1.

The vector of estimators $\tilde{A}_{n1}$ by the method of least squares can be found uniquely from the equation

$$C\tilde{A} = X^T PL, \tag{6.3.15}$$

where

$$C = X^T PX.$$

In more detailed form

$$C_{nn}\tilde{A}_{n1} = (X_{Nn})^T L_{N1}, \tag{6.3.16}$$

$$C_{nn} = (X_{Nn})^T P_{NN} X_{Nn}. \tag{6.3.17}$$

Proof. We compare (6.3.14) with (6.3.3). From (6.3.3) we have $\tilde{V} = X\tilde{A} - L$; pre-multiplying by $X^T P$ and taking into account (6.3.14) we find

$$0 = X^T P X \tilde{A} - X^T P L,$$

whence

$$X^T P X \tilde{A} = X^T P L. \tag{6.3.18}$$

Putting $C = X^T P X$ we obtain the proof of the theorem.

We will consider in more detail the matrix

$$C = C_{nn} = X^T P X.$$

Theorem 6.3.2
The matrix $C = C_{nn}$ is non-singular and

$$\det(C) = p_1 p_2 \ldots p_N \det\left(X^T X\right) = \det(P)\det\left(X^T X\right). \tag{6.3.19}$$

The proof is an immediate result of the definition of the matrix C and of theorem 6.3.1.

From theorem 6.3.2 we see that the system of equations (6.3.15) is soluble uniquely with respect to $\tilde{A}_{n1}$, and

$$\tilde{A} = C^{-1} X^T P L,$$

or in more detail

$$\tilde{A}_{n1} = (C_{nn})^{-1} (X_{Nn})^T P_{NN} L_{N1}. \tag{6.3.20}$$

Thus, the estimators $\tilde{a}_1, \tilde{a}_2, \ldots, \tilde{a}_n$ of the parameters $a_1, a_2, \ldots, a_n$ are obtained uniquely by the method of least squares.

We will also verify that $\tilde{A}_{n1}$ gives minimum $[p\tilde{v}\tilde{v}]$, so that the necessary conditions for minimizing $[pvv]$ are also sufficient.

Let $A' = A'_{n1} = \begin{Vmatrix} a'_1 \\ \vdots \\ a'_n \end{Vmatrix}$ be any arbitrary set of numbers;

$$\begin{aligned} V' &= XA' - L, \\ \tilde{V} &= X\tilde{A} - L. \end{aligned} \tag{6.3.21}$$

We will prove that

$$[pv'v'] \geqslant [p\tilde{v}\tilde{v}]. \qquad (6.3.22)$$

From (6.3.11) we find

$$V' - \tilde{V} = X(A' - \tilde{A}); \quad V' = \tilde{V} + X(A' - \tilde{A}). \qquad (6.3.23)$$

Using the last relation we obtain

$$[pv'v'] = (V')^T PV' = (\tilde{V}^T + (A' - \tilde{A})^T X^T) P (V + X(A' - \tilde{A})) =$$
$$= \tilde{V}^T P\tilde{V} + (A' - \tilde{A}) X^T PV + \tilde{V}^T PX(A' - \tilde{A}) +$$
$$+ (A' - \tilde{A})^T X^T PX(A' - \tilde{A}). \qquad (6.3.24)$$

But, from (6.3.14), $X^T P\tilde{V} = 0$. Transposing this relation we have

$$\tilde{V}^T PX = 0 \qquad (6.3.25)$$

since $P^T = P$. Thus, the second and third terms of (6.3.24) vanish. Further, from (6.3.24) $X(A' - \tilde{A}) = V' - \tilde{V}$, so that the fourth term of (6.3.24) can be written in the form

$$(V' - \tilde{V})^T P(V' - \tilde{V}) = [p(v' - \tilde{v})(v' - \tilde{v})],$$

and we have

$$[pv'v'] = [p\tilde{v}\tilde{v}] + [p(v' - \tilde{v})(v' - \tilde{v})]. \qquad (6.3.26)$$

The quantity

$$[p(v' - \tilde{v})(v' - \tilde{v})] = \sum_{i=1}^{N} p_r (v'_r - \tilde{v}_r)^2 \geqslant 0,$$

so that $\tilde{A}_{n1}$ really does give the minimum of $[p\tilde{v}\tilde{v}]$.

4. The Normal Equations, and Statistical Properties of Their Solutions

We will return to the system of equations (6.3.15), obtained for the determination of the parameters $\tilde{A}_{n1}$. We have

$$C\tilde{A} = X^T PL,$$

or

$$C_{nn}\tilde{A}_{n1} = (X_{Nn})^T PL_{N1}, \qquad (6.4.1)$$

where

$$C = X^T PX. \qquad (6.4.2)$$

This system is called a system of normal equations. Its matrix is a symmetrical matrix; in fact $P^T = P$, therefore

$$C^T = (X^T P X)^T = X^T P X = C.$$

Further, from the detailed representation of the matrices X_{Nn} and X^T_{Nn}, we see that

$$C = C_{nn} = \left\| \begin{matrix} [px_1x_1] & [px_1x_2] & \dots & [px_1x_n] \\ \cdot & \cdot & \cdot & \cdot \\ [px_nx_1] & [px_nx_2] & \dots & [px_nx_n] \end{matrix} \right\|, \tag{6.4.3}$$

i.e. that C is a generalized Gram's matrix of the vectors $x_1, x_2, \dots, x_n$ $(x_i = (x_{1i}, x_{2i}, \dots, x_{Ni}))$; corresponding scalar products taking the weights of the co-ordinates, $p_1, p_2, \dots, p_N$.

Further, $X^T PL = (X_{Nn})^T P_{NN} L_{N1}$ is a one-column matrix of the form

$$\left\| \begin{matrix} [px_1l] \\ [px_2l] \\ \vdots \\ [px_nl] \end{matrix} \right\|. \tag{6.4.4}$$

Then the system of normal equations (6.4.1) can be written in the form

$$\sum_{\nu=1}^{n} [px_i x_\nu] \tilde{a}_\nu = [px_i l], \quad i = 1, 2, \dots, n \tag{6.4.5}$$

$$x_i = (x_{i1}, x_{i2}, \dots, x_{iN}), \quad l = (l_1, l_2, \dots, l_N).$$

From (6.4.5) it is also easy to see the symmetry of the matrix C of the system of normal equations. Many of the calculating devices used in solving the normal equations (6.4.5) are based on the symmetry of matrix C; they are very well described in old textbooks (see, for instance, Edelson [10]. We refer these methods in section 12, where some examples are also given. Now we will study the statistical properties of $A = (a_1, a_2, \dots, a_n)$.

We have

$$\tilde{A} = C^{-1} X^T PL, \tag{6.4.6}$$

$$L = L_{N1} = Y_{N1} + \Delta_{N1},$$

where

$$\Delta = \Delta_{N1} = \left\| \begin{matrix} \Delta_1 \\ \vdots \\ \Delta_N \end{matrix} \right\| \tag{6.4.7}$$

is the matrix of 'true errors of measurement Y'. By the statement of the problem we have

$$E\Delta = 0; \quad EL = Y. \tag{6.4.8}$$

Theorem 6.4.1.

The estimators $\tilde{A}_{n1}$ of the parameters A_{n1}, obtained by the method of least squares are unbiased, i.e.

$$E(\tilde{A}_{n1}) = A_{n1}. \tag{6.4.9}$$

To prove this, we make use of (6.4.6) and (6.4.7). We note that, in the equation (6.4.6), only $\tilde{A}$ and L represent random matrices; the matrix $C^{-1}X^TP$ is a fixed matrix. In view of this

$$E(\tilde{A}) = E(C^{-1}X^TPL) = C^{-1}X^TPE(L) = C^{-1}X^TPY.$$

But from the statement of the problem we have

$$Y = XA, \tag{6.4.10}$$

whence

$$E(\tilde{A}) = C^{-1}X^TPXA = C^{-1}CA = A,$$

which is what it was required to prove.

Theorem 6.4.2.

The unbiased estimators, $\tilde{A}_{n1}$, form a normal, n-dimensional vector with correlation matrix

$$B_{\tilde{A}} = \sigma^2 C^{-1}. \tag{6.4.11}$$

Proof. We put

$$D = D_{nN} = C^{-1}X^TP, \tag{6.4.12}$$

so that

$$\tilde{A} = DL. \tag{6.4.13}$$

Further, we have the identity

$$A = C^{-1}CA = C^{-1}X^TPXA, \tag{6.4.14}$$

from which

$$\tilde{A} - A = C^{-1}X^TP(L - XA) = C^{-1}X^TP(\Delta + Y - XA) = C^{-1}X^TP\Delta,$$

because $Y - XA = 0$.

By virtue of (6.4.12)

$$\tilde{A} - A = D\Delta \tag{6.4.15}$$

(in detailed form $\tilde{A}_{n1} - A_{n1} = D_{nN}\Delta_{N1}$).

Further, we note that $\Delta = \begin{Vmatrix} \Delta_1 \\ \vdots \\ \Delta_n \end{Vmatrix}$ is a random normal vector with zero mean vector and independent components having variances

$$\sigma_r^2 = \frac{\sigma^2}{p_r} (r = 1, 2, \ldots, N), \tag{6.4.16}$$

so that its correlation matrix is, of course, of the form

$$B_\Delta = \sigma^2 P^{-1} = \sigma^2 P_{NN}^{-1}. \tag{6.4.17}$$

By formula (2.3.11), from (6.4.15) and (6.4.12) we conclude that the correlation matrix of the vector $\tilde{A}$ is of the form

$$B = B_{nn} = D\sigma^2 P^{-1} D^T = C^{-1} X^T P \sigma^2 P^{-1} P X (C^{-1})^T = \sigma^2 C^{-1} X^T P X (C^{-1})^T.$$

But $C = X^T P X$ is a symmetrical matrix, so that (see section 4, chapter I)

$$(C^{-1})^T = C^{-1}, \quad \text{and} \quad B_{\tilde{A}} = \sigma^2 C^{-1} X^T P X C^{-1} = \sigma^2 C^{-1},$$

which proves what we require.

We can now write down the joint probability density function of $(\tilde{a}_1, \tilde{a}_2, \ldots, \tilde{a}_n)$; it is of the form (see (2.2.10))

$$f(x_1, x_2, \ldots, x_n) =$$

$$= (2\pi)^{-\frac{n}{2}} \sigma^{-n} (\det (C))^{\frac{1}{2}} \exp\left\{ -\frac{1}{2\sigma^2} \left[(X - A)^T C (X - A)\right] \right\}, \tag{6.4.18}$$

where

$$X = \begin{Vmatrix} x_1 \\ x_2 \\ \vdots \\ x_n \end{Vmatrix} = X_{n1}; \quad A = A_{n1} = \begin{Vmatrix} a_1 \\ \vdots \\ a_n \end{Vmatrix}; \quad C = X^T P X.$$

We will now consider the problem of jointly efficient estimators, $\tilde{A}_{n1}$, and try to formulate ideas about the real theoretical-probabilistic meaning of point estimation by the method of least squares (see section 3, chapter III). We will construct Fisher's information matrix, I, (see (3.3.21)) for the likelihood function $L(l_1, \ldots, l_n)$ (see section 2 of this chapter) with given σ, for the parameters $a_1, a_2, \ldots, a_n$. It is

$$I = I_{nn} = \left\| E\left(-\frac{\partial^2 \ln L}{\partial a_i \, \partial a_j}\right)\right\|; \qquad i, j = 1, 2, \ldots, n. \tag{6.4.19}$$

From section 2 we find, immediately

$$-\frac{\partial^2 \ln L}{\partial a_i \, \partial a_j} = \frac{1}{\sigma^2} \sum_{r=1}^{N} x_{ri} p_r x_{rj} = \frac{1}{\sigma^2} [p x_i x_j] = \frac{1}{\sigma^2} (X^T P X)_{ij}$$

whence

$$I = I_{nn} = \frac{1}{\sigma^2} X^T P X = \frac{C}{\sigma^2} \tag{6.4.20}$$

and, according to (6.4.11),

$$I^{-1} = \sigma^2 C^{-1} = B_{\tilde{A}}. \tag{6.4.21}$$

From theorem 3.3.1, for a very wide class of unbiased estimators $(a_1', a_2', \ldots, a_n')$ with correlation matrix B_1, the correlation ellipsoid of the estimators $(\tilde{a}_1, \tilde{a}_2, \ldots, \tilde{a}_n)$ is contained inside the correlation ellipsoid of $(a_1', a_2', \ldots, a_n')$.

Using the results of section 5, chapter II, we can give some real theoretical-probabilistic meaning to estimation by the method of least squares.

5. The Real Meaning of Point Estimation by the Method of Least Squares

We will satisfy ourselves that the estimators $\tilde{a}_1, \ldots, \tilde{a}_n$, among a very wide class of unbiased and asymptotically normal estimators $a_1', \ldots, a_n'$ have, in some sense, an optimal character. Let

$$\tilde{\Delta}_i = \tilde{a}_i - a_i; \quad \Delta_i' = a_i' - a_i; \tag{6.5.1}$$

and let $\beta_1, \beta_2, \ldots, \beta_n$ be any arbitrary fixed numbers;

$$\xi = \sum_{i=1}^{n} \beta_i \tilde{\Delta}_i; \quad \eta = \sum_{i=1}^{n} \beta_i \Delta_i'. \tag{6.5.2}$$

Then, for any arbitrary fixed $\varepsilon > 0$, given n, and sufficiently large N, we have

$$P\{|\xi| \leqslant \varepsilon\} \geqslant P\{|\eta| \leqslant \varepsilon\}. \tag{6.5.3}$$

The proof follows immediately from (6.4.21) and from theorem 2.5.1. We note, in particular, that putting $\beta_{i_0}=1;\ \beta_i=0\ (i \neq i_0)$ we obtain

$$P\{|\tilde{\Delta}_{i_0}| \leqslant \varepsilon\} \geqslant P\{|\Delta'_{i_0}| \leqslant \varepsilon\} \tag{6.5.4}$$

for sufficiently large samples. Thus, every random deviation, separately, is better estimated by the method of least squares than by any other method among a very wide class of methods leading to unbiased and asymptotically normal estimators. But it is necessary to note that we do not affirm this in regard to a number of errors simultaneously. We can find some additional properties of the asymptotical behaviour of estimators obtained by the method of least squares.

Let $g(a_1, \ldots, a_n)$ be any function of measurable parameters, which can be developed in Taylor's series in the neighbourhood a of the point $(a_1, \ldots, a_n)$, and let $a'_1, \ldots, a'_n$ be a set of asymptotically normal and unbiased estimators of $a_1, \ldots, a_n$. We will compare the behaviour of $g(\tilde{a}_1, \ldots, \tilde{a}_n)$ and $g(a'_1, \ldots, a'_n)$. If we put $\tilde{a}_i = a_i + \tilde{\delta}_i$, $a'_i = a_i + \delta'_i$, where $\tilde{\delta}_i$, δ'_i are errors which are small with probability near to one (for given n and large N), then we can write the approximate equations

$$g(\tilde{a}_1, \ldots, \tilde{a}_n) \approx g(a_1, \ldots, a_n) + \sum_{i=1}^{n} \tilde{\delta}_i \frac{\partial g}{\partial a_i},$$

$$g(a'_1, \ldots, a'_n) \approx g(a_1, \ldots, a_n) + \sum_{i=1}^{n} \delta'_i \frac{\partial g}{\partial a_i}.$$

Therefore $g(\tilde{a}_1, \ldots, \tilde{a}_n)$ and $g(a'_1, \ldots, a'_n)$ are approximately linear and we can apply to them our previous reasoning on linear functions of errors so that

$$P\{|g(\tilde{a}_1, \ldots, \tilde{a}_n) - g(a_1, \ldots, a_n)| \leqslant \varepsilon\} \geqslant$$
$$\geqslant P\{|g(a'_1, \ldots, a'_n) - g(a_1, \ldots, a_n)| \leqslant \varepsilon\} \tag{6.5.5}$$

for given ε, fixed n and large N.

6. The Statistical Behaviour of the Deviations $\tilde{V}$

In the estimation of the accuracy of derived results, and the construction of confidence intervals, the one-column matrix of deviations $\tilde{V} = \tilde{V}_{N1}$, and functions thereof, for example, $[p\tilde{v}\tilde{v}] = \tilde{V}^T P \tilde{V}$, are of great importance. We will study the statistical behaviour of $\tilde{V}$. By definition

$$\tilde{V} = X\tilde{A} - L = \tilde{L} - L; \quad \tilde{L} = X\tilde{A}. \tag{6.6.1}$$

Theorem 6.6.1.
We have

$$\tilde{V} = \tilde{V}_{N1} = (U_{NN} - E_{NN})\Delta_N, \tag{6.6.2}$$

where

$$U = U_{NN} = XC^{-1}X^TP = X(X^TPX)^{-1}X^TP. \tag{6.6.3}$$

Proof. We have

$$\tilde{V} = X\tilde{A} - L; \quad \tilde{A} = C^{-1}X^TPL,$$

so that

$$\tilde{V} = XC^{-1}X^TPL - L = (XC^{-1}X^TP - E)L = (U - E)L;$$
$$U = XC^{-1}X^TP.$$

Further,

$$L = Y + \Delta, \quad Y = XA.$$

Thus,

$$\tilde{V} = (U - E)\Delta + (U - E)XA;$$

further

$$(U - E)XA = X(X^TPX)^{-1}X^TPXA - XA = XA - XA = 0$$

and

$$\tilde{V} = (U - E)\Delta,$$

which proves what we require.

We know that the correlation matrix Δ is of the form (see (6.4.17))

$$B_\Delta = \sigma^2P^{-1}.$$

For later work the following theorem is important.

Theorem 6.6.2.
The correlation matrix of the vector of deviations $\tilde{V} = \tilde{V}_{n1}$ is of the form

$$B_{\tilde{V}} = \sigma^2P^{-1}(E - U^T) = \sigma^2P^{-1}(E - PX(X^TPX)^{-1}X^T). \tag{6.6.4}$$

To prove this, it is convenient to reduce to the case of observations of equal accuracy: $P = E = E_{NN}$, and then, following the text of section 1 of this chapter (formulae (6.1.5) and (6.1.6)), to replace $\tilde{V}$ by $P^{-\frac{1}{2}}\tilde{V}$ and X by $P^{\frac{1}{2}}X$ in the formulae found for measurements of equal accuracy. Then, the matrix

$$U = X(X^T P X)^{-1} X^T P$$

takes the form

$$U = X(X^T X)^{-1} X^T. \text{ *)}$$

for measurements of equal accuracy.

From this definition of U we have, immediately,

$$U^T = U, \quad U^2 = U. \tag{6.6.5}$$

In fact,

$$U^T = X(X^T X)^{-1} X^T = U;$$
$$U^2 = X(X^T X)^{-1} X^T X (X^T X)^{-1} X^T = X(X^T X)^{-1} X^T = U;$$

and from the equations

$$\tilde{V} = (U - E)\Delta \quad \text{and} \quad B_L = \sigma^2 E$$

(equal accuracy), applying theorem 2.3.1, we find

$$B_{\tilde{V}} = (U - E) B_L (U - E)^T = \sigma^2 (U - E)^2 = \sigma^2 (E - U), \tag{6.6.6}$$

since $(U - E)^2 = U^2 - 2U + E = U - 2U + E = E - U$ from (6.3.5).

Now it only remains to pass from observations of equal accuracy to observations of unequal accuracy. Writing (6.6.6) in the form

$$B_{\tilde{V}} = \sigma^2 (E - X(X^T X)^{-1} X^T),$$

we obtain, by theorem 2.3.1 and the equation $\left(P^{-\frac{1}{2}}\right)^T = P^{-\frac{1}{2}}$,

$$B_{\tilde{V}} = \sigma^2 P^{-\frac{1}{2}} \left(E - P^{\frac{1}{2}} X (X^T P X)^{-1} X^T P^{\frac{1}{2}}\right) P^{-\frac{1}{2}} =$$
$$= \sigma^2 P^{-1} \left(E - P X (X^T P X)^{-1} X^T\right) = \sigma^2 P^{-1} \left(E - U^T\right),$$

which is what it was required to prove.

---

* In this case, using the language of multi-dimensional geometry, the matrix U has a rather simple meaning - it is a projection matrix (see, for example, Smirnov [46], pp. 158-163).

Now we prove a very important theorem.

Theorem 6.6.3.

The random vectors $\tilde{A}=\tilde{A}_{n1}$ and $\tilde{V}=\tilde{V}_{N1}$ are normal and independent.

The proof is based directly on theorem 2.3.3.

We have

$$\tilde{V}=(U-E)\Delta;\quad U=X(X^TPX)^{-1}X^TP,$$
$$\tilde{A}-A=(X^TPX)^{-1}X^TP\Delta=W\Delta$$

(see (6.4.14)). Here $W=(X^TPX)^{-1}X^TP$. From this it follows that $\tilde{V}$ and $\tilde{A}$ are normal vectors (see theorem 2.3.3). Further,

$$B_\Delta=\sigma^2P^{-1}E. \tag{6.6.7}$$

From theorem 2.3.3 it follows that it is sufficient to examine only the matrix equation

$$(U-E)B_\Delta W^T=0. \tag{6.6.8}$$

Putting, as before, $C=X^TPX$, we have

$$(U-E)B_\Delta W^T=\sigma^2(XC^{-1}X^TP-E)P^{-1}PXC^{-1}=$$
$$=\sigma^2(XC^{-1}X^TPXC^{-1}-XC^{-1})=$$
$$=\sigma^2(XC^{-1}CC^{-1}-XC^{-1})=\sigma^2(XC^{-1}-XC^{-1})=0,$$

which proves (6.6.8) and so the whole theorem. We note that the proof of theorem 2.3.3 is rather complicated; it is possible to give another derivation of this theorem, based on the arguments presented in Kolmogorov's paper [22]. We will pass on to the following important theorem.

Theorem 6.6.4.

The random vector $\tilde{A}$ is an n-dimensional normal vector, and the random vector $\tilde{V}$ is an $(N-n)$-dimensional normal vector. These random vectors are independent. The random variable

$$\frac{1}{\sigma^2}[p\tilde{v}\tilde{v}] \tag{6.6.9}$$

is distributed as χ^2_{N-n} and is independent of $\tilde{A}$.

Proof. As before, we will first consider the case of measurements of equal accuracy, taking $P=E$. We obtain

$$\tilde{A}-A=W\Delta;\ \tilde{V}=(U-E)\Delta;\quad W=(X^TX)^{-1}X^T;\quad U=X(X^TX)^{-1}X^T \tag{6.6.10}$$

We have, further,

$$\text{rank}\,(W)=n; \qquad \text{rank}\,(U)=n. \tag{6.6.11}$$

In fact, $\text{rank}\,(X)=\text{rank}\,(X^T)=n$; so X^TX is a non-singular matrix. In view of this, $\text{rank}\,(W)=\text{rank}\,(X^T)=n$. Further, $\text{rank}\,(U)\leqslant\text{rank}\,(X)=n$, by virtue of the inequality (1.2.18). On the other hand

$$UX=X(X^TX)^{-1}X^TX=X \tag{6.6.12}$$

(which means that U is a projection matrix). Therefore, by virtue of the inequality (1.2.18) mentioned above, we have

$$n=\text{rank}\,(X)\leqslant\min(\text{rank}\,(U),\ \text{rank}\,(X))=\min(\text{rank}(U),\ n),$$

whence $\text{rank}\,(U)\geqslant n$. Comparing this with the relation $\text{rank}\,(U)=n$, obtained before, we deduce that $\text{rank}\,(U)=n$. Thus, $\tilde{A}-A$ and $\tilde{A}$ are n-dimensional vectors.

Now we show that $\text{rank}\,(E-U)=N-n$.

We have $(E-U)^T=E-U$, i.e. $E-U$ is a symmetrical matrix. Further, $U^2=U$, whence

$$(E-U)^2=E-2U+U^2=E-U. \tag{6.6.13}$$

There exists an orthogonal matrix, $F=F_{NN}$, which reduces U to the diagonal form

$$F^TUF=D=\begin{Vmatrix} d_1 & 0 & \dots & 0 \\ 0 & d_2 & \dots & 0 \\ \cdot & \cdot & \cdot & \cdot \\ 0 & 0 & \dots & d_N \end{Vmatrix}. \tag{6.6.14}$$

Also $D^2=F^{-1}U^2F=F^{-1}UF=D$, so that $d_i^2=d_i$ and $d_i=0;\,1$. Evidently, the number of d_i's, for which $d_i=1$, is equal to rank (U), i.e. to n. Further,

$$F^{-1}(E-U)F=E-F^{-1}UF=E-D=\begin{Vmatrix} 1-d_1 & 0 & \dots & 0 \\ 0 & 1-d_2 & \dots & 0 \\ \cdot & \cdot & \cdot & \cdot \\ 0 & 0 & \dots & 1-d_N \end{Vmatrix}, \tag{6.6.15}$$

whence it is clear that $\text{rank}\,(E-U)=\text{rank}\,(E-D)=N-n$. Thus, $\text{rank}\,(U-E)=N-n$ and we conclude from (6.6.10), and from theorem 2.3.1, that $\tilde{V}$ is an $(N-n)$-dimensional normal vector. As a consequence of these arguments we can note that the matrices

U and $(E-U)$ are reduced to a diagonal form by the same orthogonal matrix F. And also, if we introduce a one-column matrix $Z=Z_{N1}=\begin{Vmatrix} z_1 \\ \vdots \\ z_N \end{Vmatrix}$ and construct the quadratic forms

$$Z^T U Z; \quad Z^T (E-U) Z, \tag{6.6.16}$$

then, by substituting $Z=FY$ and $Y=Y_{N1}$, we obtain the new quadratic forms

$$Y^T DY = \sum_{i=1}^{n} y^2_{\alpha_i}; \quad Y^T (E-D) Y = \sum_{j=1}^{N-n} y^2_{\beta_j}. \tag{6.6.17}$$

As is clear from (6.6.14) and (6.6.15) the set of variables y_{α_i} and y_{β_j} includes all the variables $y_1, \ldots, y_N$, and also $\alpha_i \neq \beta_j$ $(i=1, \ldots, n;\ j=1, \ldots, N-n)$, i.e. they are sets of different variables y_i.

We consider now the random variable (6.6.9). Putting, as before, $P=E;\ p_i=1 \quad (i=1, \ldots, N)$, we form

$$[\tilde{v}\tilde{v}] = \tilde{V}^T \tilde{V}.$$

We have

$$\tilde{V}^T \tilde{V} = \Delta^T (U-E)^T (U-E) \Delta = \Delta^T (U-E)^2 \Delta = \Delta^T (E-U) \Delta$$

by virtue of (6.6.13). Further, Δ is a normal random vector with $E(\Delta)=0$ and $B_\Delta = \sigma^2 E$, for measurements of equal accuracy. By Fisher's theorem (theorem 2.3.2), the random vector $F \cdot \Delta$ is distributed as the vector Δ, for any arbitrary orthogonal matrix F We take the orthogonal matrix, F, mentioned above. We have

$$[\tilde{v}\tilde{v}] = \Delta^T (E-U) \Delta = \Delta^T F F^T (E-U) F F^T \Delta =$$
$$= (\Delta^T F)(E-D)(F^T \Delta) = \sum_{j=1}^{N-n} y^2_{\beta_j}.$$

(see (6.6.17)). Here we have put $Y=Y_{N1}=\begin{Vmatrix} y_1 \\ \vdots \\ y_N \end{Vmatrix} = F^T \Delta.$ For reasons described above, $Y=Y_{N1}$ is a normal random vector with independent components of type $N(0, \sigma)$. Whence, according to the definition of χ^2_{N-n}, we have

$$\frac{1}{\sigma^2}[\tilde{v}\tilde{v}] = \chi^2_{N-n}.$$

The theorem is proved. It is clear that $[\tilde{v}\tilde{v}]$, as a function of the random vector $\tilde{V}$, (which is statistically independent of $\tilde{A}$), is also independent of $\tilde{A}$.

Now we return to the case of measurements of unequal accuracy. In this transition the vector $\tilde{A}$ keeps its previous form; in the place of X we must take $P^{\frac{1}{2}}X$, and also rank $\left(P^{\frac{1}{2}}X\right) =$ rank (X), so that $\tilde{A}$, as shown above, is an n-dimensional random vector. Further, $\tilde{V}$ is replaced by $P^{-\frac{1}{2}}\tilde{V}$ in the case of measurements of unequal accuracy; consequently, in the case of measurements of unequal accuracy, the quantity $\frac{1}{\sigma^2}[p\tilde{v}\tilde{v}] = \chi^2_{N-n}$ is statistically independent of $\tilde{A}$.

We will also derive some formulae relating to $[p\tilde{v}\tilde{v}]$.

Theorem 6.6.5. We have

$$[p\tilde{v}\tilde{v}] = L^T PL - \tilde{A}^T C\tilde{A} = [pll] - \tilde{A}^T C\tilde{A}. \tag{6.6.18}$$

Proof. According to formulae (6.4.1) and (6.1.1) we have

$$C\tilde{A} = X^T PL; \quad C = X^T PX; \quad \tilde{V} = X\tilde{A} - L.$$

whence $\tilde{A}^T C = L^T PX$. Further,

$J_\gamma^{(i)}$

$$\begin{aligned}[p\tilde{v}\tilde{v}] &= \tilde{V}^T P\tilde{V} = (\tilde{A}^T X^T - L^T) P (X\tilde{A} - L) = \\ &= \tilde{A}^T X^T PX\tilde{A} + L^T PL - L^T PX\tilde{A} - \tilde{A}^T X^T PL = \\ &= \tilde{A}^T C\tilde{A} + L^T PL - \tilde{A}^T C\tilde{A} - \tilde{A}^T C\tilde{A} = \\ &= L^T PL - \tilde{A}^T C\tilde{A},\end{aligned}$$

which is what it was required to prove.

The following theorem can be useful in the calculation or in verifying the calculation of $[p\tilde{v}\tilde{v}]$.

Theorem 6.6.6. We have

$$\begin{aligned}[p\tilde{v}\tilde{v}] &= L^T PL - L^T PX\tilde{A} = \\ &= [pll] - [px_1 l]\tilde{a}_1 - [px_2 l]\tilde{a}_2 - \ldots - [px_n l]\tilde{a}_n.\end{aligned} \tag{6.6.19}$$

From (6.6.18),

$$[p\tilde{v}\tilde{v}] = L^T PL - \tilde{A}^T C\tilde{A}.$$

Since $\tilde{A}^T C = L^T P X$, it follows that

$$[p\tilde{v}\tilde{v}] = L^T PL - L^T PX\tilde{A}$$

This proves the first of the equations (6.6.19). We will prove the second of the equations (6.6.19). We have

$$L^T PX = (X^T PL)^T = \| [px_1 l], [px_2 l], \ldots, [px_n l] \|,$$

whence

$$L^T PX\tilde{A} = [px_1 l]\,\tilde{a}_1 + [px_2 l]\,\tilde{a}_2 + \ldots + [px_n l]\,\tilde{a}_n,$$

which gives us the second of the equations (6.6.19).

We will also prove the formula

$$[p\tilde{v}\tilde{v}] = L^T PL - \tilde{L}^T P\tilde{L} = [pll] - [p\tilde{l}\tilde{l}], \tag{6.6.20}$$

where

$$\tilde{L} = X\tilde{A}.$$

From (6.6.18) we have

$$[p\tilde{v}\tilde{v}] = L^T PL - \tilde{A}^T C\tilde{A} = L^T PL - \tilde{A}^T X^T PX\tilde{A} =$$
$$= L^T PL - \tilde{L}^T P\tilde{L} = [pll] - [p\tilde{l}\tilde{l}],$$

which proves what we require.

We will also present an expression for $[p\tilde{v}\tilde{v}]$ given by Neyman and his pupil David [15].

We put

$$H_0 = \sum_{r=1}^{N} p_r l_r^2, \tag{6.6.21}$$

$$H_h = \sum_{r=1}^{N} p_r l_r x_{rh} \quad (h = 1, \ldots, n), \tag{6.6.22}$$

$$C_{hk} = \sum_{r=1}^{N} p_r x_{rh} x_{rk} \quad (h, k = 1, 2, \ldots, n). \tag{6.6.23}$$

Then, as it is easy to see,

$$C = \| c_{hk} \| = \left\| \begin{matrix} c_{11} & c_{12} & \cdots & c_{1n} \\ \cdot & \cdot & \cdot & \cdot \\ c_{n1} & c_{n2} & \cdots & c_{nn} \end{matrix} \right\|, \tag{6.6.24}$$

We will construct borders of the matrix C using the numbers

$H_0, H_1, \ldots, H_n$, i.e. we construct

$$C_{HH} = \begin{Vmatrix} H_0 & H_1 & H_2 & \ldots & H_n \\ H_1 & c_{11} & c_{12} & \ldots & c_{1n} \\ H_2 & c_{21} & c_{22} & \ldots & c_{2n} \\ \cdot & \cdot & \cdot & \cdot & \cdot \\ H_n & c_{n1} & c_{n2} & \ldots & c_{nn} \end{Vmatrix}. \tag{6.6.25}$$

Then, we have the following theorem.

Theorem 6.6.7.

We have

$$[p\tilde{v}\tilde{v}] = \frac{\det(C_{HH})}{\det(C)}. \tag{6.6.26}$$

To prove this, we write (6.6.21) and (6.6.22) in the matrix form

$$H_0 = L^T PL, \tag{6.6.27}$$

$$H_h = \{X^T PL\}_{h1}. \tag{6.6.28}$$

We now consider the matrix C_{HH}, and its determinant $\det(C_{HH})$. To calculate $\det(C_{HH})$, we will first develop this determinant by the elements of the first row, then by the elements of the first column, to obtain the coefficients of H_0 and $H_h H_k$. We get

$$\det(C_{HH}) = H_0 \det(C) - \sum_{h,\, k=1}^{n} H_h H_k M_{hk},$$

where M_{hk} is the cofactor of the element c_{hk} in the matrix C. Taking into account the symmetry of C $(C^T = C)$, we have

$$\|M_{hk}\| = C^{-1} \det(C);$$

$$\frac{\det(C_{HH})}{\det(C)} = H_0 - \sum_{h,\, k=1}^{n} H_h H_k \{C^{-1}\}_{hk} = H_0 - H^T C^{-1} H,$$

where H denotes the matrix

$$H = H_{n1} = \begin{Vmatrix} H_1 \\ \vdots \\ H_n \end{Vmatrix} = X^T PL,$$

according to (6.6.28). Substituting (6.6.21) here also, we find

$$\frac{\det(C_{HH})}{\det(C)} = L^T PL - L^T PXC^{-1} X^T PL. \tag{6.6.29}$$

But, according to (6.4.6), $C^{-1}X^TPL = \tilde{A}$, so that

$$\frac{\det(C_{HH})}{\det(C)} = L^TPL - L^TPX\tilde{A} = [p\tilde{v}\tilde{v}]$$

by virtue of (6.6.19), which is what it was required to prove.

7. Point Estimation of the Quantities y_i $(i = 1, 2, \ldots, N)$

The variates y_i are connected with the variates x_i by the exact relationships:

$$Y = Y_{N1} = XA = \left\| \begin{matrix} y_1 \\ \vdots \\ y_N \end{matrix} \right\|. \qquad (6.7.1)$$

We will consider the vector

$$\tilde{L} = \tilde{L}_{N1} = X\tilde{A}. \qquad (6.7.2)$$

as an estimator of $(y_1, \ldots, y_N)$.

From (6.7.2) we obtain

$$E(\tilde{L}) = XA = Y, \qquad (6.7.3)$$

so that the components of $\tilde{L}$ are unbiased estimators of the components of Y. Further, we have, for the correlation matrix $B_{\tilde{L}}$ of the vector $\tilde{L}$,

$$B_{\tilde{L}} = \sigma^2 XC^{-1}X^T. \qquad (6.7.4)$$

In fact,

$$B_{\tilde{L}} = E\left[X(\tilde{A} - A)(X(\tilde{A} - A))^T\right] = XB_{\tilde{A}}X^T = \sigma^2 XC^{-1}X^T,$$

which proves what we require.

Thus we have, for the random variable $\tilde{l}_i = \{\tilde{L}\}_{i1}$,

$$E(\tilde{l}_i) = y_i; \quad D(\tilde{l}_i) = \sigma^2 \{XC^{-1}X^T\}_{ii}. \qquad (6.7.5)$$

We will also prove a theorem on the variance of $\tilde{l}_i$:

Theorem 6.7.1.
We have

$$\sum_{i=1}^{N} p_i D(\tilde{l}_i) = [pD(\tilde{l})] = n\sigma^2. \qquad (6.7.6)$$

By virtue of (6.7.5), it is sufficient to prove that

$$\sum_{i=1}^{N} p_i \{XC^{-1}X^T\}_{ii} = n. \tag{6.7.7.}$$

We introduce the diagonal matrix of weights, P, and observe that

$$p_i \{XC^{-1}X^T\}_{ii} = \{XC^{-1}X^T P\}_{ii}.$$

Further, $XC^{-1}X^TP = U$ (see (6.6.3)), so that it is sufficient to show that

$$\sum_{i=1}^{N} \{U\}_{ii} = n, \tag{6.7.8}$$

or $\mathrm{Sp}(U) = n$ (see section 3, chapter I).

Further, we have

$$U^2 = U \text{ and rank } (U) = n$$

(see section 6 of this chapter).

The matrix $U_1 = P^{-\frac{1}{2}} U P^{\frac{1}{2}} = P^{-\frac{1}{2}} XC^{-1}X^T P^{\frac{1}{2}}$ is symmetrical and $U_1^2 = U_1$. Further, rank $(U_1) =$ rank $(U) = n$.

By formula (1.3.18) we have

$$\mathrm{Sp}(U_1) = \mathrm{Sp}(U). \tag{6.7.9}$$

As in section 6, we choose an orthogonal matrix F such that

$$FU_1F^T = D, \tag{6.7.10}$$

where D is a diagonal matrix. Since $F^T = F^{-1}$, we obtain

$$FU_1F^T = FU_1F^{-1},$$

so that

$$\mathrm{Sp}(U_1) = \mathrm{Sp}\, D \quad \text{and} \quad D^2 = D.$$

We have

$$D = \begin{Vmatrix} d_1 & 0 & \dots & 0 \\ 0 & d_2 & \dots & 0 \\ \cdot & \cdot & \cdot & \cdot \\ 0 & 0 & \dots & d_N \end{Vmatrix}; \quad d_i^2 = d_i,$$

therefore $d_i = 0;\ 1.$

Further, rank $(D) =$ rank $(U_1) = n$. Therefore, the count of numbers, d_i, which are equal to one, is n. Whence, of course

$$\mathrm{Sp}\,(D) = \sum_{i=1}^{N} d_i = n. \tag{6.7.11}$$

Since

$$\mathrm{Sp}\,(U) = \mathrm{Sp}\,(U_1) = \mathrm{Sp}\,(D),$$

then

$$\mathrm{Sp}\,(U) = n,$$

which proves the theorem.

Theorem 6.7.1 stresses the difference between the random vectors $\tilde{L}$ and L. The quantities $\tilde{l}_1, \ldots, \tilde{l}_N$ are, in general, dependent, and the quantities $l_1, \ldots, l_N$ are independent. We have

$$\sum_{r=1}^{N} p_r D(\tilde{l}_r) = [pD(\tilde{l})] = n\sigma^2 \quad \text{(see (6.7.6))},$$

and simultaneously, of course,

$$\sum_{r=1}^{N} p_r D(l_r) = [pD(l)] = N\sigma^2. \tag{6.7.12}$$

The equality (6.7.12) permits us to visualize the overall accuracy of the estimators $\tilde{l}_1, \ldots, \tilde{l}_N$. Let $p_i = 1$, for simplicity, so that the observations are of equal accuracy. Then

$$\sum_{i=1}^{N} D(\tilde{l}_i) = n\sigma^2. \tag{6.7.13}$$

Thus the 'mean variance' of $\tilde{l}_i$ is equal to

$$\frac{1}{N} \sum_{i=1}^{N} D(\tilde{l}_i) = \frac{n}{N} \cdot \sigma^2. \tag{6.7.14}$$

From this it is clear that the mean variance of $\tilde{l}_i$ is proportional to $\frac{n}{N}$ for given σ^2, i.e. the estimators are the better, the greater the number of observations in comparison to the number of measured parameters.

8. Estimation of Parameters by Confidence Intervals

Previous results allow us to construct confidence intervals for estimating the parameters $a_1, a_2, \ldots, a_n$, or linear combinations thereof separately *). We know that the vector of estimators, $\tilde{A}$, obtained by the method of least squares, has the vector of means, A, and the correlation matrix $B = \sigma^2 C^{-1}$. Thus, for the estimator $\tilde{a}_i$ we have

$$E(\tilde{a}_i) = a_i; \quad D(\tilde{a}_i) = \sigma^2 \{C^{-1}\}_{ii}. \tag{6.8.1}$$

Therefore

$$\frac{\tilde{a}_i - a_i}{\sigma \sqrt{\{C^{-1}\}_{ii}}} \in N(0, 1). \tag{6.8.2}$$

Further, the quantity $q = \frac{[p\tilde{v}\tilde{v}]}{N-n}$ is independent of the normal vector $\tilde{A}$, and consequently of the quantities (6.8.2). By theorem 6.6.4

$$\frac{1}{\sigma^2} q = \frac{1}{\sigma^2} \frac{[p\tilde{v}\tilde{v}]}{N-n} = \frac{\chi^2_{N-n}}{N-n},$$

whence it follows (section 6, chapter II) that the quantity

$$t_{N-n} = \frac{\tilde{a}_i - a_i}{\sqrt{\{C^{-1}\}_{ii} q}} = \frac{\tilde{a}_i - a_i}{\sqrt{\{C^{-1}\}_{ii} \frac{[p\tilde{v}\tilde{v}]}{N-n}}} \tag{6.8.3}$$

has Student's distribution with $(N-n)$ degrees of freedom. This allows us construct a confidence interval for estimating a_i.

We choose the necessary confidence coefficient p, for the first entry of Table I of Student's distribution; for the second entry we take the number of degrees of freedom $k = N - n$. From the distribution table we obtain a number γ such that

$$P\{|t_{N-n}| \leqslant \gamma\} = p.$$

We obtain a confidence interval with confidence coefficient p for estimating a_i in the same way, as in chapter V in the case of estimating one parameter,

$$I_\gamma^{(i)} = \left[\tilde{a}_i - \gamma \sqrt{\{C^{-1}\}_{ii} \frac{[p\tilde{v}\tilde{v}]}{N-n}},\ \tilde{a}_i + \gamma \sqrt{\{C^{-1}\}_{ii} \frac{[p\tilde{v}\tilde{v}]}{N-n}}\right]. \tag{6.8.4}$$

By analogy we can construct confidence intervals for estimating $y_1, y_2, \ldots, y_N$. For this we will use (6.7.4) and note that $\tilde{L} = X\tilde{A}$ independent of $[p\tilde{v}\tilde{v}]$. Thus, the ratio

$$t_{N-n} = \frac{\tilde{l}_i - y_i}{\sqrt{\{XC^{-1}X^T\}_{ii} q}} = \frac{\tilde{l}_i - y_i}{\sqrt{\{XC^{-1}X^T\}_{ii} \frac{[p\tilde{v}\tilde{v}]}{N-n}}} \tag{6.8.5}$$

* In chapter XIV there will be constructed confidence intervals for a more general situation of estimation by elements and confidence regions for arbitrary sets of parameters $a_1, a_2, \ldots, a_n$.

is distributed according to Student's law with $N-n$ degrees of freedom. We can choose the confidence coefficient p_0, determine the value γ as in the previous case, and construct the confidence interval

$$J_\gamma^{(i)}=\left[\tilde{l}_i-\gamma\sqrt{\{XC^{-1}X^T\}_{ii}\frac{[p\tilde{v}\tilde{v}]}{N-n}},\ \tilde{l}_i+\gamma\sqrt{\{XC^{-1}X^T\}_{ii}\frac{[p\tilde{v}\tilde{v}]}{N-n}}\right] \tag{6.8.6}$$

with confidence coefficient p_0.

We see that the length of the confidence interval $J_\gamma^{(i)}$ is a random variable

$$d_\gamma^{(i)}=2\gamma s\sqrt{\{XC^{-1}X^T\}_{ii}}, \tag{6.8.7}$$

where $s=\sqrt{\frac{[p\tilde{v}\tilde{v}]}{N-n}}$.

From (6.8.7), we can evaluate the mean square of the length of

$$E\left\{\frac{1}{N}\sum_{i=1}^{N}p_i\left(d_\gamma^{(i)}\right)^2\right\}=\frac{1}{N}E\left[pd_\gamma^2\right]. \tag{6.8.8}$$

This quantity is equal to

$$\frac{1}{N}4\gamma^2\sigma^2\sum_{i=1}^{N}p_i\{XC^{-1}X^T\}_{ii}=\frac{4\gamma^2n\sigma^2}{N},$$

using (6.7.7).

Thus, the weighted mean square of the length of the confidence interval, for a given σ^2, is proportional to $\gamma^2\frac{n}{N}$. The value of γ is determined as the number such that $P\{|t_{N-n}|\leqslant\gamma\}=p_0$. For simplicity, we assume that the observations are of equal accuracy ($p_i=1$). If $N-n\geqslant 20$, we can assume, without substantial error, that Student's ratio t_{N-n} is approximately normal $N(0, 1)$ (section 6, chapter II). Therefore, putting $p_0=0.95$, we can take $\gamma\approx 1.96$ (see 2.1.3). The mean square of the length of the confidence interval $J_\gamma^{(i)}$ is approximately equal to

$$\frac{4\times(1.96)^2\sigma^2n}{N}=\frac{15.37\sigma^2n}{N}$$

Thus, for accurate work $\frac{N}{n}$ should be large.

9. Estimation of the Accuracy of Measurements

In order to decide which estimator we want to choose, we will first derive the estimator of σ^2 by the method of maximum likelihood. The logarithm of the likelihood function is given by a formula in section 2 of this chapter, so that we have the equation

$$\frac{\partial \ln L}{\partial \sigma^2} = -\frac{N}{2\sigma^2} + \frac{1}{2\sigma^4} \sum_{r=1}^{N} p_r \left(l_r - \sum_{j=1}^{n} a_j x_{rj} \right)^2 = 0. \qquad (6.9.1)$$

We have seen, in section 2 of this chapter, that the estimators of a_i by the method of least squares are consistent with the estimators by maximum likelihood. We have

$$\sum_r p_r (l_r - \sum \tilde{a}_r x_{rj})^2 = [p\tilde{v}\tilde{v}].$$

Therefore estimation of σ^2, by the method of maximum likelihood, according to equation (6.9.1), gives

$$\hat{\sigma}^2 = \frac{[p\tilde{v}\tilde{v}]}{N}. \qquad (6.9.2)$$

We know, however, that $\frac{1}{\sigma^2}[p\tilde{v}\tilde{v}] = \chi^2_{N-n}$, so that

$$E\,[p\tilde{v}\tilde{v}] = \sigma^2 E\left(\chi^2_{N-n}\right) = (N-n)\,\sigma^2. \qquad (6.9.3)$$

Thus, the estimator $\hat{\sigma}^2$ is biased, underestimating σ^2,

$$E\,(\hat{\sigma}^2) = \sigma^2\,\frac{N-n}{N}. \qquad (6.9.4)$$

From $\hat{\sigma}^2$ is easy to obtain the unbiased estimator

$$\hat{\sigma}_1^2 = \frac{N\hat{\sigma}^2}{N-n} = \frac{[p\tilde{v}\tilde{v}]}{N-n}. \qquad (6.9.5)$$

This estimator is asymptotically equivalent to the estimator $\hat{\sigma}^2$, when a fixed number, n, of parameters is being estimated, and there is a large number of observations N. We will use it as a point estimator of σ^2; for a point estimator of σ we will use the quantity

$$\tilde{s} = \sqrt{\frac{[p\tilde{v}\tilde{v}]}{N-n}}. \qquad (6.9.6)$$

We note that the last estimator is biased, but asymptotically unbiased for given n and increasing N.

We can construct a confidence interval for estimating σ, making use of the fact that $\frac{1}{\sigma^2}[p\tilde{v}\tilde{v}] = \chi^2_{N-n}$. We do this in the same way as in chapter V, section 3. Using Table III of Appendix, with degrees of freedom $k=N-n$, we construct the confidence interval

$$I=\left[\gamma_1\sqrt{\frac{[p\tilde{v}\tilde{v}]}{N-n}},\quad \gamma_2\sqrt{\frac{[p\tilde{v}\tilde{v}]}{N-n}}\right], \tag{6.9.7}$$

covering σ with probability p_0. Since $\tilde{s}^2=\chi^2_{N-n}\sigma^2/(N-n)$, then from the properties of χ^2_{N-n}, we are able to note that

$$D(\tilde{s})\infty\frac{\sigma^2}{2(N-n)} \tag{6.9.8}$$

in the sense of asymptotic equality, i.e. $\frac{D(\tilde{s})}{\sigma^2/2(N-n)}\to 1$ for increasing $N-n$.

10. Treatment of Direct Observations from a Different Point of View. Weights

We have obtained all the results needed for estimating measured parameters by the method of least squares, using indirect unconditional measurements. The case of direct measurements of unequal accuracy with known weights, considered in chapter V, is a very common case of this. We will consider it as an example.

In this case we have one parameter a; the matrix X has the very simple form

$$X=X_{N1}=\left\|\begin{matrix}1\\1\\\vdots\\1\end{matrix}\right\|;\quad y_r=a \qquad (r=1,\,2,\,\ldots,\,N), \tag{6.10.1}$$

so that the equations of form (6.2.1) become the N equations

$$l_r=y_r+\Delta_r=a+\Delta_r \qquad (r=1,\,2,\,\ldots,\,N).$$

Taking into consideration (6.4.6) and (6.4.11), we have

$$\tilde{A}=\tilde{A}_{n1}=\tilde{A}_{11}=\tilde{a};$$

$$C=X^TPX=\sum_{i=1}^{n}p_i=[p];$$

$$\tilde{a}=\tilde{A}_{11}=C^{-1}X^TPL=\frac{[pl]}{[p]};$$

$$D(\tilde{a})=B=B_{11}=\sigma^2C^{-1}=\frac{\sigma^2}{[p]}.$$

To estimate σ^2 we use the unbiased point estimator

$$\frac{[p\tilde{v}\tilde{v}]}{N-1}=\frac{[p(l-\tilde{a})(l-\tilde{a})]}{N-1},$$

which corresponds to the earlier formula (5.2.11). Further, to estimate $D(\tilde{a}) = \frac{\sigma^2}{[p]}$ we use $\frac{[p(l-\tilde{a})(l-\tilde{a})]}{[p](N-1)}$ (corresponding to formula (5.2.11)).

We now consider the treatment of groups of observations of equal accuracy in the general processes of combination of measurements of unequal accuracy.

Suppose we have the fundamental system (6.1.1)

$$y_r = \sum_{j=1}^{n} a_j x_{rj} \qquad (r = 1, 2, \ldots, N,\ N > n),$$

with not one, but n_r, observations made for each r:

$$l_{rj} = y_r + \Delta_{rj};\quad j = 1, 2, \ldots, n_r;$$

the Δ_{rj}'s are of equal accuracy ($r = 1, 2, \ldots, N,\ j = 1, 2, \ldots, n_r$). We have, thus, observations of equal accuracy, combined into groups corresponding to the selected abscissae $(x_{r1}, \ldots, x_{rn})$. This corresponds to the same fundamental system (6.1.1), in which every set of abscissae $(x_{r1}, \ldots, x_{rn})$ is repeated n_r times. The new scheme has $N_1 = \sum_{r=1}^{N} n_r$ fundamental equations.

If we write, as before,

$$x_\mu = (x_{\mu 1}, \ldots, x_{\mu N}) \qquad (\mu = 1, 2, \ldots, n),$$

$$[x_\mu x_\nu] = \sum_{r=1}^{N} x_{\mu r} x_{\nu r}, \tag{6.10.2}$$

then, according to (6.3.17), we obtain, for the matrix, C, of the new system of N_1 fundamental equations

$$C = \begin{Vmatrix} [px_1x_1] & [px_1x_2] & \ldots & [px_1x_n] \\ \cdot & \cdot & \cdot & \cdot \\ [px_nx_1] & [px_nx_2] & \ldots & [px_nx_n] \end{Vmatrix}, \tag{6.10.3}$$

where $[px_\mu x_\nu] = \sum_{r=1}^{n} n_r x_{\mu r} x_{\nu r};\quad p_r = n_r.$

Further, the single-column matrix $X^T L$ is of the form

$$\begin{Vmatrix} z_1 \\ \cdot \\ \cdot \\ z_n \end{Vmatrix},$$

where $z_\mu = \sum_{r=1}^{N} x_{\mu r}(l_{r1} + \dots + l_{rn_r}) = \sum_{r=1}^{N} n_r x_{\mu r} \bar{l}_r, \quad \bar{l}_r = \frac{l_{r1} + \dots + l_{rn_r}}{n_r}$.

Thus, putting $p_r = n_r$, we obtain

$$X^T L = \begin{Vmatrix} [p x_1 \bar{l}] \\ \vdots \\ [p x_n \bar{l}] \end{Vmatrix} = X^T P \bar{L},$$

where

$P = \begin{Vmatrix} p_1 & 0 & \dots & 0 \\ 0 & p_2 & \dots & 0 \\ \dots & \dots & \dots & \dots \\ 0 & 0 & \dots & p_N \end{Vmatrix}$ is a diagonal matrix of weights and $\bar{L} = \begin{Vmatrix} \bar{l}_1 \\ \vdots \\ \bar{l}_N \end{Vmatrix}$.

We see that the new system of $N_1 = \sum_{r=1}^{N} n_r$ fundamental equations leads to the same system of normal equations as the previous system, replacing l_{rj} by $\bar{l}_r$:

$$\bar{l}_r - \bar{\Delta}_r = \sum_{j=1}^{n} a_j x_{rj}, \tag{6.10.4}$$

where $\bar{\Delta}_r \in N\left(0, \frac{\sigma}{\sqrt{n_r}}\right)$.

Thus the replacement of the observations $l_{r1}, \dots, l_{rn_r}$ by the sample mean, $\bar{l}_r$, and the separate errors of equal accuracy, Δ_{rj}, by $\bar{\Delta}_r = \frac{\Delta_{r1} + \dots + \Delta_{rn_r}}{n_r}$, is consistent from the point of view of the method of least squares, and leads to the optimal use of the information in the observations, in the sense of the optimality of the method of least squares for normal error vectors, as explained above.

Besides this, there is, especially in the case of non-normal errors, one advantage arising from this combination of observations; replacing $l_{r1}, \dots, l_{rn_r}$ by $\bar{l}_r$, by Liapounov's theorem (theorem 2.7.1), the quantity $\bar{\Delta}_r = \frac{\Delta_{r1} + \dots + \Delta_{rn_r}}{n_r}$ is, even for relatively small values of r, sufficiently nearly normal $N\left(0, \frac{\sigma}{\sqrt{n_r}}\right)$. Hence the use of the method of least squares in reducing observations is nearly optimal, in the sense described above.

11. Summary of Formulae and Rules of Estimation

a) Point Estimation

Detailed expressions	Matrix expressions

Fundamental system of equations

$l_r - \Delta_r = \sum_{j=1}^{n} a_j x_{rj} \quad (r=1,2,\ldots,N)$	$L - \Delta = XA$, or more detailed: (6.11.1)
$x_i = (x_{1i}, \ldots, x_{Ni})$	$L_{N1} - \Delta_{N1} = X_{Nn} A_{n1}$
$l = (l_1, \ldots, l_N)$, weights: $p_1, \ldots, p_N$.	Weight matrix $P = \begin{Vmatrix} p_1 & 0 & \ldots & 0 \\ 0 & p_2 & \ldots & 0 \\ \cdot & \cdot & \cdot & \cdot \\ 0 & 0 & \ldots & p_N \end{Vmatrix}$

Normal equations for determining $\tilde{a}_i$

$\sum_{\nu=1}^{n} [px_i x_\nu] \tilde{a}_\nu = [px_i l]$;	$C\tilde{A} = X^T PL$, (6.11.2)
$i = 1, 2, \ldots, n.$	$C = X^T PX$.

To estimate $\tilde{a}_i$ we need to solve the normal equations (6.11.2).

In section 12 there are given some calculating devices which are very often used in the solution of this system of equations; they are also described, in detail, in many text-books (see, for example, Edelson [19]).

Further, we have, to calculate $[p\tilde{v}\tilde{v}]$:

Detailed expressions	Matrix expressions
$\tilde{v}_r = l_r + \sum_{i=1}^{n} \tilde{a}_i x_{ri}$,	$\tilde{V} = X\tilde{A} - L$,
$[p\tilde{v}\tilde{v}] = \sum_{r=1}^{N} p_r \left(l_r - \sum_{i=1}^{n} \tilde{a}_i x_{ri} \right)^2$.	$\tilde{V}^T P \tilde{V}$.

To calculate $[p\tilde{v}\tilde{v}]$ there are also practical devices which we will illustrate by means of examples. To calculate $[p\tilde{v}\tilde{v}]$, or for checking this calculation, we can use formula (6.6.19)

$[p\tilde{v}\tilde{v}] = [pll] - \sum_{\nu=1}^{n} [px_\nu l] \tilde{a}_\nu$	$\tilde{V}^T P \tilde{V} = L^T PL - L^T PX\tilde{A}$ (6.11.3)

$\tilde{a}_1, \tilde{a}_2, \ldots, \tilde{a}_n$ having been calculated from the normal equations.

Further, we form $\tilde{s}=\sqrt{\frac{[p\tilde{v}\tilde{v}]}{N-n}}$ to estimate σ.

Using the quantity $\tilde{s}$ we can find the standard error of the estimator $\tilde{a}_i$. For the system of equations of the form

$$\sum_{\nu=1}^{n}[px_i x_\nu]\,\tilde{a}_\nu=\tilde{b}_i \qquad (i=1,\ 2,\ \ldots,\ n) \tag{6.11.4}$$

the inverse system

$$\sum_{\mu=1}^{n} q_{j\mu}\tilde{b}_\mu=\tilde{a}_j, \tag{6.11.5}$$

will be considered. We want to find the quantities $q_{11},\ q_{22},\ \ldots,\ q_{nn}$. The quantity $\{C^{-1}\}_{ii}$ is identical with q_{ii}. In the solutions of examples we will demonstrate ways of determining q_{ii} simultaneously with the solution of the normal equations. Now, the standard error, $\sigma(\tilde{a}_i)$, of the estimator $\tilde{a}_i$ is estimated by

$$\tilde{s}\sqrt{(C)_{ii}^{-1}}=\tilde{s}q_{ii}. \tag{6.11.6}$$

Further, σ is estimated by

$$\cdot\tilde{s}=\sqrt{\frac{[p\tilde{v}\tilde{v}]}{N-n}}, \tag{6.11.7}$$

and the standard error of the estimator $\tilde{s}$

$$\sigma(\tilde{s})\approx\frac{\sigma}{\sqrt{2(N-n)}} \tag{6.11.8}$$

is estimated by

$$\frac{\tilde{s}}{\sqrt{2(N-n)}}. \tag{6.11.9}$$

<u>b) Estimation by Confidence Intervals *)</u>

To estimate a_i we first choose the required confidence coefficient p_0. It is used as the first entry in Table I; the second entry is the number of degrees of freedom $k=N-n$. With these two entries we find γ and construct the confidence interval

$$I_\gamma^{(i)}=\left[\tilde{a}_i-\gamma\sqrt{\{C^{-1}\}_{ii}\frac{[p\tilde{v}\tilde{v}]}{N-n}},\ \tilde{a}_i+\gamma\sqrt{\{C^{-1}\}_{ii}\frac{[p\tilde{v}\tilde{v}]}{N-n}}\right]. \tag{6.11.10}$$

* As has been said before, confidence regions for a number of parameters will be discussed in chapter XIV

This covers the measured parameter a_i with probability p_0.

To estimate $y_r = \sum_{r=1}^{n} a_i x_{ri}$ $(r = 1, 2, \ldots, N)$, (see section 7 and 8 of this chapter and also chapter VII).

To estimate the accuracy of observations the quantity $[p\tilde{v}\tilde{v}]$ is used.

For a given confidence coefficient, p_0, and for $k = N - n$ degrees of freedom, we find the values γ_1 and γ_2 from Table III of the Appendix and, using them, construct the confidence interval $[\gamma_1 \tilde{s}, \gamma_2 \tilde{s}]$, covering σ with probability p_0. There is also the formula

$$\frac{1}{\sigma^2}[pD(\tilde{l})] = \sum_{r=1}^{N} p_r \{XC^{-1}X^T\}_{rr} = n, \tag{6.11.11}$$

which can be used to check the calculations. From this formula we can see that the accuracy of estimation depends, fundamentally, on the ratio $\frac{N}{n}$.

12. Some Methods of Calculation in the Solution of Normal Equations. Gauss' and Gauss-Doolittle's Methods.

We will consider the system of normal equations

$$\begin{aligned} x_{11}a_1 + x_{12}a_2 + \ldots + x_{1n}a_n &= b_1, \\ x_{21}a_1 + x_{22}a_2 + \ldots + x_{2n}a_n &= b_2, \\ \cdots\cdots\cdots\cdots\cdots\cdots\cdots & \\ x_{n1}a_1 + x_{n2}a_2 + \ldots + x_{nn}a_n &= b_n. \end{aligned}$$

The matrix X of the coefficients of the unknown a_i's is symmetrical $(x_{ij} = x_{ji})$ and positive definite. Using matrix symbols we can write the system in the form $XA = B$.

At the present time a series of different methods for solution of this system are available. Among them, historically the first, and the most widely used, is the 'exclusion method' of Gauss. It consists of successive cycles, each removing one unknown from the equations, until we reduce the initial system to a system with a 3×3 matrix, which can easily be solved.

In problems connected with the analysis of statistical data, besides the solution of the system of normal equations, we are often interested in the problem of simultaneously inverting the coefficient matrix X of this system. For example, in the calculation of confidence intervals for the parameters (see p. 167) we must know the diagonal elements of the reciprocal matrix X^{-1} Since $A = X^{-1}B$ we can, in particular, obtain a solution of the system by inverting the coefficient matrix. However, the inversion of the matrix is a heavier task than the solution of the system. In fact, the construction of the matrix $X^{-1}=C$ amounts to finding n^2 quantities, c_{mk}, (the elements of the matrix C) satisfying the conditions

$$\sum_{j=1}^{n} x_{ij}c_{jl} = \begin{cases} 1, & \text{if} \quad i=l, \\ 0, & \text{if} \quad i \neq l, \end{cases}$$

$i=1, 2, \ldots, n$, $l=1, 2, \ldots, n$, i.e. solving n systems of equations for the c_{mk}'s. Therefore, we will give here schemes of calculation, which are adapted to the inversion of the matrix as well as to the solution of the system of equations without calculating the reciprocal matrix (with a corresponding reduction in the amount of calculation and writing).

In the exclusion method we distinguish between a number of calculating schemes. *)

Among them the so-called 'compact' schemes hold a special position. At the present time, in work making so much use of computing machines, 'compact' schemes are very useful. They are based on the possibility of carrying out calculations, using these machines, by accumulation, without writing down intermediate results. In this way we have fewer rounding errors and less writing down.

Without touching on the theoretical bases of the problem, we will restrict ourselves to simple descriptions of two schemes of calculation ('extended' and 'compact') for the solution of the system of normal equations and inverting their coefficient matrix. Also, to make the schemes clearer, we will work them out for a concrete example with four unknowns.

We will consider the following system of normal equations

$$\begin{aligned} a_1 + 0.42a_2 + 0.54a_3 + 0.66a_4 &= 0.3, \\ 0.42a_1 + a_2 + 0.32a_3 + 0.44a_4 &= 0.5, \\ 0.54a_1 + 0.32a_2 + a_3 + 0.22a_4 &= 0.7, \\ 0.66a_1 + 0.44a_2 + 0.22a_3 + a_4 &= 0.9. \end{aligned}$$

Scheme A. The calculations are given in Table 18. We explain below how the table is filled in.

I. The matrix X of the system is placed in the upper left-hand corner (columns (1) - (4)). At the side of it, in column (5), there

* See V.N.Fadejeva, Methods of calculation in linear algebra, Gostekhizdat (1950); P.S.Dwyer, Linear computations (1951).

are the constant terms. In the columns (6) - (9) there is a unit matrix, i.e. the constant terms of the system of four equations, from which we can find the elements of the reciprocal matrix $C = X^{-1}$. If it is only necessary to find the solution of the initial system, then these columns may be omitted. If, however, besides this solution, we also want to find the reciprocal matrix C, we can omit column (5), because the solution of the system is easily obtained using the elements of C. Column (10) is the check column. In the first section of this column there are the values of the sums of elements in each line. In the later stages of the calculations the values in the check column are subjected to the same operations as the other values in the same row. If the calculations are correct, the numbers in the check column should be equal (within the accuracy of the rounding errors) to the sum of all elements in the corresponding row (column (11)).

For elements of the table we introduce the notation $x_{p.ij}$, where p is the number of the stage of calculations (I - IX) and i, j are the numbers of the row and column, respectively, in the pth stage.

II. We divide each element of the row by the element of the fourth column of the same row: $x_{2.ij} = \dfrac{x_{1.ij}}{x_{1.i4}}$. In dividing, particularly, we should take more significant digits than we need in the final results, to reduce the influence of rounding errors and also because of the loss of significant digits in the subtracting of numbers of nearly the same magnitude.

III. We subtract the last element in stage II from all the remainder (Column (4), which is all zeros, is not written down).

IV. We divide each value obtained in stage III by the element of column (3) in the corresponding row: $x_{4.ij} = \dfrac{x_{3.ij}}{x_{3.i3}}$.

V. We subtract the last element in stage IV from the all remainder.

VI, VII. We repeat the same operations as above.

If we only need to solve the system, then, after stage VII, we find the unknowns by the formulae

$$a_1 = \frac{x_{7.15}}{x_{7.11}},$$

$$a_2 = x_{6.i5} - x_{6.i1} \cdot a_1, \qquad i = 1 \text{ or } 2$$

$$a_3 = x_{4.i5} - x_{4.i1} \cdot a_1 - x_{4.i2} \cdot a_2, \qquad i = 1, \text{ or } 2, \text{ or } 3,$$

$$a_4 = x_{2.i5} - x_{2.i1} \cdot a_1 - x_{2.i2} \cdot a_2 - x_{2.i3} \cdot a_3, \quad i = 1, \text{ or } 2, \text{ or } 3, \text{ or } 4.$$

respectively.

TABLE 18

Scheme A

		(1)	(2)	(3)	(4)	(5)	(6)	(7)	(8)	(9)	(10)	(11)
I	$X_1 (x_{1.ij})$	1,00	0,42	0,54	0,66	0,3	1	0	0	0	3,92	
		0,42	1,00	0,32	0,44	0,5	0	1	0	0	3,68	
		0,54	0,32	1,00	0,22	0,7	0	0	1	0	3,78	
		0,66	0,44	0,22	1,00	0,9	0	0	0	1	4,22	
II	$X_2 (x_{2.ij})$	1,51515	0,63636	0,81818	1	0,45455	1,51515	0	0	0	5,93939	5,93939
		0,95455	2,27273	0,72727	1	1,13636	0	2,27273	0	0	8,36364	8,36364
		2,45455	1,45455	4,54545	1	3,18182	0	0	4,54545	0	17,18182	17,18182
		0,66000	0,44000	0,22000	1	0,90000	0	0	0	1	4,22000	4,22000
III	$X_3 (x_{3.ij})$	0,85515	0,19636	0,59818		—0,44545	1,51515	0	0	—1	1,71939	1,71939
		0,29455	1,83273	0,50727		0,23636	0	2,27273	0	—1	4,14364	4,14364
		1,79455	1,01455	4,32545		2,28182	0	0	4,54545	—1	12,96182	12,96182
IV	$X_4 (x_{4.ij})$	1,42959	0,32826	1		—0,74468	2,53293	0	0	—1,67174	2,87437	2,87436
		0,58066	3,61293	1		0,46595	0	4,48032	0	—1,97134	8,16851	8,16852
		0,41488	0,23455	1		0,52753	0	0	1,05086	—0,23119	2,99664	2,99663
V	$X_5 (x_{5.ij})$	1,01471	0,09371			—1,27221	2,53293	0	— 1,05086	—1,44055	—0,12227	—0,12227
		0,16578	3,37838			—0,06158	0	4,48032	— 1,05086	—1,74015	5,17187	5,17189
VI	$X_6 (x_{6.ij})$	10,82819	1			—13,57603	27,02945	0	—11,21396	—15,37243	—1,30477	—1,30478
		0,04907	1			—0,01823	0	1,32617	—0,31105	—0,51508	1,53087	1,53088
VII	$X_7 (x_{7.ij})$	10,77912				—13,55780	27,02945	—1,32617	—10,90291	—14,85735	—2,83564	—2,83566
VIII	$X_8 (x_{8.ij})$	1	0	0	0		2,50757	—0,12303	—1,01148	—1,37835	0,99473	0,99471
		0	1	0	0		—0,12305	1,33221	0,26142	—0,44744	1,50028	1,50030
		0	0	1	0		—1,01147	—0,26143	1,53182	0,44561	1,70452	1,70452
		0	0	0	1		—1,37832	—0,44746	0,44560	2,00855	1,62836	1,62837
IX	a_i	—1,25778	0,04349	1,03916	1,48238		— 1,25780	0,04350	1,03916	1,48239		

To find a_2, a_3, a_4 we can use various equations, putting $i=1$ or 2, or 3. We will find, for example, the unknowns using the last row of the corresponding stages. (We put $i=2$ for a_2, $i=3$ for a_3, $i=4$ for a_4). We obtain

$$a_1=\frac{-13{,}55780}{10{,}77912}=-1{,}25778,$$

$$a_2=-0{,}01823-0{,}04907\times(-1{,}25778)=0{,}04349,$$

$$a_3=0{,}52753-0{,}41488\times(-1{,}25778)-0{,}23455\times0{,}04349=1{,}03916,$$

$$a_4=0{,}90-0{,}66\times(-1{,}25778)-0{,}44\times0{,}04349-0{,}22\times \times 1{,}03916=1{,}48238.$$

The values obtained for the unknowns are given in row IX of the table.

VIII. We will explain the scheme for obtaining the reciprocal matrix written in columns (6) - (9) (VIII). The elements of the first row of the matrix C are obtained by the formula

$$c_{1k}=\frac{x_{7\cdot 1j}}{x_{7\cdot 11}}, \qquad j=6,\ 7,\ 8,\ 9 \quad (k=j-5).$$

For instance $c_{11}=\frac{27{,}02945}{10{,}77912}=2{,}50757$, $c_{12}=\frac{-1{,}32617}{10.77912}=-0{,}12303$ etc.

On the left hand side we calculate the unit matrix. The calculations are checked in the same way (by summing the elements in the row). We obtain the values of the check column by the same formulae as c_{mk} for $j=10$. The elements of the corresponding rows of matrix are obtained by the formulae

$$c_{2k}=x_{6.\,ij}-x_{6.\,i1}c_{1k}, \qquad i=1 \text{ or } 2,$$

$$c_{3k}=x_{4.\,ij}-x_{4.\,i1}c_{1k}-x_{4.\,i2}c_{2k}, \qquad i=1, \text{ or } 2, \text{ or } 3,$$

$$c_{4k}=x_{2.\,ij}-x_{2.\,i1}c_{1k}-x_{2.\,i2}c_{2k}-x_{2.\,i3}c_{3k}, \quad i=1, \text{ or } 2, \text{ or } 3, \text{ or } 4,$$

$$j=6,\ 7,\ 8,\ 9, \quad k=j-5.$$

The elements of the reciprocal matrix can also be found from different equations, putting $i=1$, or 2, or 3, i.e. choosing this or that row of the table. We find, for example, c_{2k}, using the second row of VI:

$$c_{21}=x_{6.26}-x_{6.21}c_{11}=0-0{,}04907\times2{,}50757=-0{,}12305.$$

We see that the value obtained for c_{21} is different from $c_{12}=-0{,}12303$ in the fifth decimal digit (the matrix C should be symmetrical), which shows the influence of the degree of accuracy of the calculations. Further,

$$c_{22}=1,32617-0,04907\times(-0,12303)=1,33221, \text{ etc.}$$

We will find c_{3k} and c_{4k}, using the first rows of IV and II (we put $i=1$). For example,

$$c_{32}=0-1,42959\times(-0,12303)-0,32826\times1,33221=-0,26143,$$
$$c_{43}=0-1,51515\times(-1,01148)-0,63636\times(-0,26142)-0,81818\times$$
$$\times 1,53182=0,44560.$$

To complete the check calculations for the elements of the matrix C, we can make use of the condition $XC=E$, where E is the unit matrix. The elements d_{ij} of the matrix E on the principal diagonal are equal to one, and all others are zero. Evidently, $d_{ij}=\sum_{k=1}^{4} x_{ik}c_{kj}$. We will calculate the diagonal elements d_{ii} of the matrix E in our case.

$$d_{11}=x_{11}c_{11}+x_{12}c_{21}+x_{13}c_{31}+x_{14}c_{41}=1\times2,50757+0,42\times$$
$$\times(-0,12305)+0,54\times(-1,01147)+0,66\times(-1,37832)=0,999999,$$
$$d_{22}=0,999997, \quad d_{33}=0,999998, \quad d_{44}=1,000\,000.$$

In those cases, in which we are not satisfied with the accuracy of calculation of the elements, we can, without repeating the calculations with more digits, use methods for making the values c_{mk} more accurate (for example, the iterative Hotelling processes) *).

The values of the unknowns, a_i, are calculated, using the elements of C, by the formulae

$$a_i=\sum_{j=1}^{4} c_{ij}b_j.$$

In our case they are

$$a_1=c_{11}b_1+c_{12}b_2+c_{13}b_3+c_{14}b_4=$$
$$=2,50757\times0,3-0,12303\times0,5-1,01148\times0,7-1,37835\times0,9=$$
$$=-1,25780,$$
$$a_2=0,04350, \quad a_3=1,03916, \quad a_4=1,48238.$$

After finding the a_i's, it is convenient to insert them in the initial equations

---

* V.N.Fadejeva, Methods of calculation in linear algebra, p. 103-6

$$a_1 + 0{,}42a_2 + 0{,}54a_3 + 0{,}66a_4 = -1{,}25780 + 0{,}42 \times 0{,}04350 +$$
$$+ 0{,}54 \times 1{,}03916 + 0{,}66 \times 1{,}48239 = 0{,}29999,$$
$$0{,}42a_1 + a_2 + 0{,}32a_3 + 0{,}44a_4 = 0{,}50001,$$
$$0{,}54a_1 + 0{,}32a_2 + a_3 + 0{,}22a_4 = 0{,}69999,$$
$$0{,}66a_1 + 0{,}44a_2 + 0{,}22a_3 + a_4 = 0{,}90000.$$

However, from a theoretical point of view this check appears to be insufficient.

It is possible to encounter a case, in which some element, by which we have to divide, is equal to zero. Then, so as not to make the calculations more complicated, we can use another scheme of calculation, for example, scheme B, where dividing only involves the diagonal elements, i.e. positive values.

Scheme A is rather tedious, although extremely simple in regard to calculating operations. We will now put forward one of the 'compact' schemes for solving the system of normal equations and for inversion of the symmetrical matrix X. *)

TABLE 19

SCHEME B

		(1)	(2)	(3)	(4)	(5)	(6)	(7)
I		1,00	0,42 1,00	0,54 0,32 1,00	0,66 0,44 0,22 1,00	0,3 0,5 0,7 0,9	2,92 2,68 2,78 3,22	
II	X_1 Y_1	1,00 1,00	0,42 0,42	0,54 0,54	0,66 0,66	0,3 0,3	2,92 2,92	2,92 2,92
III	X_2 Y_2		0,8236 1	0,0932 0,11316	0,1628 0,19767	0,3740 0,45410	1,4536 1,76493	1,4536 1,76493
IV	X_3 Y_3			0,69785 1	− 0,15482 − 0,22185	0,49568 0,71030	1,03871 1,48844	1,03871 1,48845
V	X_4 Y_4				0,49787 1	0,73804 1,48240	1,23591 2,48240	1,23591 2,48240

* The square root scheme (see literature cited on page 169) also appears to be very convenient for problems connected with the analysis of statistical data.

$$\text{VI.} \quad \left\| \begin{array}{rrrr} 2,50759 & -0,12304 & -1,01149 & -1,37834 \\ -0,12304 & 1,33221 & -0,26142 & -0,44746 \\ -1,01149 & -0,26142 & 1,53183 & 0,44560 \\ -1,37834 & -0,44746 & 0,44560 & 2,00856 \end{array} \right\|$$

On the left hand we place the elements of the upper right-hand corner of the initial matrix X; at their side, in the column (5), the constant terms b_i; on their right the check column (6). In the first stage the sums of all row elements are calculated and placed in the check column (considering the whole matrix and not only its corner). In the later stages of the calculation the values in the check column are obtained in the same way as the remaining values in the same row.

II. Row X_1 : we repeat the first row of I, i.e. $X_{1j}=x_{1j}$. Row Y_1 : we divide the elements of row X_1 by X_{11}. In our example $X_{11}=1$ and therefore the rows X_1 and Y_1 are identical.

Check on calculations in all stages: the sum of all elements of a row should be equal (up to the accuracy of the rounding errors) to the value appearing in check column.

III. We calculate the elements of the row X_2 by the formula

$$X_{2j}=x_{2j}-[X_{12}Y_{1j} \text{ or } X_{1j}Y_{12}],\text{-}$$

where x_{2j} are elements of the second row of I and (to the accuracy of the calculations) we have $X_{12}Y_{1j}=X_{1j}Y_{12}$. In our case the rows X_1 and Y_1 are the same and we have an identity. We find

$$X_{22}=1 \quad -0,42\times0,42=0,8236,$$
$$X_{23}=0,32-0.42\times0,54=0,0932,$$
$$X_{24}=0,44-0,42\times0,66=0,1628 \text{ etc.}$$

The elements of the row Y_2 are equal to $Y_{2j}=\frac{X_{2j}}{X_{22}}$. Then we have

$Y_{22}=1, \quad Y_{23}=0,11316$ etc.

IV. We calculate the elements of row X_3 by the formula

$$X_{3j}=x_{3j}-[(X_{13}Y_{1j}+X_{23}Y_{2j}) \text{ or } (X_{1j}Y_{13}+X_{2j}Y_{23})].$$

In our example the two sums in the large brackets are exactly, and not approximately, equal. We obtain

$$X_{33}=1-(0,54\times0,54+0,0932\times0,11316)=0,69785,$$
$$X_{34}=0,22-(0,54\times0,66+0,0932\times0,19767)=-0,15482 \text{ etc.}$$

The elements of row Y_3 are equal to $Y_{3j}=\frac{X_{3j}}{X_{33}}$.

V. We calculate the elements of row X_4 from the formula

$$X_{4j}=x_{4j}-[(X_{14}Y_{1j}+X_{24}Y_{2j}+X_{34}X_{3j}) \text{ or } (X_{1j}Y_{14}+X_{2j}Y_{24}+X_{3j}Y_{34})].$$

For example

$$X_{44}=1-(0{,}66\times0{,}66+0{,}1628\times0{,}19767+ +0{,}15482\times0{,}22185)=0{,}49787.$$

The elements of row Y_4 are calculated from the formula $Y_{4j}=\frac{X_{4j}}{X_{44}}$

Without inverting the coefficient matrix we can find the solution of the system from the formulae

$$\begin{aligned}
a_4&=Y_{45},\\
a_3&=Y_{35}-Y_{34}a_4,\\
a_2&=Y_{25}-Y_{23}a_3-Y_{24}a_4,\\
a_1&=Y_{15}-Y_{12}a_2-Y_{13}a_3-Y_{14}a_4.
\end{aligned}$$

Applying the formulae to our case we get

$$a_4=1{,}48240,\ a_3=1{,}03917,\ a_2=0{,}04348,\ a_1=-1{,}25780.$$

VI. We will describe a scheme for obtaining the elements of the reciprocal matrix. We will obtain the elements consecutively, starting with c_{44}, so that the matrix C will be filled in by columns from left to right, and also from bottom to top.

We calculate c_{i4} from the formulae

$$\begin{aligned}
c_{44}&=\frac{1}{X_{44}},\\
c_{34}&=-c_{44}Y_{34},\\
c_{24}&=-c_{34}Y_{23}-c_{44}Y_{24},\\
c_{14}&=-c_{24}Y_{12}-c_{34}Y_{13}-c_{44}Y_{14}.
\end{aligned}$$

In our example

$$\begin{aligned}
c_{44}&=\frac{1}{0{,}49787}=2{,}00856,\\
c_{34}&=-2{,}00856\times(-0{,}22185)=0{,}44560,\\
c_{24}&=-0{,}44746,\\
c_{14}&=-1{,}37834.
\end{aligned}$$

Next, we calculate c_{i3} from the formulae

$$c_{43} = c_{34},$$
$$c_{33} = \frac{1}{X_{33}} - c_{34}Y$$
$$c_{23} = -c_{33}Y_{23} - c_{34}Y_{24},$$
$$c_{13} = -c_{23}Y_{12} - c_{33}Y_{13} - c_{34}Y_{14}.$$

For example, $c_{33} = \frac{1}{0{,}69785} - 0{,}44560 \times (-0{,}22185) = 1{,}53183.$

We find c_{i2} from the formulae

$$c_{42} = c_{24}, \quad c_{32} = c_{23},$$
$$c_{22} = \frac{1}{X_{22}} - c_{23}Y_{23} - c_{24}Y_{24},$$
$$c_{12} = -c_{22}Y_{12} - c_{23}Y_{13} - c_{24}Y_{14}.$$

And finally, $c_{41} = c_{14}, \quad c_{31} = c_{13}, \quad c_{21} = c_{12},$

$$c_{11} = \frac{1}{X_{11}} - c_{12}Y_{12} - c_{13}Y_{13} - c_{14}Y_{14}.$$

The matrix reciprocal, to C is calculated below according to scheme B. The final check for c_{ij} lies in calculation of the sums of products $d_{ii} = \sum_{k=1}^{4} x_{ik}c_{ki}$ (the diagonal elements of a unit matrix) which should be equal to 1. In our example $d_{11} = 1{,}000004$, $d_{22} = 0{,}999996$, $d_{33} = 1{,}000003$, $d_{44} = 1{,}000005$.

To solve the system using the matrix C we make later the same calculations as in scheme A. To make the elements of the reciprocal matrix more precise in those cases in which it is necessary, it is helpful to employ Hôtelling's iteration method (see reference in the scheme A).

13. Examples

Example 1.

In an examination of the influence of temperature on the motion of a chronometer the results *) given in the two first columns of Table 20 were obtained.

---

* The data are taken from Yushchenko's book [56], p. 83

TABLE 20

t_i	ω_i	$t_i - 15$	$(t_i - 15)^2$	$\left(\frac{t_i - 15}{15}\right) = x'_i$	$\left(\frac{t_i - 15}{15}\right)^2 = x''_i$
5,0	2,60	−10,0	100,00	−0,667	0,445
9,6	2,01	−5,4	29,16	−0,360	0,130
16,0	1,34	1,0	1,00	0,067	0,004
19,6	1,08	4,6	21,16	0,307	0,094
24,4	0,94	9,4	88,36	0,627	0,393
29,8	1,06	14,8	219,04	0,987	0,974
34,4	1,25	19,4	376,36	1,293	1,672

We assume that the dependence of the motion of the chronometer on temperature can be expressed by the equation

$$\omega = \omega_{15} + (t - 15)\beta + (t - 15)^2 \gamma.$$

It is required to estimate the constants ω_{15}, β and γ using the metho of least squares; to find confidence intervals for these quantities, and to estimate the accuracy of the observations.

Before forming the system of normal equations for ω_{15}, β and γ it is useful to make a transformation of the variables in the initial equations, since the multipliers $(t_1 - 15)^2$ are very large and so the coefficients in the normal equations will vary over a wide range of values, and this complicates the calculations. We put $a_1 = 15\beta$, $a_2 = 225\gamma$, $a_3 = \omega_{15}$. Then the initial equation is transformed into the form

$$\left(\frac{t - 15}{15}\right) a_1 + \left(\frac{t - 15}{15}\right)^2 a_2 + a_3 = \omega;$$

The values of the quantities $x'_i = \frac{t_i - 15}{15}$ and $x''_i = \left(\frac{t_i - 15}{15}\right)^2$

are given in the fifth and sixth columns, respectively, of table 20.

We construct the system of normal equations for determining a_1, a_2, a_3. The coefficients x_{ij} in the normal equations, which are equal to $x_{11} = [x'x']$, $x_{12} = [x'x'']$, etc., we obtain by accumulation, without writing down the intermediate results. We write them in the matrix form

$$X = \begin{Vmatrix} 3,712 & 3,055 & 2,254 \\ 3,055 & 4,122 & 3,712 \\ 2,254 & 3,712 & 7 \end{Vmatrix}.$$

The constant terms are equal to: $b_1 = 1,215$, $b_2 = 5,017$, $b_3 = 10,280$

Thus, the system of normal equations is of the form

$$3{,}712a_1 + 3{,}055a_2 + 2{,}254a_3 = 1{,}215,$$
$$3{,}055a_1 + 4{,}122a_2 + 3{,}712a_3 = 5{,}017,$$
$$2{,}254a_1 + 3{,}712a_2 + 7{,}000a_3 = 10{,}280.$$

We will solve this system, and invert the matrix of its coefficients, using a 'compact' calculating scheme (scheme B, p. 174). In Table 21 are given the results of calculations according to this scheme. The reciprocal matrix X^{-1} is placed under this table.

TABLE 21

	(1)	(2)	(3)	(4)	Check	Sum of row elements
	3,712	3,055 4,122	2,254 3,712 7,000	1,215 5,017 10,280	10,236 15,906 23,246	
X_1 Y_1	3,712 1	3,055 0,8230	2,254 0,6072	1,215 0,3273	10,236 2,7575	10,236 2,7575
X_2 Y_2		1,608 1	1,857 1,155	4,017 2,498	7,482 4,653	7,482 4,653
X_3 Y_3			3,487 1	4,903 1,406	8,390 2,406	8,390 2,406

$$C = X^{-1} = \begin{Vmatrix} 0{,}72444 & -0{,}62555 & 0{,}09847 \\ -0{,}62555 & 1{,}00446 & -0{,}33123 \\ 0{,}09847 & -0{,}33123 & 0{,}28678 \end{Vmatrix}.$$

To check the elements of the matrix $X^{-1} = C$ we calculate the diagonal elements of the unit matrix $E = XC$ from the formula $d_{ii} = \sum_{k=1}^{3} x_{ik}c_{ki}$. We obtain $d_{11} = 1{,}00002$, $d_{22} = 0{,}99980$, $d_{33} = 0{,}99989$.

We find the solution of the system from the formula $\tilde{a}_i = \sum_{j=1}^{3} c_{ij}\omega_j$; $\tilde{a}_1 = -1{,}246$, $\tilde{a}_2 = 0{,}874$, $\tilde{a}_3 = 1{,}406$. Then, the point estimates of ω_{15}, β, γ are $\tilde{\omega}_{15} = 1{,}406$, $\tilde{\beta} = \frac{\tilde{a}_1}{15} = -0{,}0831$, $\tilde{\gamma} = \frac{\tilde{a}_2}{225} = 0{,}00388$.

Thus, the equation expressing the dependence of motion of the chronometer on temperature is written in the form

$$\tilde{\omega} = 1,406 - 0,0831\,(t-15) + 0,0039\,(t-15)^2.$$

Now we want to find confidence intervals for the parameters, which are determined by the formula

$$I_{\gamma_1}^{(i)} = \left[\tilde{a}'_i - \gamma_1 \sqrt{c_{ii}\frac{[\tilde{v}\tilde{v}]}{N-n}},\ \tilde{a}'_i + \gamma_1 \sqrt{c_{ii}\frac{[\tilde{v}\tilde{v}]}{N-n}}\right],$$

where $\tilde{a}'_i$ are the point estimates of the parameters, N is the number of observations, n is the number of parameters, γ_1 is determined from the table of Student's distribution to satisfy the condition $P\{|t| < \gamma_1\} = p$, for $k = N - n$ degrees of freedom, c_{ii} is the diagonal element of the matrix $C = X^{-1}$ and

$$[\tilde{v}\tilde{v}] = [\tilde{\omega}\tilde{\omega}] - \sum_{i=1}^{n} [a'_i\tilde{\omega}]\,\tilde{a}'_i.$$

In our case $[\tilde{\omega}\tilde{\omega}] = 17,3318$, $[a'_1\tilde{\omega}] = [(t-15)\tilde{\omega}] = 18,228$, $[a'_2\tilde{\omega}] = [(t-15)^2\,\tilde{\omega}] = 1128,50$, $[a'_3\tilde{\omega}] = [1\times\tilde{\omega}] = 10,28$.

Then

$$[\tilde{v}\tilde{v}] = 17,3318 - (-18,228\times0,0831 + 1128,50\times0,00388 + 10,28\times1,406) = 0,01429.$$

We take the confidence coefficient $p = 0,90$. Then, from the table of the t-distribution, for $k = 7 - 3 = 4$, we find $\gamma_1 = 2,132$. The diagonal elements of the matrix C are: $c_{11} = 0,7244$, $c_{22} = 1,0045$, $c_{33} = 0,2868$; the point estimates of the parameters are: $\tilde{a}'_1 = -0,0831$ (for β), $\tilde{a}'_2 = 0,0039$ (for γ), $\tilde{a}'_3 = 1,406$ (for ω_{15}). Substituting the values of the corresponding quantities into the formula given above, we obtain the confidence intervals:

for β:

$$I^{(1)} = [-0,191;\ 0,025],$$

for γ:

$$I^{(2)} = [-0,124;\ 0,132],$$

for ω_{15}:

$$I^{(3)} = [1,338;\ 1,474].$$

We estimate the accuracy of the observations by using the relationship

$$P\{\gamma_1\tilde{s} < \sigma < \gamma_2\tilde{s}\} = P_2 - P_1 = p.$$

We calculate

$$\tilde{s}=\sqrt{\frac{[\tilde{v}\tilde{v}]}{N-n}}=\sqrt{\frac{0{,}01429}{4}}=0{,}0598.$$

We choose as the confidence coefficient $p=0{,}90$. Then, for the number of degrees of freedom $k=N-n=4$, we find, from Table III of Appendix, the values $\gamma_1=0{,}649$, $\gamma_2=2{,}37$. Then, the confidence interval for σ is determined by the inequality

$$0{,}038<\sigma<0{,}142.$$

Example 2.

In Table 22 *) are given barometer readings from an aneroid (A) and a quicksilver barometer (B_0) at different temperatures (t).

TABLE 22

№	t (°C)	A (мм)	B_0 (мм)
1	10,0	749,0	744,4
2	6,2	746,1	741,3
3	6,3	756,6	752,7
4	5,3	758,9	754,7
5	4,8	751,7	747,9
6	3,8	757,5	754,0
7	17,1	752,4	747,8
8	22,2	752,5	748,6
9	20,8	752,2	747,7
10	21,0	759,5	755,6

There is known an empirical formula

$$B_0=A+a_1+a_2t+a_3(760-A). \qquad (6.12.1)$$

Here a_1, a_2, a_3 are unknown constants.

We will find estimates for a_1, a_2, a_3 by the method of least squares, confidence intervals for these quantities and we will estimate the accuracy of the observations.

Putting $x_1=1$, $x_2=t$, $x_3=760-A$, $b=B_0-A$, we write formula (6.13.1) in the form

$$x_1a_1+x_2a_2+x_3a_3=b.$$

* The data are taken from Chebotariev's book [51], p. 231

The data in Table 22, for the quantities x_i, b respectively, then become as in Table 23. (We denote the observed values of corresponding quantities by the same letters with dashes).

TABLE 23

№	x'_1	x'_2	x'_3	b'
1	1	10,0	11,0	—4,6
2	1	6,2	13,9	—4,8
3	1	6,3	3,4	—3,9
4	1	5,3	1,1	—4,2
5	1	4,8	8,3	—3,8
6	1	3,8	2,5	—3,5
7	1	17,1	7,6	—4,6
8	1	22,2	7,5	—3,9
9	1	20,8	7,8	—4,5
10	1	21,0	0,5	—3,9
Sum	10	117,5	63,6	—41,7

The system of normal equations for the determination of a_1, a_2, a_3 is of the form

$$\begin{aligned} x_{11}a_1+x_{12}a_2+x_{13}a_3&=b_1,\\ x_{21}a_1+x_{22}a_2+x_{23}a_3&=b_2,\\ x_{31}a_1+x_{32}a_2+x_{33}a_3&=b_3, \end{aligned}$$

where the coefficients of the unknowns are determined by the formulae

$$x_{11}=[x'_1x'_1],\quad x_{12}=[x'_1x'_2],\quad x_{13}=[x'_1x'_3],\quad b_1=[x'_1b'],$$
$$\cdots\cdots\cdots\cdots\cdots\cdots\cdots\cdots$$
$$x_{31}=[x'_3x'_1],\quad \cdots\cdots\cdots\cdots \quad b_3=[x'_3b'],$$

and of course, $x_{ij}=x_{ji}$.

Without writing down the values of the separate terms (the results are obtained by accumulation) we give the values x_{ij} in the form of the coefficient matrix X and the matrix B of the constant terms in the normal equations:

$$X=\begin{Vmatrix} 10 & 117{,}5 & 63{,}6 \\ 117{,}5 & 1902{,}59 & 741{,}97 \\ 63{,}6 & 741{,}97 & 577{,}22 \end{Vmatrix},\qquad B=\begin{Vmatrix} -41{,}7 \\ -494{,}87 \\ -276{,}75 \end{Vmatrix}.$$

Thus, the system of normal equations, in our case, has the form

$$10,0a_1 + 117,5a_2 + 63,6a_3 = -41,7,$$
$$117,5a_1 + 1902,59a_2 + 741,97a_3 = -494,87,$$
$$63,6a_1 + 741,97a_2 + 577,22a_3 = -276,75.$$

We solve the system using a 'compact' calculating scheme (scheme B). In Table 24 are given the results of the calculations for this scheme. There is a complete description of the scheme in pp. 174-177.

TABLE 24

	(1)	(2)	(3)	(4)	Check	Sum of row elements
	10	117,5 1902,59	63,6 741,97 577,22	—41,70 —494,87 —276,75	149,40 2267,19 1106,04	
X_1 Y_1	10 1	117,5 11,75	63,6 6,36	—41,70 —4,17	149,40 14,94	149,40 14,94
X_2 Y_2		521,965 1	—5,330 —0,01021141	—4,895 —0,00937802	511,740 0,98041056	511,740 0,98041057
X_3 Y_3			172,6696 1	—11,5880 —0,0671	161,0816 0,9329	161,0816 0,9329

$$X^{-1} = C = \left\| \begin{matrix} 0,6076815 & -0,0228938 & -0,0375282 \\ -0,0228938 & 0,0019164 & 0,00005914 \\ -0,0375282 & 0,00005914 & 0,0057914 \end{matrix} \right\|.$$

The elements of the corresponding rows of Table 24 are obtained from the formulae

$$X_{1j} = x_{1j}, \qquad Y_{1j} = \frac{X_{1j}}{X_{11}},$$
$$X_{2j} = x_{2j} - X_{12}Y_{1j}, \qquad Y_{2j} = \frac{X_{2j}}{X_{22}},$$
$$X_{3j} = x_{3j} - (X_{13}Y_{1j} + X_{23}Y_{2j}), \qquad Y_{3j} = \frac{X_{3j}}{X_{33}}.$$

For example $X_{23}=741{,}97-117{,}5\times 6{,}36=-5{,}330$,
$X_{34}=-276{,}75-(-63{,}6\times 4{,}17+5{,}330\times 0{,}00937802)=-11{,}5880.$

As has been said before, we can obtain the solutions of the system from the formulae

$$\begin{aligned}\tilde{a}_3&=Y_{34},\\ \tilde{a}_2&=Y_{24}-Y_{23}\tilde{a}_3,\\ \tilde{a}_1&=Y_{14}-Y_{12}\tilde{a}_2-Y_{13}\tilde{a}_3,\end{aligned}$$

the application of which, in our case, gives

$$\begin{aligned}\tilde{a}_3&=-0{,}0671,\\ \tilde{a}_2&=-0{,}00937802-(-0{,}01021141)\times(-0{,}0671)=-0{,}0101,\\ \tilde{a}_1&=-3{,}6246.\end{aligned}$$

However, to determine the confidence limits for a_i we need the diagonal elements of the reciprocal matrix $X^{-1}=C$.

We will describe the way of finding the elements c_{ij} of the matrix C. First we find

$$c_{33}=\frac{1}{X_{33}}=\frac{1}{172{,}6696}=0{,}0057914.$$

Further,

$$\begin{aligned}c_{23}&=-c_{33}Y_{23}=-0{,}0057914\times(-0{,}01021141)=0{,}00005914,\\ c_{13}&=-c_{23}Y_{12}-c_{33}Y_{13}=-0{,}00005914\times 11{,}75-0{,}0057914\times 6{,}36=\\ &=-0{,}0375282.\end{aligned}$$

Then we find

$$\begin{aligned}c_{22}&=\frac{1}{X_{22}}-c_{23}Y_{23}=0{,}0019164,\\ c_{12}&=-c_{22}Y_{12}-c_{23}Y_{13}=-0{,}0228938,\end{aligned}$$

and finally,

$$c_{11}=\frac{1}{X_{11}}-c_{12}Y_{12}-c_{13}Y_{13}=0{,}6076815.$$

We write down the remaining elements of the matrix C, using the condition of symmetry, $c_{ij}=c_{ji}$. To check the matrix C we calculate the diagonal elements of matrix $E=XC$ from the formula $d_{ii}=\sum_{k=1}^{3} x_{ik}c_{ki}$. We obtain $d_{11}=1{,}000000$, $d_{22}=0{,}999982$, $d_{33}=0{,}999998$. We find the solution of the system from the formula $a_i=\sum_{j=1}^{3} c_{ij}b_j$; whence we have

$$\tilde{a}_1=-3{,}6249,\quad \tilde{a}_2=-0{,}0101,\quad \tilde{a}_3=-0{,}0671.$$

We see that the solution obtained previously is different from the solution obtained by reciprocal matrix only in the last digit of $\tilde{a}_1$. The difference is due to rounding errors.

Remark. In the normal equations, for the examples considered, the order of the coefficients of the unknowns varied markedly (from 10 to 1902). Heterogeneity of coefficients of this kind is encountered very often and creates difficulties in the calculations. It makes it necessary to increase the number of significant figures so as ensure the necessary precision in the final results. To achieve a greater homogeneity in the orders of the coefficients we can, by dividing the observational values of some x_i's by certain factors, simultaneously multiply the values of the corresponding unknown by the same factor. For example, in our case we can decrease all values of x_2' and x_3' 10 times and seek for the solution of the system

$$\begin{aligned} 10a_1'+11{,}75a_2'+6{,}36a_3'&=-41{,}7,\\ 11{,}75a_1'+19{,}03a_2'+7{,}42a_3'&=-49{,}49,\\ 6{,}36a_1'+7{,}42a_2'+5{,}772a_3'&=-27{,}67. \end{aligned}$$

Then, the solution of the initial system is,

$$a_1=a_1',\quad a_2=\frac{a_2'}{10},\quad a_3=\frac{a_3'}{10}.$$

Now we will find confidence intervals for the parameters a_1, a_2, a_3.

The confidence interval for a_i is the interval

$$I_\gamma^{(i)}=\left[\tilde{a}_i-\gamma\sqrt{c_{ii}\frac{[\tilde{v}\tilde{v}]}{N-n}},\ \tilde{a}_i+\gamma\sqrt{c_{ii}\frac{[\tilde{v}\tilde{v}]}{N-n}}\right].$$

Here $\tilde{a}_i$ is the point estimator of the parameter a_i, which is obtained from the system of normal equations, N is the number of observations and n is the number of parameters a_i; the value of γ is determined from tables of Student's distribution, to satisfy the condition $P(|t|<\gamma)=p$ (p is the specified confidence coefficient) for $k=N-n$ degrees of freedom, c_{ii} is a diagonal element of the matrix $C=X^{-1}$, and, finally,

$$[\tilde{v}\tilde{v}]=[b'b']-\sum_{i=1}^{n}[x'_i b']\tilde{a}_i.$$

We will calculate $[\tilde{v}\tilde{v}]$ for our example. Substituting into the formula the values: $[b'b']=175{,}57$, $[x'_1 b']=b_1=-41{,}7$, $[x'_2 b']=b_2=-494{,}87$, $[x'_3 b']=b_3=-276{,}75$, $\tilde{a}_1=-3{,}6249$, $\tilde{a}_2=-0{,}0101$, $\tilde{a}_3=-0{,}0671$, we obtain

$$[\tilde{v}\tilde{v}]=175{,}57-(41{,}70\times3{,}6249+494{,}87\times0{,}0101+ \\ +276{,}75\times0{,}0671)=0{,}8436.$$

We choose the confidence coefficient $p=0{,}90$ and from the table of Student's distribution we find, for $p=0{,}90$ and number of degrees of freedom $k=N-n=10-3=7$, the value $\gamma=1{,}895$. The diagonal elements of the matrix C are equal to

$$c_{11}=0{,}6076815, \quad c_{22}=0{,}0019164, \quad c_{33}=0{,}0057914,$$

and so the confidence interval for a_1 is determined by the inequalities

$$-3{,}625-1{,}895\sqrt{0{,}6077\frac{0{,}8436}{7}}<a_1<-3{,}625+ \\ +1{,}895\sqrt{0{,}6077\frac{0{,}8436}{7}},$$

or

$$-4{,}138<a_1<-3{,}112.$$

Carrying out the calculations, we obtain confidence intervals for a_2 and a_3, with confidence coefficient $p=0{,}90$:

$$I^{(2)}=[-0{,}0389;\ 0{,}0187],$$
$$I^{(3)}=[-0{,}1172;\ -0{,}0170].$$

We now estimate the accuracy of the observations. The confidence interval for σ is obtained from the relationship $P\{\gamma_1\tilde{s}<\sigma<\gamma_2\tilde{s}\}=$ $=P_2-P_1=p$. Here $\tilde{s}$ is the point estimator of σ, $\tilde{s}=\sqrt{\frac{[\tilde{v}\tilde{v}]}{N-n}}$,

p is the given confidence coefficient, γ_1 and γ_2 are determined from the γ-limits for confidence intervals in Table III, with the number of degrees of freedom, $k=N-n$.

We take $p=0{,}90$. We calculate $\tilde{s}=\sqrt{\frac{0{,}8436}{7}}=0{,}347$.

From Table III, for $k=N-n=7$, we find $\gamma_1=0{,}705$, $\gamma_2=1{,}797$. Then, the confidence interval for σ is determined by the inequalities

$$0{,}245<\sigma<0{,}624.$$

CHAPTER VII

THE ESTIMATION OF LINEAR FORMS IN FUNDAMENTAL PARAMETERS FROM INDIRECT OBSERVATIONS. THEOREMS OF NEYMAN AND DAVID *)

1. Statement of the Problem

The method of least squares is often applied to problems of estimation of parameters in a linear regression. We have encountered this problem before, in the introduction, (section 1), where we considered the problem of 'fitting' a line to a series of points by the method of least squares. Similar operations, with a simple probabilistic interpretation, are used in problems of linear regression; for example, when two random variables Y and X are connected by the relationship

$$E(Y|X)=g_1+g_2X, \tag{7.1.1}$$

where the left had side is the conditional expected value of Y for given X, and g_1, g_2 are known. Let $E(X)=a$, and suppose we wish to estimate the linear function g_1+g_2a on the basis of observations of Y for given X. This is a problem of estimation of a linear form. We will describe some examples of similar situations. First we will give a general statement of the problem.

Suppose that there are, as in Chapter VI, observations of linear functions of the fundamental parameters $a_1, \ldots, a_n$:

$$y_r=l_r-\Delta_r=a_1x_{r1}+a_2x_{r2}+\ldots+a_nx_{rn}\ (r=1, 2, \ldots, N), \tag{7.1.2}$$

where the quantities l_r are observed, $\Delta_r\in N\left(0, \frac{\sigma}{\sqrt{p_r}}\right)$ and the p_r's are known weights.

We wish to obtain an estimator of the linear function of the parameters

$$a=g_1a_1+g_2a_2+\ldots+g_n a_n, \tag{7.1.3}$$

* J.Neyman - American statistician. F.David - English statistician, a pupil of J.Neyman

where the quantities g_i are known. It is natural to consider estimating $a_1, a_2, \ldots, a_n$ by the method of least squares (according to the theory given in chapter VI) and to use the estimators $\tilde{a}_1, \ldots, \tilde{a}_n$ so obtained in place of $a_1, \ldots, a_n$ in (7.1.3). Thus, for a we obtain the following estimator

$$\tilde{a} = g_1\tilde{a}_1 + \ldots + g_n\tilde{a}_n. \tag{7.1.4}$$

Evidently, it is unbiased:

$$E(\tilde{a}) = E(g_1\tilde{a}_1 + \ldots + g_n\tilde{a}_n) = \sum_{j=1}^{n} g_j E(\tilde{a}_j) = \sum_{j=1}^{n} g_j a_j = a.$$

But its other properties are not clear without further investigation. We will show later that the estimator $\tilde{a}$ is optimal in a certain sense.

2. Theorems of Neyman and David

Let the rank of the matrix X in the equation

$$Y = XA, \tag{7.2.1}$$

(having the same meaning as in the previous chapter) be equal to n. We also introduce the matrix

$$G = G_{1n} = \| g_1, g_2, \ldots, g_n \|,$$

so that

$$a = GA; \quad \tilde{a} = G\tilde{A}. \tag{7.2.2}$$

Thus,

$$E(\tilde{a}) = GE(\tilde{A}) = GA = a. \tag{7.2.3}$$

Further, $B_{\tilde{A}} = \sigma^2 C^{-1}$, where $B_{\tilde{A}}$ is the correlation matrix of the vector $\tilde{A}$, whence, according to section 3 of chapter II,

$$D(\tilde{a}) = \sigma^2 GC^{-1}G^T. \tag{7.2.4}$$

It is natural to enquire how near is $D(\tilde{a})$ to the lower limit given by the theory of estimation (section 3, chapter III).

We will show later that in the class of linear unbiased estimators of the form $\lambda_1 l_1 + \lambda_2 l_2 + \ldots + \lambda_N l_N$ the estimator $\tilde{a}$ has the minimum variance, even if the errors Δ_i are not normally distributed. (This is essentially the basic assertion of Neyman and David). Now we derive some formulae for $\tilde{a}$, analogous to the formulae of chapter VI. We introduce, as in section 6, chapter VI, the quantities and matrices

$$H_h = \sum_{r=1}^{N} p_r l_r x_{rh} = \{X^T PL\}_{h1} \qquad (h = 1, 2, \ldots, n), \qquad (7.2.5)$$

$$H = X^T PL,$$

$$C = X^T PX = \|c_{hk}\|; \qquad C^T = C, \qquad (7.2.6)$$

and the bordered matrices

$$C_{gg} = \begin{Vmatrix} 0 & g_1 & g_2 \cdots g_n \\ g_1 & c_{11} & c_{12} \cdots c_{1n} \\ \cdot & \cdot & \cdots \\ g_n & c_{n1} & c_{n2} \cdots c_{nn} \end{Vmatrix} \quad (c_{ij} = c_{ji}), \qquad (7.2.7)$$

$$C_{gH} = \begin{Vmatrix} 0 & g_1 & g_2 \cdots g_n \\ H_1 & c_{11} & c_{12} \cdots c_{1n} \\ \cdot & \cdot & \cdots \\ H_n & c_{n1} & c_{n2} \cdots c_{nn} \end{Vmatrix}. \qquad (7.2.8)$$

We will prove a theorem due to Neyman and David [15].

Theorem 7.2.1.

$$\tilde{a} = -\frac{\det(C_{gH})}{\det(C)}. \qquad (7.2.9)$$

and

$$D(\tilde{a}) = -\sigma^2 \frac{\det(C_{gg})}{\det(C)}. \qquad (7.2.10)$$

To prove this we will study, as at the end of section 6, chapter VI, the bordered matrices (7.2.7) and (7.2.8). We have

$$\det(C_{gH}) = -\sum_{h,k=1}^{n} g_h H_k \{C^{-1}\}_{hk} \det(C)$$

and

$$-\frac{\det(C_{gH})}{\det(C)} = GC^{-1}X^T PL = G\tilde{A} = \tilde{a}, \qquad (7.2.11)$$

which proves (7.2.9).

Further, from (7.2.4), $D(\tilde{a}) = \sigma^2 GC^{-1}G^T$. From the bordered matrix (7.2.8) we find

$$\det(C_{gg}) = -\sum_{h,k=1}^{n} g_h g_k \{C^{-1}\}_{hk} \det(C)$$

and

$$-\frac{(\det (C_{gg})}{\det (C)}=GC^{-1}G^{T}=\frac{D(\tilde{a})}{\sigma^{2}},$$

from which (7.2.10) follows.

We will now prove another theorem, also due to Neyman and David.

Theorem 7.2.2.
Among all unbiased linear estimators of the form

$$\lambda_1 l_1+\lambda_2 l_2+\ldots+\lambda_N l_N \tag{7.2.12}$$

for the function a, the estimator $\tilde{a}$ possesses the minimum variance.

We will prove this using matrices. Let

$$\Lambda=\|\lambda_1, \lambda_2, \ldots, \lambda_N\|. \tag{7.2.13}$$

Then the estimators, which we are considering, are of the form:

$[\lambda l]=\Lambda L$, where L, as usual, is the matrix $\left\|\begin{matrix} l_1 \\ \vdots \\ l_N \end{matrix}\right\|$. Further,

the unbiasedness of ΛL means that

$$E([\lambda l])=GA,$$

i.e.

$$\Lambda E(L)=\Lambda Y=\Lambda XA=GA. \tag{7.2.14}$$

The meaning of the requirement of unbiasedness is precisely that the equality (7.2.14) must be fulfilled for any arbitrary set of parameters

$$A=\left\|\begin{matrix} a_1 \\ \vdots \\ a_n \end{matrix}\right\|.$$

It is easy to see that this is possible if and only if

$$\Lambda X=G, \tag{7.2.15}$$

which we will assume to be true.

Further, by virtue of (7.2.12), the independence of the observations l_r and the equation

$$D(l_r) = \frac{\sigma^2}{p_r} \qquad (i = 1, 2, \ldots, N),$$

we have

$$D([\lambda l]) = \sigma^2 \sum_{i=1}^{N} \frac{\lambda_i^2}{p_i} = \sigma^2 \Lambda P^{-1} \Lambda^T. \tag{7.2.16}$$

We see, from (7.2.4), that $D(\tilde{a}) = \sigma^2 G C^{-1} G^T$ or, by virtue of (7.2.15),

$$D(\tilde{a}) = \sigma^2 \Lambda X C^{-1} X^T \Lambda^T. \tag{7.2.17}$$

To prove that $D([\lambda l]) \geqslant D(\tilde{a})$, it is sufficient to show that, for any arbitrary $\Lambda = \| \lambda_1, \lambda_2, \ldots, \lambda_n \|$,

$$\Lambda P^{-1} \Lambda^T \geqslant \Lambda X C^{-1} X^T \Lambda^T = \Lambda X (X^T P X)^{-1} X^T \Lambda^T \tag{7.2.18}$$

(since $C = X^T P X$).

To prove this inequality we proceed as in section 6 of chapter VI. We considered there the matrix

$$U = X (X^T P X)^{-1} X^T P; \quad U^2 = U$$

(see (6.6.3) and (6.6.5)).

Putting $U P^{-1} = X (X^T P X)^{-1} X^T = W$, we see that $W^T = W$ and also that the right hand side of (7.2.18) can be written in the form $\Lambda W \Lambda^T$.

We put $\Lambda P^{-\frac{1}{2}} = M$; then

$$M^T = \left(P^{-\frac{1}{2}}\right)^T \Lambda^T = P^{-\frac{1}{2}} \Lambda^T$$

and

$$\Lambda W \Lambda^T = M P^{\frac{1}{2}} W P^{\frac{1}{2}} M^T. \tag{7.2.19}$$

The matrix $P^{\frac{1}{2}} W P^{\frac{1}{2}}$, is, of course, symmetrical, and since

$$W = U P^{-1}, \quad P^{\frac{1}{2}} W P^{\frac{1}{2}} = P^{\frac{1}{2}} U P^{\frac{1}{2}},$$

we have

$$\left(P^{\frac{1}{2}} W P^{\frac{1}{2}}\right)^2 = P^{\frac{1}{2}} U^2 P^{-\frac{1}{2}} = P^{\frac{1}{2}} U P^{-\frac{1}{2}} = P^{\frac{1}{2}} W P^{\frac{1}{2}}. \tag{7.2.20}$$

We choose an orthogonal matrix $F = F_{NN}$, such that

$$F^T P^{\frac{1}{2}} W P^{\frac{1}{2}} F = D \tag{7.2.21}$$

is a diagonal matrix. Then, since $F^T = F^{-1}$, and by reason of (7.2.20), we find

$$D^2 = D.$$

Putting

$$D = \begin{Vmatrix} d_1 & 0 & \dots & 0 \\ 0 & d_2 & \dots & 0 \\ \cdot & \cdot & \cdot & \cdot \\ 0 & 0 & \dots & d_N \end{Vmatrix},$$

we have $d_i^2 = d_i$, i.e. $d_i = 0$ or $d_i = 1$.

Thus, $MF\left(F^T P^{\frac{1}{2}} W P^{\frac{1}{2}}\right) F F^T M^T = MFDF^T M^T$; if

$$MF = \|\mu_1, \mu_2, \dots \mu_N\|, \tag{7.2.22}$$

then

$$MFDF^T M^T = \sum_{i=1}^{N} d_i \mu_i^2, \quad d_i = 0;\ 1.. \tag{7.2.23}$$

Further,

$$\Delta P^{-1} \Delta^T = \Delta P^{-\frac{1}{2}} P^{-\frac{1}{2}} \Delta^T = MM^T = MFF^T M^T = \sum_{i=1}^{N} \mu_i^2. \tag{7.2.24}$$

Hence, of course,

$MFF^T M^T \geqslant MFDF^T M^T$, or $\Delta P^{-1} \Delta^T \geqslant \Delta W \Delta^T$ for any arbitrary Δ,

which proves (7.2.18) and also our theorem.

We now stop to consider the real interpretation of the estimator $\tilde{a}$. From the considerations of section 5, chapter VI, it follows that if $a'_1, \dots, a'_n$ belong to a very wide class of asymptotically normal and asymptotically unbiased estimators of the parameters $a_1, \dots, a_n$, then the linear form $[g\tilde{a}] = g_1\tilde{a}_1 + \dots + g_n\tilde{a}_n$ is the most suitable estimator of $[ga]$, among all estimators of the form $a' = g_1 a'_1 + \dots + g_n a'_n$ (with the same g's), in a certain sense, viz.: that for given $\varepsilon > 0$ and n,

$$P\{|\tilde{a} - [ga]| \leqslant \varepsilon\} \geqslant P\{|a' - [ga]| \leqslant \varepsilon\} \tag{7.2.25}$$

for large N. If we limit ourselves to linear unbiased estimators of a of the form (7.2.12) only, then, for a normal error vector Δ, these estimators are also normal and, by virtue of theorem 7.2.2, inequalities analogous to (7.2.25) are satisfied for all $N > n$, and not only for large N, i.e.

$$P\{|\tilde{a}-a| \leqslant \varepsilon\} \geqslant P\{|[\lambda l]-a| \leqslant \varepsilon\}. \qquad (7.2.26)$$

3. Estimation of Linear Forms

The knowledge we possess of the properties of the estimator $\tilde{a}$ is sufficient for good point estimation of $a=[ga]$. However, for estimation by confidence intervals and for estimation of the accuracy of working with $\tilde{a}$, we must obtain an estimator for $D(\tilde{a})$.

Theorem 7.3.1.
An unbiased estimator of $D(\tilde{a})$ is

$$\tilde{S}^2 = -\frac{[p\tilde{v}\tilde{v}]}{N-n}\frac{\det(C_{gg})}{\det(C)} = -\frac{\det(C_{gg})\det(C_{HH})}{(N-n)(\det(C))^2}. \qquad (7.3.1)$$

We note that in the second expression of (7.3.1) the only random quantity is $\det(C_{HH})$.

The proof follows immediately from earlier theorems. From theorem 7.2.1 (see (7.2.10)) we have

$$D(\tilde{a}) = -\sigma^2\frac{\det(C_{gg})}{\det(C)},$$

further, from (6.9.3)

$$E\left(\frac{[p\tilde{v}\tilde{v}]}{N-n}\right)=\sigma^2, \text{ so that } E(\tilde{S}^2) = -\sigma^2\frac{\det(C_{gg})}{\det(C)} = D(\tilde{a}).$$

Further, from theorem 6.6.7,

$$[p\tilde{v}\tilde{v}] = \frac{\det(C_{HH})}{\det(C)}.$$

This completely proves the two equalities (7.3.1). Now we construct confidence intervals for estimating $a=[ga]$.

We have seen, in chapter VI, that the random vectors $\tilde{A}$ and $\tilde{V}$ are independent; in particular, $\tilde{A}$ is independent of $[p\tilde{v}\tilde{v}]$, and, consequently, of $\tilde{S}$. The estimator $\tilde{a}=\sum_{i=1}^{n} g_i\tilde{a}_i$ is a linear function of the random vector $\tilde{A}$ and therefore is statistically independent of $\tilde{S}$. From theorem 6.6.4 we have

$$\frac{[p\tilde{v}\tilde{v}]}{\sigma^2} = \chi^2_{N-n}. \qquad (7.3.2)$$

Further, the random variable

$$\frac{\tilde{a}-a}{\sigma}\sqrt{-\frac{\det(C)}{\det(C_{gg})}} \tag{7.3.3}$$

is normal $N(0, 1)$. Therefore we have the following theorem.

Theorem 7.3.2.
The quantity

$$t_{N-n}=\frac{\tilde{a}-a}{\sqrt{-\frac{[p\tilde{v}\tilde{v}]\det(C_{gg})}{(N-n)\det(C)}}}=\frac{\tilde{a}-a}{\tilde{S}} \tag{7.3.4}$$

has Student's distribution with $N-n$ degrees of freedom.

We construct a confidence interval for a in the usual way: for a given confidence coefficient p_0, and the number of degrees of freedom $N-n$, we find, from Table 1, a value γ, such that $P(|t_{N-n}|\leqslant\gamma)=p_0$.

The confidence interval

$$I_\gamma=[\tilde{a}-\gamma\tilde{S},\ \ \tilde{a}+\gamma\tilde{S}] \tag{7.3.5}$$

covers a with probability p_0.

We will give alternative expressions for $\tilde{S}^2$ and $D(\tilde{a})$.

Theorem 7.3.3.
If we write $\tilde{a}$ in the form of a linear function of the observations $l_1, l_2, \ldots, l_N$, i.e.

$$G\tilde{A}=GC^{-1}X^TPL=\tilde{a}=[\lambda l]=\Lambda L, \tag{7.3.6}$$

then

$$D(\tilde{a})=\sigma^2\left[\frac{\lambda^2}{p}\right]=\sigma^2\sum_{i=1}^{N}\frac{\lambda_i^2}{p_i} \tag{7.3.7}$$

and

$$\tilde{S}^2=\frac{[p\tilde{v}\tilde{v}]}{N-n}=\left[\frac{\lambda^2}{p}\right]. \tag{7.3.8}$$

To prove this we note that, from (7.3.1), it follows that

$$D(\tilde{a})=\sigma^2\Lambda P^{-1}\Lambda^T=\sigma^2\left[\frac{\lambda^2}{p}\right]. \tag{7.3.9}$$

Further, from (7.3.1), by virtue of the unbiasedness of $\tilde{S}^2$, and (6.9.3),

$$E(\tilde{S}^2) = D(\tilde{a}) = \sigma^2\left(-\frac{\det(C_{gg})}{\det(C)}\right);$$

comparing this with (7.3.9) we find

$$-\frac{\det(C_{gg})}{\det(C)} = \left[\frac{\lambda^2}{p}\right], \tag{7.3.10}$$

which leads to (7.3.8).

4. Summary of Estimation Formulae for Linear Functions of Parameters

The notation used in the fundamental equations and parameters is here the same as in chapter VI, section 6. We have to estimate the linear form

$$a = g_1 a_1 + \dots + g_n a_n, \tag{7.4.1}$$

where $g_1, \dots, g_n$ are given.

a) Point Estimation

$$\tilde{a} = g_1\tilde{a}_1 + g_2\tilde{a}_2 + \dots + g_n\tilde{a}_n, \tag{7.4.2}$$

where $\tilde{a}_1, \tilde{a}_2, \dots, \tilde{a}_n$ are estimated by the method of least squares. The estimator $\tilde{a}$ can also be expressed in terms of the symmetrical matrix of the system of normal equations,

$$C = \begin{Vmatrix} c_{11} & c_{12} & \dots & c_{1n} \\ c_{21} & c_{22} & \dots & c_{2n} \\ \cdot & \cdot & \cdot & \cdot \\ c_{n1} & c_{n2} & \dots & c_{nn} \end{Vmatrix} \qquad (c_{ij} = c_{ji}).$$

We construct the quantities

$$H_0 = \sum_{r=1}^{N} p_r l_r^2,$$

$$H_h = \sum_{r=1}^{N} p_r l_r x_{rh} \qquad (h = 1, 2, \dots, n) \tag{7.4.3}$$

and the bordered matrices of C:

$$C_{HH} = \begin{Vmatrix} H_0 & H_1 & \dots & H_n \\ H_1 & c_{11} & \dots & c_{1n} \\ \cdot & \cdot & \cdot & \cdot \\ H_n & c_{n1} & \dots & c_{nn} \end{Vmatrix},$$

$$C_{gg} = \begin{Vmatrix} 0 & g_1 & g_2 & \cdots & g_n \\ g_1 & c_{11} & c_{12} & \cdots & c_{1n} \\ \cdot & \cdot & \cdot & \cdot & \cdot \\ g_n & c_{n1} & c_{n2} & \cdots & c_{nn} \end{Vmatrix},$$

$$C_{gH} = \begin{Vmatrix} 0 & g_1 & g_2 & \cdots & g_n \\ H_1 & c_{11} & c_{12} & \cdots & c_{1n} \\ \cdot & \cdot & \cdot & \cdot & \cdot \\ H_n & c_{n1} & c_{n2} & \cdots & c_{nn} \end{Vmatrix}.$$

Hence

$$\tilde{a} = -\frac{\det(C_{gH})}{\det(C)}. \tag{7.4.4}$$

If the estimators $\tilde{a}_1, \ldots, \tilde{a}_n$ by the method of least squares, have already been obtained, then it is relatively convenient to use formula (7.4.2) in the calculations.

Further

$$D(\tilde{a}) = -\sigma^2 \frac{\det(C_{gg})}{\det(C)} = \sum_{h,\,k=1}^{n} g_h g_k \{C^{-1}\}_{hk}. \tag{7.4.5}$$

An unbiased estimator of $D(\tilde{a})$ is the estimator

$$\begin{aligned} \tilde{S}^2 &= -\frac{[p\tilde{v}\tilde{v}]}{N-n} \cdot \frac{\det(C_{gg})}{\det(C)} = \\ &= -\frac{\det(C_{gg})\det(C_{HH})}{(N-n)(\det(C))^2} = -\frac{[p\tilde{v}\tilde{v}]}{N-n}\left[\frac{\lambda^2}{p}\right], \end{aligned} \tag{7.4.6}$$

where the λ_i are such that $\tilde{a} = [\lambda l]$.

This formula is also applicable to the case when the errors are non-normal, but possess the following properties:

$$E(\Delta_i) = 0; \quad D(\Delta_i) = \frac{\sigma^2}{p_i}.$$

An approximate estimator of the standard deviation $\sigma(\tilde{S})$ of the estimator $\tilde{S}$ for large $(N-n)$ is

$$\sigma(\tilde{S}) \approx \sqrt{-\frac{\det(C_{gg})}{2\det(C)(N-n)}}. \tag{7.4.7}$$

b) Estimation by Confidence Intervals

We choose a confidence coefficient p_0, given in Table 1 of

Student's distribution. The second entry is for the number of degrees of freedom $N-n$. Using these entries we find γ_0. The confidence interval

$$I_\gamma = [\tilde{a} - \gamma_0 \tilde{S},\ \tilde{a} + \gamma_0 \tilde{S}] \tag{7.4.8}$$

covers a with probability p_0.

5. Special Cases Encountered in Practice. The Problem of Linear Regression

Let X be a random variable and Y a random variable statistically connected with X, so that (Y, X) is a random vector. Cases are often encountered in which Y has a linear regression on X, i.e. for given X

$$E(Y|X) = a_1 + a_2 X, \tag{7.5.1}$$

and the conditional variance of Y is constant. Here a_1, a_2 are unknown. Using independent observed values $y_1, y_2, \ldots, y_N$ corresponding to $x_1, x_2, \ldots, x_N$, it is required to estimate

$$a = a_1 + a_2 \alpha, \tag{7.5.2}$$

where α is a given value *). We will consider some practical examples, in which this situation is encountered. If we assume the vector (Y, X) is normal, so that the observations $y_1, \ldots, y_N$ are independent and normal, then the estimation of $a = a_1 + a_2\alpha$ by the method of least squares will have the real interpretation described at the end of section 5, chapter VI. If we do not assume this and only admit the existence of the variance of y_i, then all the previous results are valid but the estimators so obtained are good only in the sense that they have the minimum variance in some class or other of unbiased estimators, i.e. essentially, they are good only in the sense of the method of least squares, and also they are obtained by relatively complicated calculations.

In the present problem we have the same situation as in chapter VI, but the previous random variables, l_i, are denoted here by y_i. We have $p_i = 1$, $g_1 = 1$, $g_2 = \alpha$, $x_{r1} = 1$, $x_{r2} = x_r$; so that

$$E(y_r) = a_1 x_{r1} + a_2 x_{r2} = a_1 + a_2 x_r; \quad y_r = \Delta_r + E(y_r),$$

---

* Sometimes cases are met with in which $\alpha = E(X)$. From elementary courses in probability it is known that

$$E(Y) = E(E(Y|X)) = a_1 + a_2 E(X) = a_1 + a_2 \alpha,$$

so that then we have the problem of estimating $E(Y)$.

$$X=\begin{Vmatrix} 1 & x_1 \\ 1 & x_2 \\ \vdots & \vdots \\ 1 & x_N \end{Vmatrix}; \qquad X^T=\begin{Vmatrix} 1 & \dots & 1 \\ x_1 & \dots & x_N \end{Vmatrix};$$

$$C=X^TPX=X^TX=\begin{Vmatrix} N & [x] \\ [x] & [x^2] \end{Vmatrix},$$

$$\det(C)=N[x^2]-[x]^2 \tag{7.5.3}$$

(it is instructive to compare this with example 1 in the introduction).

$$H_1=\sum_{r=1}^{N} y_r=[y]; \qquad H_2=\sum_{r=1}^{N} y_r x_r=[xy];$$

$$H_0=\sum_{r=1}^{N} y_r^2=[y^2];$$

$$C_{gg}=\begin{Vmatrix} 0 & 1 & \alpha \\ 1 & N & [x] \\ \alpha & [x] & [x^2] \end{Vmatrix}; \qquad C_{HH}=\begin{Vmatrix} [y^2] & [y] & [xy] \\ [y] & N & [x] \\ [xy] & [x] & [x^2] \end{Vmatrix};$$

$$C_{gH}=\begin{Vmatrix} 0 & 1 & \alpha \\ [y] & N & [x] \\ [xy] & [x] & [x^2] \end{Vmatrix}.$$

To calculate

$$\tilde{a}=-\frac{\det(C_{gH})}{\det(C)}$$

we find $\det(C_{gH})$, developing this determinant by the elements of the first row:

$$\det(C_{gH})=[x][xy]-[x^2][y]+\alpha([x][y]-n[xy]).$$

Hence

$$\tilde{a}=\frac{[x^2][y]-[x][xy]+\alpha(N[xy]-[x][y])}{N[x^2]-[x]^2}. \tag{7.5.4}$$

We note that in these calculations it is not essential that $\alpha=E(X)$; α could be any arbitrary given number.

We will give an expression for $\tilde{a}$ in a form appropriate to the theory of correlation. We put (see section 1 of introduction)

$\bar{x}=\frac{[x]}{N}$, $\bar{y}=\frac{[y]}{N}$ and

$$r_{xy}=\frac{[(x-\bar{x})(y-\bar{y})]}{\sqrt{[(x-\bar{x})^2]\,[(y-\bar{y})^2]}}; \tag{7.5.5}$$

the quantity r_{xy} is called the sample correlation coefficient between X and Y; we always have $|r_{xy}| \leqslant 1$. Further

$$[(x-\bar{x})^2] = [x^2] - N\bar{x}^2 = [x^2] - \frac{[x]^2}{N},$$

$$[(y-\bar{y})^2] = [y^2] - N\bar{y}^2 = [y^2] - \frac{[y]^2}{N}, \tag{7.5.6}$$

$$[(x-\bar{x})(y-\bar{y})] = [xy] - \frac{1}{N}[x]\,[y]. \tag{7.5.7}$$

We now put

$$s_x^2 = \frac{1}{N}[(x-\bar{x})^2]; \qquad s_y^2 = \frac{1}{N}[(y-\bar{y})^2]. \tag{7.5.8}$$

Hence we find

$$\tilde{a} = (\alpha - \bar{x})\, r_{xy}\frac{s_y}{s_x} + \frac{[x^2]\,[y] - [x]\,[xy] + \bar{x}\,(N\,[xy] - [x]\,[y])}{N \cdot s_x^2}.$$

The second term can be transformed to the form

$$\frac{[x^2]\,\bar{y} - \bar{x}\,[xy] + \bar{x}\,[xy] - \frac{1}{N}[x]^2\,\bar{y}}{s_x^2} = \bar{y},$$

so that we obtain

$$\tilde{a} = \bar{y} + r_{xy}\frac{s_y}{s_x}(\alpha - \bar{x}), \tag{7.5.9}$$

(see (0.1.10) of the introduction). Further from (7.3.1) the unbiased estimator for $D(\tilde{a})$, is the estimator

$$\tilde{S}^2 = -\frac{\det(C_{\xi\xi})\,\det(C_{HH})}{(N-2)(\det(C))^2}. \tag{7.5.10}$$

We give only the final expression for $\tilde{S}^2$ (David [15], chapter XIII, pp. 160-178)

$$\tilde{S}^2 = \frac{s_y^2\left(1 - r_{xy}^2\right)}{N-2}\left[1 + \frac{(\alpha - \bar{x})^2}{s_x^2}\right]. \tag{7.5.11}$$

If the set of abscissae are selected at our pleasure, i.e. if we can define them in advance, then, from formula (7.5.11), is clear that to decrease the second term it is desirable to choose the system of values $x_1, \ldots, x_n$ so that $|\alpha - \bar{x}|$ is as small as possible and $s_x^2 \neq 0$ is as large as possible, i.e. to arrange the x_i's as near as possible to the ends of the range of observations of x in such a way that their mean is as near as possible to α (coincident with α, if possible). If we estimate the coefficients a_1 and a_2 in the linear dependence separately by the method of least squares it is also convenient if s_x^2 is as large as possible; for this we can divide the observations into two groups distributed near the ends of the range of possible values of x.

The general problem of the most suitable distribution of the abscissae x_i, when using the method of least squares, in the case when the abscissae are chosen at our pleasure, has been studied but little up to the present.

Using (7.5.11) we can write the confidence interval for estimating $a = a_1 + a_2\alpha$: in the explicit form

$$I_\gamma = [\tilde{a} - \gamma\tilde{S}, \quad \tilde{a} + \gamma\tilde{S}],$$

where

$$\tilde{a} = \bar{y} + r_{xy}\frac{s_y}{s_x}(\alpha - \bar{x});$$

$$\tilde{S} = s_y\sqrt{\frac{1-r_{xy}^2}{N-2}}\cdot\sqrt{1+\frac{(\alpha-\bar{x})^2}{s_x^2}}.$$

We will now turn our attention to problems of multiple correlation. Suppose we have a random vector (X, Y, Z) and, also, the conditional expected value of Z, for given X, Y, is a linear function of X, Y

$$E(Z|X, Y) = A + BX + CY, \tag{7.5.12}$$

where A, B, C are unknown.

We assume that the conditional variance of Z, for fixed X and Y, is constant, but not known to us. We have observations x_r, y_r, z_r, for which

$$E(Z|x_r, y_r) = A + Bx_r + Cy_r,$$
$$z_r = \Delta_r + E(Z|x_r, y_r);$$

the quantities Δ_r are independent and have unknown variance σ^2. Thus

$$z_r + \Delta_r = A + Bx_r + Cy_r \qquad (r = 1, 2, \ldots, N), \tag{7.5.13}$$

and we have the usual situation of the method of least squares. The problem is to find a point estimator of the linear form $a = A + B\xi + C\eta$ for given ξ, η. We will give explicit formulae for this estimator, without proof. In particular, putting $\xi, \eta = 0$ and making use of the symmetry of the formulae, we will obtain explicit formulae for point estimators of A, B, C based on observations of equal accuracy.

If the errors Δ_r are normal (for example, if the vector (X, Y, Z) is assumed to be normal) then the estimators obtained have the real interpretation previously described; if this is not assumed, we can only affirm that they are good in regard to smallness of variance.

Here

$$g_1 = 1, \quad g_2 = \xi, \quad g_3 = \eta; \quad x_{r1} = 1, \quad x_{r2} = x_r, \quad x_{r3} = y,$$
$$H_0 = [z^2]; \quad H_1 = [z]; \quad H_2 = [xz]; \quad H_3 = [yz];$$
$$X = \begin{Vmatrix} 1 & x_1 & y_1 \\ 1 & x_2 & y_2 \\ \vdots & \vdots & \vdots \\ 1 & x_N & y_N \end{Vmatrix}; \qquad X^T = \begin{Vmatrix} 1 & 1 & \dots & 1 \\ x_1 & x_2 & \dots & x_N \\ y_1 & y_2 & \dots & y_N \end{Vmatrix};$$
$$C = X^T X = \begin{Vmatrix} N & [x] & [y] \\ [x] & [x^2] & [xy] \\ [y] & [xy] & [y^2] \end{Vmatrix}; \tag{7.5.14}$$
$$C_{gH} = \begin{Vmatrix} 0 & 1 & \xi & \eta \\ [z] & N & [x] & [y] \\ [xz] & [x] & [x^2] & [xy] \\ [yz] & [y] & [xy] & [y^2] \end{Vmatrix}. \tag{7.5.15}$$

For the quantity a we have the estimator

$$\tilde{a} = -\frac{\det(C_{gH})}{\det(C)}. \tag{7.5.16}$$

The simple correlation coefficients r_{xy}, r_{xz}, r_{yz} are introduced exactly as in the analogous formulae (7.5.5) and also quantities

$$s_x^2 = \frac{1}{N}[(x-\bar{x})^2]; \quad s_y^2 = \frac{1}{N}[(y-\bar{y})^2]; \quad s_z^2 = \frac{1}{N}[(z-\bar{z})^2].$$

From formula (7.5.16) we obtain after elementary, but lengthy, calculations:

$$\tilde{a} = \bar{z} + (\xi - \bar{x})\frac{s_z}{s_x}\left[\frac{r_{xz} - r_{xy} r_{yz}}{1 - r_{xy}^2}\right] + (\eta - \bar{y})\frac{s_z}{s_y}\left[\frac{r_{yz} - r_{xy} r_{xz}}{1 - r_{xy}^2}\right]. \tag{7.5.17}$$

In particular, for $\xi = \eta = 0$ we obtain the estimator for A

$$\tilde{A} = \bar{z} - \bar{x}\frac{s_z}{s_x}\left[\frac{r_{xz} - r_{xy} r_{yz}}{1 - r_{xy}^2}\right] - \bar{y}\frac{s_z}{s_y}\left[\frac{r_{yz} - r_{xy} r_{xz}}{1 - r_{xy}^2}\right], \tag{7.5.18}$$

To obtain $\tilde{B}$ it is sufficient to assume that $\eta=0$ and obtain an estimator of $a=A+B\xi$, divide it by ξ and then let ξ tend to ∞, i.e. find $\lim\limits_{\xi\to\infty}\frac{\tilde{A}}{\xi}$. Then we obtain from (7.5.13)

$$\tilde{B}=\frac{s_z}{s_x}\left(\frac{r_{xz}-r_{xy}r_{yz}}{1-r_{xy}^2}\right); \tag{7.5.19}$$

similarly, for $\xi=0$, $\eta\to\infty$ we obtain

$$\tilde{C}=\frac{s_z}{s_y}\left(\frac{r_{yz}-r_{xy}r_{xz}}{1-r_{xy}^2}\right). \tag{7.5.20}$$

Further

$$\tilde{S}^2=-\frac{\det(C_{gg})\det(C_{HH})}{(N-3)(\det(C))^2};$$

after some calculations we obtain

$$\tilde{S}^2=\frac{s_z^2}{(N-3)\left(1-r_{xy}^2\right)}\left(1-r_{xy}^2-r_{yz}^2-r_{xz}^2+2r_{xy}r_{yz}r_{xz}\right)\times$$
$$\times\left[1+\frac{1}{1-r_{xy}^2}\left(\left(\frac{\xi-\bar{x}}{s_x}\right)^2-2r_{xy}\left(\frac{\xi-\bar{x}}{s_x}\right)\left(\frac{\eta-\bar{y}}{s_y}\right)+\left(\frac{\eta-\bar{y}}{s_y}\right)^2\right)\right]. \tag{7.5.21}$$

whence we can obtain the equations for unbiased estimators of the variances $\tilde{S}_A^2$, $\tilde{S}_B^2$, $\tilde{S}_C^2$

$$\left.\begin{aligned}\tilde{S}_A^2&=\frac{s_z^2}{(N-3)\left(1-r_{xy}^2\right)}R,\\ \tilde{S}_B^2&=\frac{s_z^2}{(N-3)\,s_x^2\left(1-r_{xy}^2\right)}R,\\ \tilde{S}_C^2&=\frac{s_z^2}{(N-3)\,s_y^2\left(1-r_{xy}^2\right)}R,\end{aligned}\right\} \tag{7.5.22}$$

where

$$R=1-r_{xy}^2-r_{yz}^2-r_{xz}^2+2r_{xy}r_{yz}r_{xz}. \tag{7.5.23}$$

6. Examples

Example 1. As a first example we take Mendelejev's data from the Introduction (page 4).

The straight line

$$y = 67{,}5 + 0{,}87x \tag{0.1.11}$$

was obtained by the method of least squares. The temperature $x = 32°$ was not observed; the point estimate of the solubility of $NaNO_3$ when $x = 32°$, is

$$\tilde{y} = 67{,}5 + 0{,}87 \times 32 = 95{,}3.$$

We will construct a confidence interval covering the solubility at 32° with confidence coefficient $p = 0{,}90$. In order to do this we find an estimate $\tilde{S}$, from the formula

$$\tilde{S} = s_y \sqrt{\frac{1 - r_{xy}^2}{N-2}\left(1 + \frac{(\alpha - \bar{x})^2}{s_x^2}\right)}.$$

In our case $N = 9$, $[x] = 234$, $[y] = 811{,}3$, $[x^2] = 10\,144$, $[y^2] = 76\,218{,}2$, $[xy] = 24\,628{,}6$.
Then

$$s_x^2 = \frac{1}{N}\left([x^2] - \frac{[x]^2}{N}\right) = \frac{1}{9}(10\,144 - 6084) = 451{,}1; \quad s_x = 21{,}24:$$

$$s_y^2 = \frac{1}{N}\left([y^2] - \frac{[y]^2}{N}\right) = 342{,}7; \quad s_y = 18{,}51;$$

$$r_{xy} = \frac{[xy] - \frac{[x]\,[y]}{N}}{N s_x s_y} = 0{,}9990; \quad r_{xy}^2 = 0{,}9980.$$

Hence for $\alpha = 32\ (\bar{x} = 26)$ we find

$$\tilde{S} = 18{,}51 \sqrt{\frac{0{,}0020}{7}\left(1 + \frac{36}{451{,}1}\right)} = 0{,}33.$$

From table I of the t-distribution, for $p = 0{,}90$ and $k = N - 2 = 7$ we find $\gamma = 1{,}895$.

Hence a confidence interval for y with confidence coefficient 0.90 is the interval $[\tilde{y} - 1{,}895\,\tilde{S};\ \tilde{y} + 1{,}895\,\tilde{S}]$, or $[94{,}6;\ 96{,}0]$.

Example 2. As a second example we take example 2 of the introduction. The assumptions of the existence of linear correlation between velocity and stopping distance, and also of the normality of the distribution of stopping distance for a given velocity are needed in these investigations. Investigations of such assumptions, in general, go beyond the framework of the method of least squares and are studied in mathematical statistics. We will not concern ourselves with them. Assuming the existence of the properties described above, for the data of example 2 of the introduction, we will estimate the value, y_i, of the stopping distance for the velocity $x_i = 36$ km/hour and construct a confidence interval for y_i with confidence coefficient $p = 0{,}90$.

From formula (0.1.13): $y = -5{,}362 + 0{,}7454\,x$, we find a point estimate of y_i for $x_i = 36$. We have

$$\tilde{y}_i = -5{,}362 + 0{,}7454 \times 36 = 21{,}47.$$

We now construct a confidence interval for y_i. In our example $N = 50$, $[x] = 1238{,}98$, $[y] = 655{,}43$, $[x^2] = 34\,248{,}4$, $[y^2] = 11\,618{,}5$, $[xy] = 18\,885{,}2$. Then

$$s_x^2 = \frac{[x^2] - \frac{[x]^2}{N}}{N} = \frac{34\,248{,}4 - 30\,701{,}4}{50} = 70{,}94; \quad s_x = 8{,}423,$$

Similarly $s_y^2 = 60{,}53$, $s_y = 7{,}780$, and further

$$r_{xy} = \frac{[xy] - \frac{[x]\,[y]}{50}}{50 \times s_x \times s_y} = 0{,}8069, \quad r_{xy}^2 = 0{,}6511.$$

Hence for $\alpha = 36$ $(\bar{x} = 24{,}78)$

$$\tilde{S} = 7{,}78 \sqrt{\frac{0{,}3489}{48}\left(1 + \frac{(11{,}22)^2}{70{,}94}\right)} = 1{,}105.$$

From table 1 of the t-distribution we find, for $p = 0{,}90$ and $k = N - 2 = 48$, the value $\gamma = 1{,}678$.

Then the confidence interval for y, for $x = 36$, is the interval $[\tilde{y} - 1{,}678\,\tilde{S};\ \tilde{y} + 1{,}678\,\tilde{S}]$, or $[19{,}61;\ 23{,}32]$.

Example 3 *). From the practice firing of a gun with increasing velocity of wind perpendicular to the direction of firing, we obtain the values of the lateral deviations for 10 rounds fired at equal intervals of time τ (table 25)**).

---

* The data in the example are taken from the book [2], p. 236

** For simplicity we take τ as unit time.

TABLE 25

Moment of time t_i	Values of lateral deviation y_i	Moment of time t_i	Values of lateral deviation y_i
0	57,2	5	59,8
1	58,0	6	60,4
2	58,1	7	60,0
3	59,1	8	60,0
4	59,3	9	62,2

Assuming that the lateral deviation is a linear function of time, $y = a + bt$, we will estimate a and b. We will also give estimates of y_i for the moments $t = 2{,}5;\ 6{,}5;\ 10$.

We find estimates of a and b by the method of least squares from formulae (0.1.9), written in the form

$$b = \frac{[ty] - \frac{[t][y]}{N}}{[t^2] - \frac{[t]^2}{N}} \quad \text{and } a = \bar{y} - b\bar{t}.$$

We calculate: $[t] = 45$, $[y] = 594{,}1$, $[t^2] = 285$, $[y^2] = 35\,313{,}79$, $[ty] = 2709{,}9$, $\bar{t} = 4{,}5$, $\bar{y} = 59{,}41$.

Then, $b = 0{,}441$, $a = 57{,}4$ and the dependence of lateral deviation on time is expressed by the equation

$$y = 57{,}4 + 0{,}441\, t.$$

We find point estimates of the lateral deviations for y_1, y_2, y_3 at the moments $t = 2{,}5; 6{,}5; 10$. They are equal to: $\tilde{y}_1 = 58{,}5$, $\tilde{y}_2 = 60{,}3$, $\tilde{y}_3 = 61{,}8$. We form confidence intervals for y_1, y_2, y_3. For this we calculate $s_t^2 = 8{,}250$, $s_t = 2{,}872$, $s_y^2 = 1{,}831$, $s_y = 1{,}353$, $r_{ty} = 0{,}9380$ and $r_{ty}^2 = 0{,}8798$. The estimates, $\tilde{S}$, determined by the formula

$$\tilde{S} = s_y \sqrt{\frac{1 - r_{ty}^2}{N - 2}\left(1 + \frac{(\alpha - \bar{x})^2}{s_t^2}\right)}$$

are equal to: $\tilde{S}_1 = 0{,}2021$, $\tilde{S}_2 = 0{,}2021$, $\tilde{S}_3 = 0{,}3583$ for the three cases $\alpha_1 = 2{,}5$, $\alpha_2 = 6{,}5$, $\alpha_3 = 10$ respectively.

We take the confidence coefficient $p=0,90$. From table 1 of the t-distribution, for $p=0,90$ and $k=N-2=8$, we find $\gamma=1,860$. Then, the confidence intervals for y_1, y_2, y_3 are the intervals: $[\tilde{y}_i-\gamma\tilde{S}_i;\ \tilde{y}_i+\gamma\tilde{S}_i]$, $i=1, 2, 3$, i.e. [58,1; 58,9], [59,9; 60,7], [61,1; 62,5].

Example 4 *). In table 26 are given the results of measuring the velocity y (in km/sec) and distance x (in millions of parsecs) for ten extragalactic nebulae.

TABLE 26

x	y	x	y
1,20	630	9,12	4 820
1,82	890	10,97	5 230
3,31	2 350	14,45	7 500
7,24	3 810	22,91	11 800
8,92	4 630	36,31	19 600

Assuming that y is a linear function of $x\,(y=a+bx)$, we will estimate the parameters a and b, and also obtain estimates of y for $x=2;\ 8;\ 37$.

We find the estimates for a and b by the method of least squares, using formula (0.1.9). We calculate $[x]=116,25$, $[y]=61\,260$, $[x^2]=$ $=2403,2945$, $[y^2]=672\,899\,800$, $[xy]=1\,270\,758,80$, $\bar{x}=11,625$, $\bar{y}=6126$. Then $b=531,06$, $a=-47,6$, and the equation of linear regression of y on x is written in the form

$$y=-47,6+531,06x.$$

The point estimates for the velocity y_i $(i=1, 2, 3)$ for $x=2;\ 8$ and 37 are

$$\tilde{y}_1=1014,5,\quad \tilde{y}_2=4\,200,9,\quad \tilde{y}_3=19\,601,6.$$

respectively.

We find confidence intervals for the y_i's. We calculate $s_x^2=105,19$, $s_x=10,256$, $s_y^2=29\,762,104$, $s_y=5455,5$, $r_{xy}=0,99838$, $r_{xy}^2=0,99676$.

* The data are taken from the book [2], p. 237

Then the estimates $\tilde{S}$ for $\alpha_1 = 2$, $\alpha_2 = 8$, $\alpha_3 = 37$, are equal to $\tilde{S}_1 = 106$, $\tilde{S}_2 = 82{,}4$, $\tilde{S}_3 = 207$, respectively.

We take a confidence coefficient $p = 0{,}90$. For this confidence coefficient and $k = N - 2 = 8$ degrees of freedom, we find, from the table of Student's distribution, $\gamma = 1{,}860$.

The confidence intervals for y_1, y_2, y_3 are the intervals $[\tilde{y}_i - \gamma\tilde{S}_i;\ \tilde{y}_i + \gamma\tilde{S}_i]$, $i = 1, 2, 3$, or $[817;\ 1212]$, $[4047;\ 4354]$, $[19\,216;\ 19\,987]$ respectively.

Example 5. In table 27 are given the results of experimental studies on the quantity of heat radiated during the hardening of Portland cement.*) Data already obtained have established the relationship between the chemical structure of the mixture from which the bricks radiating the heat have been manufactured, and the amount of heat radiated; x and y express the proportions, in the mixture, of calcium aluminate $3CaO \cdot Al_2O_3$ and calcium silicate $3CaO \cdot SiO_2$ (in percentages by weight of the mixture) respectively; z is the quantity of heat radiated in calories per gram of cement.

TABLE 27

x	y	z
7	26	78,5
1	29	74,3
11	56	104,3
11	31	87,6
7	52	95,9
11	55	109,2
3	71	102,7
1	31	72,5
2	54	93,1
21	47	115,9
1	40	83,8
11	66	113,3
Sum 87	558	1131,1

Assuming that the dependence of z on x and y is linear, we will obtain a point estimate of z for $x = 10$, $y = 68$ and compare the results obtained with the observed value of z for these values of x and y (equal to 109.4) (see the corresponding observation in [48] p. 543).

* The data are borrowed from the book [48], p. 543

We obtain the point estimate of z from formula (7.5.17)

$$\tilde{z}=\bar{z}+(\xi-\bar{x})\frac{s_z}{s_x}\left[\frac{r_{xz}-r_{xy}r_{yz}}{1-r_{xy}^2}\right]+(\eta-\bar{y})\frac{s_z}{s_y}\left[\frac{r_{yz}-r_{xy}r_{xz}}{1-r_{xy}^2}\right].$$

Calculating the quantities occuring in the formula, we obtain

$$\begin{array}{lll} \bar{x}=7.25; & \bar{y}=46.50; & \bar{z}=94.26; \\ s_x^2=34.02; & s_y^2=206.6; & s_z^2=208.7; \\ s_x=5.833; & s_y=14.37; & s_z=14.45; \\ r_{xy}=0.1954; & r_{xz}=0.7292; & r_{yz}=0.7996; \\ r_{xy}^2=0.0382. & & \end{array}$$

Putting $\xi=10$, $\eta=68$ and substituting the values given above into the formula for $\tilde{z}$, we find the point estimate of the quantity z for $x=10$, $y=68$. It is equal to $\tilde{z}=113.09$.

CHAPTER VIII

INDIRECT CONDITIONAL MEASUREMENTS (REDUCTION BY MEANS OF ELEMENTS)

1. Statement of the Problem

In the introduction we encountered problems in the measurement of quantities, in which certain natural conditions were imposed on the estimators of our quantities. A typical case is example 4 - on measurements of the angles of a triangle; a more general statement of the problem is given in formulae (0.1.31) and (0.1.32). Here we define the statement more precisely.

Suppose that N measurable quantities $\lambda_1, \lambda_2, \ldots, \lambda_N$ satisfy $q < N$ relationships called fundamental equations

$$F_j(\lambda_1, \lambda_2, \ldots, \lambda_N) = 0 \qquad (j = 1, 2, \ldots, q), \qquad (8.1.1)$$

where $F_j(\lambda_1, \ldots, \lambda_N)$ are functions which may be developed in Taylor series.

Suppose that measurements of the quantities $\lambda_1, \ldots, \lambda_N$ have been obtained, which have random errors and give results $l_1, l_2, \ldots, l_N$. Introducing corrections $\delta_1, \delta_2, \ldots, \delta_N$ into these results so that equations (8.1.1) are satisfied exactly, we have $l_i + \delta_i = \lambda_i$ $(i = 1, 2, \ldots, N)$;

$$F_j(l_1 + \delta_1, l_2 + \delta_2, \ldots, l_N + \delta_N) = 0, \quad j = 1, 2, \ldots, q. \quad (8.1.2)$$

The values $\delta_1, \delta_2, \ldots, \delta_N$ are the true corrections for the observations, which are unknown to us. We replace the unknown quantities λ_i by the estimates $\tilde{l}_1, \tilde{l}_2, \ldots, \tilde{l}_N$, so that for the fundamental equations to be satisfied.

$$F_j(\tilde{l}_1, \tilde{l}_2, \ldots, \tilde{l}_N) = 0 \qquad (j = 1, 2, \ldots, q). \qquad (8.1.3)$$

Such an operation is often called reduction. To find the necessary estimates we again start with the method of maximum likelihood.

Let the quantities $l_1, l_2, \ldots, l_N$ be independent, normal with $l_i \in N\left(\lambda_i, \frac{\sigma}{\sqrt{p_i}}\right)$, so that $l_i = \lambda_i + \Delta_i$; $D(\Delta_i) = \frac{\sigma^2}{p_i}$; $p_i (i = 1, 2, \ldots, N)$ are the weights.

We construct the likelihood function of the sample $(l_1, l_2, \ldots, l_N)$:

$$L = (2\pi)^{-\frac{N}{2}} \sigma^{-N} p_1 p_2 \ldots p_N \exp\left\{-\frac{1}{2\sigma^2} \sum_{i=1}^{N} p_i (l_i - \lambda_i)^2\right\}. \quad (8.1.4)$$

According to the principle of maximum likelihood, to estimate the quantities $\lambda_1, \lambda_2, \ldots, \lambda_N$ they should be replaced by the quantities $\tilde{l}_1, \tilde{l}_2, \ldots, \tilde{l}_N$, which give the conditional maximum of the function L, subject to conditions (8.1.3). For any arbitrary value of σ^2 this requirement is equivalent to the following

$$\left.\begin{aligned} &\sum_{i=1}^{N} p_i (\tilde{l}_i - l_i)^2 = \min, \\ &F_j(\tilde{l}_1, \tilde{l}_2, \ldots, \tilde{l}_N) = 0, \quad j = 1, 2, \ldots, q \end{aligned}\right\} \quad (8.1.5)$$

i.e. to the requirements of the method of least squares, when it is applied to a conditional minimum.

We now note that in future the fundamental equations (8.1.1) will be supposed to be linear, i.e. of the form

$$f_{j0} + \lambda_1 f_{j1} + \lambda_2 f_{j2} + \ldots + \lambda_N f_{jN} = 0 \quad (j = 1, 2, \ldots, q). \quad (8.1.6)$$

The reasons for this are as follows. In those cases, where the problems under consideration (problems of indirect conditional measurements) arise, as in problems of reduction in geodesy, astronomy and other disciplines, the quantities which are measured, for example, angles in geodesy, are known to a first approximation. We will know approximations λ_i^0 to the quantities λ_i and assume that the true errors $\Delta\lambda_i = \lambda_i - \lambda_i^0$ are such that we cannot neglect them, but we can ignore their squares $(\Delta\lambda_i)^2$ in comparison to the chosen unit of length. Later, we will have some practical examples of such situations. In such cases, remembering that the functions $F_j(\lambda_1, \ldots, \lambda_N)$ can be developed in Taylor series, and carrying out this development in the neighbourhood of the point $(\lambda_1^0, \ldots, \lambda_N^0)$, we find

$$F_j(\lambda_1, \ldots, \lambda_N) = F_j(\lambda_1^0, \lambda_2^0, \ldots, \lambda_N^0) + \Delta\lambda_1 \left(\frac{\partial F_j}{\partial \lambda_1}\right)_0 + \Delta\lambda_2 \left(\frac{\partial F_j}{\partial \lambda_2}\right)_0 +$$

$$+ \ldots + \Delta\lambda_N \left(\frac{\partial F_j}{\partial \lambda_N}\right)_0 + \text{quantities of the order of smallness of } (\Delta_1^2 + \Delta_2^2 + \ldots + \Delta_N^2).$$

Here the partial derivatives $\left(\frac{\partial F_j}{\partial \lambda_i}\right)_0$ are evaluated at the point $(\lambda_1^0, \ldots, \lambda_N^0)$ and appear as known constant values, as also does $F_j(\lambda_1^0, \ldots, \lambda_N^0)$.

The basic idea of the method lies in the fact that if the values $\lambda_1^0, \lambda_2^0, \ldots, \lambda_N^0$ are known, we can take, as the measurable quantities, not $\lambda_1, \ldots, \lambda_N$, but the true corrections $\Delta\lambda_1, \Delta\lambda_2, \ldots, \Delta\lambda_N$.

Writing

$$F_j(\lambda_1^0, \ldots, \lambda_N^0) = f_{j0}, \left(\frac{\partial F_j}{\partial \lambda_i}\right)_0 = f_{ji} \qquad (i = 1, 2, \ldots, N),$$

we get, in place of (8.1.1), linear fundamental equations of the form (8.1.6), where $\Delta\lambda_1, \ldots, \Delta\lambda_N$ are denoted, for brevity, by $\lambda_1, \ldots, \lambda_N$. These equations are correct to an accuracy neglecting quantities of the order of smallness of $(\Delta_1^2 + \ldots + \Delta_N^2)$.

From the q equations (8.1.6) we can eliminate some of the numbers $\lambda_1, \lambda_2, \ldots, \lambda_N$, expressing them as a linear form in the remainder. The number of parameters remaining 'free' is determined by the rank of the matrix $F = F_{qN}$ and is equal to $m = \text{rank}\,(F)$. We denote the remaining parameters by $\xi_1, \xi_2, \ldots, \xi_n$, and obtain the equations in the parametric form

$$\lambda_r = \xi_1 x_{r1} + \xi_2 x_{r2} + \ldots + \xi_n x_{rn} \qquad (r = 1, 2, \ldots, N), \quad (8.1.7)$$

where $x_{rs} (r = 1, 2, \ldots, N,\ s = 1, 2, \ldots, n)$ are known numbers.

If we transform $\xi_1, \ldots, \xi_n$ into $\xi_1', \ldots, \xi_n'$, by means of a non-singular linear transformation, then we obtain new linear expressions for λ_r of type (8.1.7) with known coefficients. Therefore, in the equations (8.1.7), we can regard $\xi_1, \ldots, \xi_n$ as parameters which do not necessarily coincide with any particular λ_i. In this case equations (8.1.7) are called the fundamental equations in parametric form and the parameters $\xi_1, \xi_2, \ldots, \xi_n$ are called elements. The estimation of $\lambda_1, \ldots, \lambda_N$ in this case is called reduction by means of elements (in contradistinction to reduction by correlates, which will be considered later). If we change $\xi_1, \xi_2, \ldots, \xi_n$ into $a_1, a_2, \ldots, a_n$ and λ_r into y_r, then we obtain equations which are close in form and in meaning to equations (6.1.1) of chapter VI:

$$y_r = x_{r0} + \sum_{j=1}^{n} a_j x_{rj} \qquad (r = 1, 2, \ldots, N;\ N > n), \quad (8.1.8)$$

where we have $l_r = y_r + \Delta_r$, in place of y_r and the errors Δ_r can be assumed independent, random and normal $N\left(0, \frac{\sigma}{\sqrt{p_r}}\right)$. The difference from equations (6.1.1) lies in the presence of the 'free terms' x_{r0}. To transform the equations (8.1.8) into complete similarity to (6.1.1) we write them in the form

$$y_r - x_{r0} = \sum_{j=1}^{n} a_j x_{rj}. \tag{8.1.9}$$

Here x_{r0} are known numbers. We compare the observations l_r with the auxiliary values $l_r - x_{r0}$, which can be assumed to be values of independent random normal variables $N\left(y_r - x_{r0}, \frac{\sigma}{\sqrt{p_r}}\right)$. It is true that in the present case the basic emphasis is on the estimation of the left-hand elements $y_1, \ldots, y_N$, and not of the elements $a_1, \ldots, a_n$, as in chapter VI, but in view of the linear dependence (8.1.8) the corresponding estimates should be closely related.

The exact statement of the problem of reduction by means of elements is: to find the unbiased estimators $\tilde{a}_1, \tilde{a}_2, \ldots, \tilde{a}_n$ and $\tilde{l}_1, \tilde{l}_2, \ldots, \tilde{l}_N$ so that the equations

$$\tilde{l}_r = x_{r0} + \sum_{j=1}^{n} \tilde{a}_j x_{rj} \qquad (r = 1, 2, \ldots, N), \tag{8.1.10}$$

which are called conditional (or equations of condition), are satisfied. These estimators should possess, if possible, better properties in regard to their joint efficiency.

2. Reduction by Means of Elements Using the Method of Least Squares

As has been said before, the statement of the problem of reduction by means of elements is, essentially, identical with the statement of the problem in chapter VI. If we select the estimators $\tilde{a}_1, \ldots, \tilde{a}_n$ by the method of least squares, then they are jointly efficient. The real advantage of estimation by the method of least squares has been explained in section 5, chapter VI. The estimators $\tilde{l}_1, \ldots, \tilde{l}_N$ for $l_1, \ldots, l_N$ are obtained directly from formula (8.1.9) with $\tilde{a}_1, \ldots, \tilde{a}_n$ known.

To calculate the required estimators it suffices to use the results of chapter VI, replacing the numbers y_r by numbers $y_r - x_{r0}$. We will write down the results obtained in this way.

We introduce the matrix

$$X_0 = \begin{Vmatrix} x_{10} \\ x_{20} \\ \vdots \\ x_{N0} \end{Vmatrix}.$$

We write the fundamental equations (8.1.8) in the form

$$Y - X_0 = X \cdot A, \tag{8.2.1}$$

where, as in chapter VI,

$$X = X_{Nn} = \begin{Vmatrix} x_{11} & \dots & x_{1n} \\ x_{21} & \dots & x_{2n} \\ \cdot & \cdot & \cdot \\ x_{N1} & \dots & x_{Nn} \end{Vmatrix}.$$

As in chapter VI, we find that rank $(X) = n$. Further, we suppose (in the notation of chapter VI)

$$\tilde{V} = XA + X_0 - L = X\tilde{A} - (L - X_0), \tag{8.2.2}$$

where $\tilde{A}$ is chosen so that

$$[p\tilde{v}\tilde{v}] = \min. \tag{8.2.3}$$

All the calculations are the same as in chapter VI, replacing L by $L - X_0$.

The normal equations are of the form

$$C\tilde{A} = X^T P(L - X_0); \quad C = X^T PX. \tag{8.2.4}$$

Further, $\tilde{A}$ is an unbiased estimator of A, with correlation matrix

$$B_{\tilde{A}} = \sigma^2 C^{-1}. \tag{8.2.5}$$

We take the quantities $\tilde{l}_1, \dots, \tilde{l}_N$, where

$$\tilde{l}_r = x_{r0} + \sum_{j=1}^{n} \tilde{a}_j x_{rj} \qquad (r = 1, 2, \dots, N), \tag{8.2.6}$$

i.e.

$$\tilde{L} = X_0 + X\tilde{A}, \tag{8.2.7}$$

as estimators of $y_1, \dots, y_N$.

The estimators $\tilde{L}$ are unbiased estimators of Y, because

$$E(\tilde{L}) = X_0 + XE(\tilde{A}) = X_0 + XA = Y.$$

Further, according to section 7 of chapter VI (here $\tilde{L} - X_0$ plays the rôle of $\tilde{L}$), the correlation matrix, $B_{\tilde{L}}$ of $\tilde{L}$ is

$$B_{\tilde{L}} = \sigma^2 X C^{-1} X^T. \tag{8.2.8}$$

Exactly similarly to theorem 6.7.1, we also have here the relationship

$$\frac{1}{\sigma^2} \sum_{r=1}^{N} p_r D(\tilde{l}_r) = \frac{1}{\sigma^2} [pD(\tilde{l})] = \sum \{XC^{-1}X^T\}_{rr} = n, \tag{8.2.9}$$

which can be used to check the calculations.

Besides this, we see that the weighted mean variance of the estimators is proportional to $\frac{n}{N}$, so that it is convenient to make the ratio of the number of observations to the number of elements as large as possible.

We will now derive formulae for calculating $[p\tilde{v}\tilde{v}]$ and for checking the calculations. We denote $L - X_0$ by M.

Theorem 8.2.1.

$$[p\tilde{v}\tilde{v}] = M^T P M - M^T P X \tilde{A} = [pmm] - [px_1 m] \tilde{a}_1 - \ldots - [px_n m] \tilde{a}_n, \tag{8.2.10}$$

$$[p\tilde{v}\tilde{v}] = M^T P M - \tilde{A}^T C \tilde{A}, \tag{8.2.11}$$

$$[p\tilde{v}\tilde{v}] = L^T P L - \tilde{L}^T P \tilde{L} + 2 X_0^T P \tilde{V}. \tag{8.2.12}$$

Formula (8.2.10) is obtained immediately from (6.6.19), replacing L by $M = L - X_0$; in the same way (8.2.11) follows from (6.6.18). To prove (8.2.12) we write

$$\begin{aligned}
[p\tilde{v}\tilde{v}] &= M^T P M - \tilde{A}^T C \tilde{A} = M^T P M - \tilde{A}^T X^T P X \tilde{A} = \\
&= M^T P M - (\tilde{L} - X_0)^T P (\tilde{L} - X_0) = \\
&= L^T P L - L^T P X_0 - X_0^T P L - \tilde{L}^T P \tilde{L} + X_0^T P \tilde{L} + \tilde{L}^T P X_0.
\end{aligned}$$

Further, $L^T P X_0$ is a number, i.e. a matrix of first order; consequently

$$\begin{aligned}
(L^T P X_0)^T &= X_0^T P L = L^T P X_0; \\
(\tilde{L}^T P X_0)^T &= X_0^T P \tilde{L} = \tilde{L}^T P X_0,
\end{aligned}$$

so that

$$[p\tilde{v}\tilde{v}] = L^T PL - \tilde{L}^T P\tilde{L} - 2X_0^T PL + 2X_0^T P\tilde{L} = \\ = L^T PL - \tilde{L}^T P\tilde{L} + 2X_0^T P(\tilde{L} - L).$$

Further,

$$\tilde{L} = X_0 + X\tilde{A}; \quad \tilde{V} = X_0 + X\tilde{A} - L = \tilde{L} - L,$$

so that

$$[p\tilde{v}\tilde{v}] = L^T PL - \tilde{L}^T P\tilde{L} + 2X_0^T P\tilde{V},$$

which was to be proved.

Confidence intervals for estimating the quantities $a_1, a_2, \ldots, a_n$ are constructed in the same way as in the chapter VI, replacing L by $L - X_0$ in the estimators $\tilde{A}$. Hence

$$\tilde{A} = C^{-1}X^T P(L - X_0), \tag{8.2.13}$$

$$I_\gamma^{(i)} = \left[\tilde{a}_i - \gamma\sqrt{\{C^{-1}\}_{ii}\frac{[p\tilde{v}\tilde{v}]}{N-n}}, \quad \tilde{a}_i + \gamma\sqrt{\{C^{-1}\}_{ii}\frac{[p\tilde{v}\tilde{v}]}{N-n}}\right]. \tag{8.2.14}$$

To estimate y_i $(i = 1, 2, \ldots, N)$ we obtain the confidence intervals

$$J_\gamma^{(i)} = \left[\tilde{l}_i - \gamma\sqrt{\{XC^{-1}X^T\}_{ii}\frac{[p\tilde{v}\tilde{v}]}{N-n}}, \quad \tilde{l}_i + \gamma\sqrt{\{XC^{-1}X^T\}_{ii}\frac{[p\tilde{v}\tilde{v}]}{N-n}}\right]. \tag{8.2.15}$$

The length of the confidence interval $J_\gamma^{(i)}$ is the random variable

$$d_\gamma^{(i)} = 2\gamma s\sqrt{\{XC^{-1}X^T\}_{ii}}.$$

As in chapter VI, we can consider the quantity

$$\frac{1}{N}E\left(p_i\sum_{i=1}^{N}(d_\gamma^{(i)})^2\right) = \frac{4\gamma^2\sigma^2 n}{N}. \tag{8.2.16}$$

For $N - n \geqslant 20$ we can assume

$$\frac{4\gamma^2\sigma^2 n}{N} \approx \frac{15.37\sigma^2 n}{N},$$ (if the confidence coefficient, p_0, is equal to 0.95).

To estimate the accuracy of measurement we use as the point

estimator

$$\tilde{s}=\sqrt{\frac{[p\tilde{v}\tilde{v}]}{N-n}}. \tag{8.2.17}$$

We can give a confidence interval for σ in the form $[\gamma_1\tilde{s}, \gamma_2\tilde{s}]$, as described in section 9 of chapter VI.

3. Rules for Reduction by Means of Elements

The fundamental equations are

$$y_r=x_{r0}+\sum_{j=1}^{n}a_j x_{rj} \quad (r=1, 2, \ldots, N, N>n). \tag{8.3.1}$$

To find point estimators of a_j and y_r we construct the normal equations for $x_j=(x_{1j}, x_{2j}, \ldots, x_{Nj})$

$$\sum_{\nu=1}^{n}[px_i x_\nu]\tilde{a}_\nu=[px_i(l-x_0)]. \tag{8.3.2}$$

Solving the normal equations (8.3.2) we obtain the estimators $\tilde{a}_1, \ldots, \tilde{a}_n$. The estimators of y_r are obtained from the formulae

$$\tilde{y}_r=x_{r0}+\sum_{j=1}^{n}\tilde{a}_j x_{rj} \qquad (r=1, 2, \ldots, N, N>n). \tag{8.3.3}$$

Further, we must calculate $[p\tilde{v}\tilde{v}]$, where

$$\tilde{v}_r=\sum_{i=1}^{n}\tilde{a}_i x_{ri}+x_{r0}-l_r. \tag{8.3.4}$$

To calculate $[p\tilde{v}\tilde{v}]$, or as a check on such calculations, we can use the formulae

$$[p\tilde{v}\tilde{v}]=[pmm]-[px_1m]\tilde{a}_1-\ldots-[px_nm]\tilde{a}_n, \tag{8.3.5}$$

where $m=(m_1, \ldots, m_N)$; $m_r=l_r-x_{r0}$;

$$[p\tilde{v}\tilde{v}]=[pmm]-\sum_{h,k=1}^{n}[px_h x_k]\tilde{a}_h\tilde{a}_k. \tag{8.3.6}$$

If we put

$$\tilde{l}_r=x_{r0}+\sum_{j=1}^{n}\tilde{a}_j x_{rj},$$

then

$$[p\tilde{v}\tilde{v}] = [pll] - [p\tilde{l}\,\tilde{l}] - 2[p\tilde{v}x_0]. \tag{8.3.8}$$

To estimate the accuracy of the observations we calculate the quantity

$$\tilde{s} = \sqrt{\frac{[p\tilde{v}\,\tilde{v}]}{N-n}}, \tag{8.3.9}$$

which is used as an estimator of σ. This estimator is asymptotically unbiased in regard to σ, with increasing $N-n$. Its standard deviation is $\sigma(\tilde{s}) \approx \frac{\sigma}{\sqrt{2(N-n)}}$ for large $N-n$. It is estimated approximately by $\frac{\tilde{s}}{\sqrt{2(N-n)}}$.

To estimate the standard deviations, $\sigma(\tilde{a}_i)$, of the estimators $\tilde{a}_i$, we need to find the diagonal elements of the matrix inverse to the matrix C of the normal equations (8.3.2), i.e. the values $\{C^{-1}\}_{ii}$. Then, $\sigma(\tilde{a}_i)$ is estimated by the quantity

$$\tilde{s}\sqrt{\{C^{-1}\}_{ii}}. \tag{8.3.10}$$

Further, for the estimators, $\tilde{l}_r$, of the parameters y_r we have to construct the matrix

$$X^T C^{-1} X, \text{ where } X = \begin{Vmatrix} x_{11} & x_{12} & \dots & x_{1n} \\ x_{21} & x_{21} & \dots & x_{2n} \\ \cdot & \cdot & \cdot & \cdot \\ x_{N1} & x_{N2} & \dots & x_{Nn} \end{Vmatrix},$$

in which we need only the diagonal elements $\{X^T C^{-1} X\}_{rr}$. Then

$$\sigma(\tilde{l}_r) = \sigma\sqrt{\{X^T C^{-1} X\}_{rr}}. \tag{8.3.11}$$

An approximate estimator of $\sigma(\tilde{l}_r)$, for large $N-n$, is the quantity

$$\tilde{s}\sqrt{\{X^T C^{-1} X\}_{rr}}. \tag{8.3.12}$$

To check the calculations we can use the formula

$$\frac{1}{\sigma^2}[pD(\tilde{l})] = \sum_{r=1}^{N} \{XC^{-1}X^T\}_{rr} = n. \tag{8.3.13}$$

From this it is also clear that the precision of observations, for given weights and σ^2, depends on the ratio $\frac{N}{n}$, which it is convenient to make as large as possible.

Estimation by Confidence Intervals

We use Table 1 of Student's distribution. We choose a confidence coefficient p_0, and, for the second entry, take $N-n$ degrees of freedom. With these two entry values we find the number γ_0. The confidence interval

$$I_\gamma^{(i)}=\left[\tilde{a}_i-\gamma_0\sqrt{\{C^{-1}\}_{ii}\frac{[p\tilde{v}\tilde{v}]}{N-n}},\quad \tilde{a}_i+\gamma_0\sqrt{\{C^{-1}\}_{ii}\frac{[p\tilde{v}\tilde{v}]}{N-n}}\right] \quad (8.3.14)$$

covers a_i with probability p_0.

To estimate y_r we construct the confidence interval

$$J_\gamma^{(r)}=\left[\tilde{l}_r-\gamma_0\sqrt{(X^TC^{-1}X)_{rr}\frac{[p\tilde{v}\tilde{v}]}{N-n}},\ \tilde{l}_r+\gamma_0\sqrt{(X^TC^{-1}X)_{rr}\frac{[p\tilde{v}\tilde{v}]}{N-n}}\right], \quad (8.3.15)$$

covering y_r with probability p_0.

To estimate σ by confidence intervals we use Table III of the Appendix. For a given p_0, we find γ_1 and γ_2. The confidence interval

$$I=\left[\gamma_1\sqrt{\frac{[p\tilde{v}\tilde{v}]}{N-n}},\quad \gamma_2\sqrt{\frac{[p\tilde{v}\tilde{v}]}{N-n}}\right] \quad (8.3.16)$$

covers σ with probability p_0.

Examples of applications of this method will be given, together with examples of applications of the method of correlates, in chapter IX.

CHAPTER IX

REDUCTION BY MEANS OF CORRELATES

1. Statement of the Problem

The method of reduction by means of correlates is different from the method of reduction by means of elements only in its analytical form; the mathematico-statistical formulation and ideas remain as before.

We have to estimate the parameters $y_1, \ldots, y_N$, which are connected by $q\,(q < N)$ relationships

$$x_{j0} + y_1 x_{j1} + y_2 x_{j2} + \ldots + y_N x_{jN} = 0 \quad (j = 1, 2, \ldots, q). \tag{9.1.1}$$

We assume these relations to be linear in the same way as in chapter VIII; transitions, with little error, from non-linear to linear relationships will be described in specific examples.

We have to find estimators $\tilde{l}_1, \tilde{l}_2, \ldots, \tilde{l}_N$ for $y_1, y_2, \ldots, y_N$ on the basis of observations $l_1, l_2, \ldots, l_N$, which we assume to have random errors $\Delta_1, \ldots, \Delta_N$, so that the l_r's are independent, normal $N\left(y_r, \frac{\sigma}{\sqrt{p_r}}\right)$ random variables. Following the methods used in chapter VIII, we will look for estimators $\tilde{l}_1, \ldots, \tilde{l}_N$ satisfying the conditions

$$\left.\begin{aligned} &\sum_{i=1}^{N} p_i (\tilde{l}_i - l_i)^2 = [p(\tilde{l} - l)^2] = \min \\ &x_{j0} + \tilde{l}_1 x_{j1} + \tilde{l}_2 x_{j2} + \ldots + \tilde{l}_N x_{jN} = 0 \quad (j = 1, 2, \ldots, q). \end{aligned}\right\} \tag{9.1.2}$$

The estimators obtained, $\tilde{l}_1, \ldots, \tilde{l}_N$, should coincide with the estimators found by means of elements and also those determined in chapter VIII. In fact, there also, estimators $\tilde{l}_1, \ldots, \tilde{l}_N$ were sought which would satisfy the condition $[p(\tilde{l} - l)^2] = \min$, while the $\tilde{l}_i$'s satisfy the relationships (8.1.10), which are completely equivalent to the linear relationships in (9.1.2). The relations (8.1.10) were specially chosen, so that they would be equivalent to (9.1.2), i.e. so that every set of values $\tilde{l}_1, \ldots, \tilde{l}_N$, represented in the form (8.1.10), with arbitrary parameters $\tilde{a}_1, \ldots, \tilde{a}_n$, should satisfy the q linear relationships (9.1.2) and, conversely, every set of values $\tilde{l}_1, \ldots, \tilde{l}_N$, satisfying the linear relationships in (9.1.2) (and not necessarily satisfying the first of the relations (9.1.2)), could be represented in the form (8.1.10), for arbitrary values of the parameters $\tilde{a}_1, \ldots, \tilde{a}_n$ (not necessarily for the estimators we have calculated). Hence, in finding the conditional minimum in (9.1.2), we will obtain the old values of the estimators. However, we will not obtain them by the old method - using the parametric form of the linear relationships (9.1.2) and reducing by means of elements, because this requires the operation of exclusion of the variables $\tilde{l}_r$ from the equations (9.1.2); we will consider the process of calculating the estimators $\tilde{l}_r$, i.e. we want to find the conditional minimum of $[p(\tilde{l}-l)^2]$ using the linear realtionships (conditional equations) (9.1.1) directly. This process is essentially, the method of correlates. Here we will apply Lagrange's method to find the conditional minimum.

We recall Lagrange's rule. Let $\Phi(z_1, \ldots, z_N)$ be a function which is everywhere twice differentiable, and $F_1(z_1, \ldots, z_N), \ldots, F_q(z_1, \ldots, z_N)$, $(q < N)$ functions with the same property. We have to find values $z_1, \ldots, z_N$, for which

$$\Phi(z_1, \ldots, z_N) = \min \text{ and } F_j(z_1, \ldots, z_N) = 0 \qquad (j = 1, 2, \ldots, q).$$

To find these values we construct the auxiliary function

$$\Psi(z_1, \ldots, z_N) = \Phi - k_1 F_1 - k_2 F_2 - \ldots - k_q F_q,$$

where $k_1, k_2, \ldots, k_q$ are undetermined Lagrange's multipliers. Then we make the complete differential of Ψ equal to zero: $d\Psi = 0$, i.e.

$$\frac{\partial \Psi}{\partial z_1} = \frac{\partial \Psi}{\partial z_2} = \ldots = \frac{\partial \Psi}{\partial z_N} = 0.$$

To the system of equations so obtained we add the q conditional equations $F_j(z_1, \ldots, z_N) = 0$ $(j = 1, 2, \ldots, q)$, which gives $N + q$ equations for the determination of $z_1, z_2, \ldots, z_N$ and $k_1, k_2, \ldots, k_q$. Among the solutions $(z_1, \ldots z_N)$ of these equations we have to seek for the solution we need.

2. Calculation of the Estimators by Means of Correlates

We will make the calculations in matrix form. To write the equations of condition (9.1.1) we introduce the matrices:

$$X_0 = \begin{Vmatrix} x_{10} \\ x_{20} \\ \vdots \\ x_{q0} \end{Vmatrix}; \quad X = X_{qN} = \begin{Vmatrix} x_{11} & x_{12} & \dots & x_{1N} \\ \cdot & \cdot & \cdot & \cdot \\ x_{q1} & x_{q2} & \dots & x_{qN} \end{Vmatrix}. \tag{9.2.1}$$

The matrices L and Y have the same meaning as in chapter VIII. The conditional equations (9.1.1) are written in the form

$$X_0 + XY = 0. \tag{9.2.2}$$

We will assume that rank $(X) = q$; otherwise the conditional equations will be dependent, which could be avoided by introducing a new, shortened system of equations of condition.

We will denote the corrections, unknown to us, which must be added to L to give Y, by $V = V_{N1}$;

$$L + V = Y. \tag{9.2.3}$$

We also put

$$X_0 + XL = M. \tag{9.2.4}$$

Then, inserting (9.2.3) in (9.2.2), we find

$$M + XV = 0. \tag{9.2.5}$$

There are q conditional linear equations for the true corrections $v_1, v_2, \dots, v_N$. Subject to these conditions, we should choose $V = \tilde{V}$, so that $[p\tilde{v}\tilde{v}] = \min$. We will show that this V exists and is determined uniquely.

Working with Lagrange's method we must introduce q multipliers $k_1, k_2, \dots, k_q$, which are called correlates. We denote the one-column correlate matrix by $K = K_{q1}$;

$$K = K_{q1} = \begin{Vmatrix} k_1 \\ k_2 \\ \vdots \\ k_q \end{Vmatrix}. \tag{9.2.6}$$

Then, Lagrange's function is of the form

$$\Psi = [pvv] - K^T(M + XV) = V^T PV - K^T(M + XV). \tag{9.2.7}$$

We construct the complete differential of Ψ:

$$d\Psi = d\,[pvv] - d\,[K^T(M + XV)]. \tag{9.2.8}$$

Evidently, we have

$$d\,[pvv] = 2\,[pv\,dv].$$

We write

$$dV = \begin{Vmatrix} dv_1 \\ dv_2 \\ \vdots \\ dv_N \end{Vmatrix}. \qquad (9.2.9)$$

It is easy to see that

$$2\,[pv\,dv] = 2V^T P\,dV. \qquad (9.2.10)$$

Further, we easily find

$$d\,[K^T(M+XV)] = dK^T M + dK^T XV = K^T X\,dV. \qquad (9.2.11)$$

For convenience in writing, we double the undetermined multipliers k_i in the formula for the Lagrange function Ψ.

We obtain

$$d\Psi = 2V^T P\,dV - 2K^T X\,dV = 2(V^T P - K^T X)\,dV = 0 \qquad (9.2.12)$$

and

$$V^T P - K^T X = 0. \qquad (9.2.13)$$

Or, in more detail

$$(V_{N1})^T P_{NN} - (K_{q1})^T X_{qN} = 0_{1N}. \qquad (9.2.14)$$

This gives N equations in the unknowns V and K ($N+q$ unknowns). To them there are added the equations of condition

$$M + XV = 0, \quad \text{or} \quad M_{q1} + X_{qN} V_{N1} = 0_{q1}, \qquad (9.2.15)$$

which gives q equations in V. We will show that these equations have unique solutions. We have, from (9.2.13),

$$V^T P = K^T X.$$

Transposing, we find

$$PV = X^T K, \qquad (9.2.16)$$

$$V = P^{-1} X^T K. \qquad (9.2.17)$$

Substituting into (9.2.15) we obtain

$$M+XP^{-1}X^TK=0. \qquad (9.2.18)$$

The matrix $XP^{-1}X^T$ will be a symmetrical $q\times q$ matrix. Since rank $(X)=q$ and P^{-1} is a diagonal matrix of rank N (the reciprocal matrix of the weights); it is non-singular. This follows from theorem 1.3.1.

We write

$$XP^{-1}X^T=G=G_{qq}; \qquad (9.2.19)$$

then, G is non-singular, so G^{-1} exists and from (9.2.18) it follows that

$$K=-G^{-1}M. \qquad (9.2.20)$$

Thus, K is uniquely determined and from (9.2.17) we get the explicit expression for V:

$$V=\tilde{V}=-P^{-1}X^TG^{-1}M; \quad G=XP^{-1}X^T. \qquad (9.2.21)$$

V is uniquely determined; we denote the V so determined by $\tilde{V}$ and use it as the correction to L.

Equation (9.2.20), written in the form

$$GK+M=0,$$

gives the normal system of equations for the q correlates with the symmetric matrix $G=XP^{-1}X^T$. We will write it in more detail.

We have

$$M=X_0+XL=\begin{Vmatrix} m_1 \\ \vdots \\ m_q \end{Vmatrix}.$$

Since

$$X=\begin{Vmatrix} x_{11} & x_{12} \ldots x_{1N} \\ \ldots & \ldots \\ x_{q1} & x_{q2} \ldots x_{qN} \end{Vmatrix}; \qquad X_0=\begin{Vmatrix} x_{10} \\ x_{20} \\ \vdots \\ x_{q0} \end{Vmatrix},$$

then

$$m_i=x_{i0}+x_{i1}l_1+x_{i2}l_2+\ldots+x_{iN}l_N \qquad (i=1,\ 2,\ \ldots,\ q). \qquad (9.2.22)$$

Introducing the q vectors obtained from the rows of X,

$$x_i=(x_{i1},\ x_{i2},\ \ldots,\ x_{iN}) \qquad (i=1,\ 2,\ \ldots,\ q), \qquad (9.2.23)$$

we can write

$$m_i = x_{i0} + [x_i l] \qquad (i = 1, 2, \ldots, q). \tag{9.2.24}$$

We will write the $XP^{-1}X^T$ in terms of the vectors x_i. We have

$$X^T = \begin{Vmatrix} x_{11} & x_{21} & \ldots & x_{q1} \\ x_{12} & x_{22} & \ldots & x_{q2} \\ \cdot & \cdot & \cdot & \cdot \\ x_{1N} & x_{2N} & \ldots & x_{qN} \end{Vmatrix};$$

$$P^{-1}X^T = \begin{Vmatrix} \frac{x_{11}}{p_1} & \frac{x_{21}}{p_1} & \ldots & \frac{x_{q1}}{p_1} \\ \frac{x_{12}}{p_2} & \frac{x_{22}}{p_2} & \ldots & \frac{x_{q2}}{p_2} \\ \cdot & \cdot & \cdot & \cdot \\ \frac{x_{1N}}{p_N} & \frac{x_{2N}}{p_N} & \ldots & \frac{x_{qN}}{p_N} \end{Vmatrix};$$

$$G = XP^{-1}X^T = \begin{Vmatrix} \left[\frac{x_1x_1}{p}\right] & \left[\frac{x_1x_2}{p}\right] & \ldots & \left[\frac{x_1x_q}{p}\right] \\ \left[\frac{x_2x_1}{p}\right] & \left[\frac{x_2x_2}{p}\right] & \ldots & \left[\frac{x_2x_q}{p}\right] \\ \cdot & \cdot & \cdot & \cdot \\ \left[\frac{x_qx_1}{p}\right] & \left[\frac{x_qx_2}{p}\right] & \ldots & \left[\frac{x_qx_q}{p}\right] \end{Vmatrix}.$$

Therefore the normal equations for the correlates (9.2.18) are written in the form

$$\left[\frac{x_\nu x_1}{p}\right]k_1 + \left[\frac{x_\nu x_2}{p}\right]k_2 + \ldots + \left[\frac{x_\nu x_q}{p}\right]k_q + [x_\nu l] + x_{\nu 0} = 0 \tag{9.2.25}$$
$$(\nu = 1, 2, \ldots, q).$$

These equations were obtained in this form by Gauss. Having found the correlates $k_1, \ldots, k_q$ from the normal equations (9.2.25) we can find the apparent corrections from (9.2.17): $\tilde{V} = P^{-1}X^TK$, or, in more detail

$$\tilde{v}_r = \frac{1}{p_r}(x_{1r}k_1 + x_{2r}k_2 + \ldots + x_{qr}k_q). \tag{9.2.26}$$

The estimators of Y are of the form

$$\tilde{L} = L + \tilde{V}. \tag{9.2.27}$$

As was explained above, the estimators $\tilde{L}$ are identical with those obtained by means of elements, and therefore, $\tilde{V}$ gives precisely the conditional minimum of $[p\tilde{v}\tilde{v}]$, and the estimators, $\tilde{L}$, possess unbiasedness, and other desirable properties. We will, however, derive some of these properties by a new method, so as to have the bases of analysis by means of correlates independent of the theory of analysis by means of elements.

3. Proof of Minimum-ness

Theorem 9.3.1.

The 'corrections'

$$\tilde{V} = -P^{-1}X^T G^{-1} M \tag{9.3.1}$$

found from (9.2.21), give the unique minimum of $[pvv]$, subject to the condition

$$M + X\tilde{V} = 0. \tag{9.3.2}$$

Proof. We have

$$\begin{aligned}\tilde{V}^T P \tilde{V} &= M^T (G^{-1})^T X P^{-1} P P^{-1} X^T G^{-1} M = \\ &= M^T (G^{-1})^T X P^{-1} X^T G^{-1} M = M^T (G^{-1})^T M = \\ &= M^T (G^T)^{-1} M = M^T (X P^{-1} X^T)^{-1} M\end{aligned} \tag{9.3.3}$$

by virtue of (9.2.21). Further,

$$\tilde{V}^T P \tilde{V} = \tilde{V}^T X^T (X P^{-1} X^T)^{-1} X \tilde{V}, \tag{9.3.4}$$

by virtue of (9.3.2).

For every matrix $V = V_{N1}$, satisfying the condition

$$M + XV = 0, \tag{9.3.5}$$

we have

$$V^T X^T (X P^{-1} X^T)^{-1} X V = M^T (X P^{-1} X^T)^{-1} M. \tag{9.3.6}$$

We now prove that, for any arbitrary matrix $V = V_{N1}$

$$V^T P V \geqslant V^T X^T (X P^{-1} X^T) X V. \tag{9.3.7}$$

If this inequality is proved, then, for the matrix V, satisfying (9.3.5), we will have, by virtue of (9.3.6),

$$V^T P V \geqslant M^T (X P^{-1} X^T)^{-1} M = \tilde{V}^T P \tilde{V}, \tag{9.3.8}$$

which it is required to prove.

Inequality (9.3.7) can be proved analogously to inequality (7.2.18).

We introduce the matrix

$$U = X^T(XP^{-1}X^T)^{-1}XP^{-1}, \tag{9.3.9}$$

so that

$$U^2 = U. \tag{9.3.10}$$

Putting $UP = X^T(XP^{-1}X^T)^{-1}X = W$, we see that $W^T = W$ and that the right hand side of (9.3.7) can be written in the form

$$V^TWV.$$

We put $P^{\frac{1}{2}}V = Z$, $V^TP^{\frac{1}{2}} = Z^T$, so that

$$V^TPV = Z^TZ \tag{9.3.11}$$

and

$$V^TWV = Z^TP^{-\frac{1}{2}}WP^{-\frac{1}{2}}Z. \tag{9.3.12}$$

If W is a symmetric matrix, then $P^{-\frac{1}{2}}WP^{-\frac{1}{2}}$ is also symmetrical. Since $W = UP$, then $P^{-\frac{1}{2}}WP^{-\frac{1}{2}} = P^{-\frac{1}{2}}UP^{\frac{1}{2}}$, whence, by virtue of (9.3.10), we have

$$\left(P^{-\frac{1}{2}}WP^{-\frac{1}{2}}\right)^2 = P^{-\frac{1}{2}}WP^{-\frac{1}{2}} \tag{9.3.13}$$

We choose an orthogonal matrix $F = F_{qq}$, such that

$$F\left(P^{-\frac{1}{2}}WP^{-\frac{1}{2}}\right)F^T = D = D_{qq} \tag{9.3.14}$$

is a diagonal matrix. Since $F^T = F^{-1}$, from (9.3.10) we find: $D^2 = D$. Putting

$$D = \begin{Vmatrix} d_1 & 0 & 0 \\ 0 & d_2 & 0 \\ \cdot & \cdot & \cdot \\ 0 & 0 & d_q \end{Vmatrix}, \tag{9.3.15}$$

we find $d_i^2 = d_i$, т. е. $d_i = 0;\ 1$ $(i = 1, 2, \ldots, q)$. Hence

$$Z^TF^TF\left(P^{-\frac{1}{2}}WP^{-\frac{1}{2}}\right)F^TFZ = Z^TF^TDFZ. \tag{9.3.16}$$

If we put $FZ = \begin{Vmatrix} \mu_1 \\ \mu_2 \\ \vdots \\ \mu_q \end{Vmatrix}$, then

$$Z^T F^T DFZ = \sum_{i=1}^{q} d_i \mu_i^2; \quad d_i = 0;\ 1. \tag{9.3.17}$$

Hence, obviously,

$$Z^T F^T FZ = \sum_{i=1}^{q} \mu_i^2 \geqslant \sum_{i=1}^{q} d_i \mu_i^2 = Z^T F^T DFZ.$$

Or, by virtue of (9.3.9) and the definitions of W and Z, we have

$$V^T PV \geqslant V^T X^T (XP^{-1} X^T) XV,$$

which coincides with (9.3.7) and proves the theorem. We will now prove the unbiasedness of the estimators '$\tilde{L}$'. We have

$$\tilde{V} = -P^{-1} X^T G^{-1} M; \quad M = X_0 + XL.$$

Hence

$$E(\tilde{V}) = -P^{-1} X^T G^{-1} (X_0 + XE(L)) =$$
$$= -P^{-1} X^T G^{-1} (X_0 + XY) = 0$$

by virtue of (9.2.2).

This means that

$$E\tilde{V} = 0, \text{ and } \quad E\tilde{L} = E(L + \tilde{V}) = EL = Y, \tag{9.3.18}$$

which is what it was required to prove.

We will now give an explicit expression for $\tilde{L}$ in terms of L.

Theorem 9.3.2.

$$\tilde{L} = -P^{-1} X^T G^{-1} X_0 + (E - P^{-1} X^T G^{-1} X) L. \tag{9.3.19}$$

To prove this, we note that

$$\tilde{L} = L + \tilde{V} = L - P^{-1} X^T G^{-1} M.$$

Substituting the expression $M = X_0 + XL$, we obtain (9.3.19).

4. The Statistical Behaviour of Correlates and Estimators

The expression (9.2.20) for the matrix of correlates

$$K = -G^{-1} M$$

after substituting the expression for M, takes the form

$$K = -G^{-1} X_0 - G^{-1} XL = -G^{-1} (X_0 + XL), \tag{9.4.1}$$

whence is clear that $K=\begin{Vmatrix} k_1 \\ k_2 \\ \cdot \\ \cdot \\ k_q \end{Vmatrix}$ is a random normal vector. Its properties are demonstrated by the following theorem.

Theorem 9.4.1.

The normal random vector of correlates

$$K=\begin{Vmatrix} k_1 \\ \cdot \\ \cdot \\ k_q \end{Vmatrix}$$

is n-dimensional and has zero mean vector and correlation matrix

$$B_K=\sigma^2 G^{-1};\ G=XP^{-1}X^T. \tag{9.4.2}$$

Proof. We note that

$$K=-G^{-1}M;\ M=X_0+XL;\ EM=X_0+XY=0,$$

so that

$$EK=-G^{-1}EM=0.$$

Further,

$$K=-G^{-1}(X_0+XL)=-G^{-1}X_0-G^{-1}XL. \tag{9.4.3}$$

From theorem 2.3.1 the correlation matrix of K is of the form

$$B_K=-G^{-1}XB_LX^TG^{-1}=G^{-1}X\sigma^2P^{-1}X^TG^{-1}=$$
$$=\sigma^2G^{-1}GG^{-1}=\sigma^2G^{-1}, \tag{9.4.4}$$

which is what it was required to prove.

We now find the correlation matrix $B_{\tilde{L}}$ of the vector of estimators $\tilde{L}$.

Theorem 9.4.2.

$$B_{\tilde{L}}=\sigma^2(P^{-1}-P^{-1}X^TG^{-1}XP^{-1}). \tag{9.4.5}$$

Proof. Since $E(\tilde{L})=Y$, $B_{\tilde{L}}=E[(\tilde{L}-Y)(\tilde{L}-Y)^T]$.

From (9.3.19) (theorem 9.3.2), we find

$$\tilde{L}-Y=-P^{-1}X^TG^{-1}X_0+(E-P^{-1}X^TG^{-1}X)(Y+\Delta)-Y=$$
$$=-P^{-1}X^TG^{-1}(X_0+XY)+(E-P^{-1}X^TG^{-1}X)\Delta.$$

By virtue of (9.2.2), we have $X_0+XY=0$, so that

$$\tilde{L}-Y=(E-P^{-1}X^TG^{-1}X)\Delta. \tag{9.4.6}$$

Further, $B_\Delta=\sigma^2P^{-1}$.

Writing

$$U=P^{-1}X^TG^{-1}X, \tag{9.4.7}$$

we find, from the equation $G=XP^{-1}X^T$

$$U^2=U;\quad U^T=PUP^{-1} \tag{9.4.8}$$

We now write (9.4.6) in the form

$$\tilde{L}-Y=(E-U)\Delta. \tag{9.4.9}$$

From theorem 2.3.1 we have

$$B_{\tilde{L}}=\sigma^2(E-U)P^{-1}(E-U)^T=\sigma^2(E-U)P^{-1}(E-PUP^{-1})=$$
$$=\sigma^2(P^{-1}-UP^{-1}-UP^{-1}+U^2P^{-1})=$$
$$=\sigma^2(P^{-1}-UP^{-1}-UP^{-1}+UP^{-1})=$$
$$=\sigma^2(P^{-1}-UP^{-1})=\sigma^2(P^{-1}-P^{-1}X^TG^{-1}XP^{-1}),$$

which proves (9.4.5).

We now stop to consider the real meaning of the estimators $\tilde{l}_1, \ldots, \tilde{l}_N$, obtained for the measurable quantities $y_1, \ldots, y_N$ after reduction by means of correlates. This reduction, as the name indicates, leads to estimators $\tilde{l}_1, \ldots, \tilde{l}_N$, satisfying q equations of condition, by adding to the observations $l_1, \ldots, l_N$, which do not, in general, satisfy these equations, the indicated corrections $\tilde{v}_i=\tilde{l}_i-l_i$. Further, the estimators $\tilde{l}_1, \ldots, \tilde{l}_N$ can be expressed in terms of $N-q$ of them; this corresponds to the introduction of $N-q$ elements from the values of the parameters $y_1, \ldots, y_N$. The estimators corresponding to these parameters will be taken to be the corresponding ones mentioned in section 5 of chapter VI. In fact, with respect to a very wide class of asymptotically unbiased estimators of these parameters, every individual estimator $\tilde{l}_i$, (and any arbitrary linear combination of estimators $\tilde{l}_i$) will differ from the corresponding parameter (or linear combinations of these parameters) by less than a given value $\varepsilon > 0$ with greater probability than any other estimator (or linear combination of estimators, respectively). These estimators, expressed linearly in terms of $N-q$ known estimators, are extremal in a certain sense, as was shown in section 2 of chapter VII.

The case when the number of conditional equations q is not large in comparison to N, and consequently, to the number $N-q$ of basic (sometimes called 'free') parameters, approximates to the trivial case $q=0$, where there are no equations of condition and all the parameters are free. In this case the estimators of y_r by the method of least squares are simply l_r; also $D(l_r)=\frac{\sigma^2}{p_r}$, so that the quality of the estimator depends only on the weight of the observation. Here, also, it is true that the estimator l_r is extremal among the wide class of asymptotically normal and asymptotically unbiased estimators y'_r of the parameters y_r, so that

$$P\{|l_r-y_r|\leqslant\varepsilon\}>P\{|y'_r-y_r|\leqslant\varepsilon\} \tag{9.4.10}$$

for each r separately and for sufficient great N. In the intermediate case, when the numbers q and N are both great, the asymptotic properties of estimators by the method of least squares, as compared with those of other estimators, have not been studied. It seems desirable to use reduction by means of elements when the numbers of elements and observations are both large.

About the accuracy of these estimators - see below.

5. Alternative Expressions for $[p\tilde{v}\tilde{v}]$, and its Statistical Behaviour

The statistical behaviour of $[p\tilde{v}\tilde{v}]$ can be studied using a knowledge of reduction by means of correlates and of reduction by means of elements. Since the number of observations is equal to N and the number of (independent) equations of condition is q, the number of elements (obtained, for example, by exclusion) will be $N-q$. This number plays the rôle of the number n in the previous chapter; hence $N-n=q$ and $\frac{1}{\sigma^2}[p\tilde{v}\tilde{v}]$ must be distributed as χ^2_q. We will, however, give a derivation of this property, not depending on the theory of reduction by means of elements and give some expressions which are needed in calculating $[p\tilde{v}\tilde{v}]$, and in checking this calculation.

Theorem 9.5.1.
The formulae

$$[p\tilde{v}\tilde{v}]=M^TG^{-1}M, \tag{9.5.1}$$

$$[p\tilde{v}\tilde{v}] = -M^T K, \tag{9.5.2}$$
$$[p\tilde{v}\tilde{v}] = K^T G K; \tag{9.5.3}$$

are valid.

The first of these formulae is identical with (9.3.3). The second follows from the first, using (9.2.20): $K = -G^{-1}M$; finally, (9.5.3) is obtained from (9.5.1) by writing it in the form

$$[p\tilde{v}\tilde{v}] = M^T G^{-1} G G^{-1} M; \quad G^T = G; \quad K^T = -M^T G^{-1}.$$

We will now prove that the quantity $\frac{1}{\sigma^2}[p\tilde{v}\tilde{v}]$ is distributed as χ_q^2

Theorem 9.5.2.

$$\frac{1}{\sigma^2}[p\tilde{v}\tilde{v}] = \chi_q^2.$$

Proof. From (9.3.19) we find

$$\tilde{V} = \tilde{L} - L = -P^{-1}X^T G^{-1}(X_0 + XL), \tag{9.5.4}$$
$$L = Y + \Delta, \tag{9.5.5}$$

and $\Delta = \begin{Vmatrix} \Delta_1 \\ \vdots \\ \Delta_N \end{Vmatrix}$ is a normal vector with $E(\Delta) = 0$, $B_\Delta = \sigma^2 P^{-1}$.

Further, $X_0 + XY = 0$, so that

$$\tilde{V} = P^{-1}X^T G^{-1} X\Delta. \tag{9.5.6}$$

Putting

$$U = P^{-1}X^T G^{-1} X, \tag{9.5.7}$$

we have

$$U^2 = U; \quad U^T = PUP^{-1}. \tag{9.5.8}$$

We also put

$$\Delta^{(0)} = P^{-\frac{1}{2}}\Delta, \tag{9.5.9}$$

so that

$$E\Delta^{(0)} = 0; \quad B_{\Delta^{(0)}} = \sigma^2 E_{NN}. \tag{9.5.10}$$

Then we obtain, from (9.5.6) and (9.5.7),

$$-\tilde{V} = UP^{\frac{1}{2}}\Delta^{(0)} \tag{9.5.11}$$

and

$$[p\tilde{v}\tilde{v}] = \tilde{V}^T P \tilde{V} = (\Delta^{(0)})^T P^{-\frac{1}{2}} U^T P U P^{-\frac{1}{2}} \Delta^{(0)} =$$
$$= (\Delta^{(0)})^T P^{-\frac{1}{2}} P U^2 P^{-\frac{1}{2}} \Delta^{(0)} = (\Delta^{(0)})^T P^{\frac{1}{2}} U P^{-\frac{1}{2}} \Delta^{(0)} \tag{9.5.12}$$

We put

$$W = P^{\frac{1}{2}} U P^{-\frac{1}{2}}. \tag{9.5.13}$$

The matrix $W = P^{-\frac{1}{2}} X^T G^{-1} X P^{-\frac{1}{2}}$ is symmetrical and also

$$W^2 = W. \tag{9.5.14}$$

According to section 4 of chapter 1, an orthogonal matrix F can be found such that

$$FWF^T = D = \begin{Vmatrix} d_1 & 0 & \dots & 0 \\ 0 & d_2 & \dots & 0 \\ \cdot & \cdot & \cdot & \cdot \\ 0 & 0 & \dots & d_q \end{Vmatrix}. \tag{9.5.15}$$

Since $F^T = F^{-1}$, $D^2 = D$, so that $d_i = 0$; or 1. Further, rank (D) is equal to the number of units among the numbers d_i. But rank $(D) =$ rank (U).

We will prove that rank $(U) = q$. In fact, the matrix G is non-singular, so that rank $(G^{-1}) = q$. Further, rank $(X) =$ rank $(X^T) = q$.

According to inequality (1.2.18)

$$\text{rank } (U) \leqslant q. \tag{9.5.16}$$

But from expression (9.5.7) we see that $XU = X$, so that rank $(X) = = q \leqslant$ rank (U). Hence rank $(U) = q$ and $d_i = 1$ $(i = 1, 2, \dots, q)$.

Hence

$$FWF^T = E. \tag{9.5.17}$$

From this we find, in (9.5.12)

$$[p\tilde{v}\tilde{v}] = (\Delta^{(0)})^T F^T F W F^T F \Delta^{(0)} = Z^T Z,$$

where $Z = F\Delta^{(0)}$ is an orthogonal transformation of $\Delta^{(0)}$ and consequently by Fisher's theorem 2.3.2, Z is a normal vector with independent components $z_i \in N(0, \sigma)$ $(i=1, 2, \ldots, q)$.

Hence

$$[p\tilde{v}\tilde{v}] = \sum_{i=1}^{q} z_i^2 = \chi_q^2,$$

which is what it was required to prove.

Theorem 9.5.3.

The random normal vectors $\tilde{V} = \tilde{L} - L$ and $\tilde{L}$ are stochastically independent. Also $\tilde{V}$ is a $(N-q)$-dimensional, and $\tilde{L}$ is a q-dimensional, normal vector.

Proof. On the basis of theorem 2.3.3 and the equation $E(\tilde{V})=0$ it is sufficient to show that

$$E\tilde{V}(\tilde{L}-Y)^T = 0. \tag{9.5.18}$$

to prove the independence of $\tilde{V}$ and $\tilde{L}$.

We have from (9.5.6),

$$\tilde{V} = -U\Delta; \quad U = P^{-1}X^T G^{-1}X. \tag{9.5.19}$$

From (9.4.9) we obtain

$$\tilde{L} - Y = (E-U)\Delta, \tag{9.5.20}$$

$$E(\Delta\Delta^T) = \sigma^2 P^{-1}. \tag{9.5.21}$$

Hence, by virtue of the relations $U^2 = U$; $U^T = PUP^{-1}$, we have

$$E\tilde{V}(\tilde{L}-Y) = -U\left(E(\Delta\Delta^T)(E-U)^T\right) = -\sigma^2 UP^{-1}\left(E - PUP^{-1}\right) \tag{9.5.22}$$

Further, the right-hand side of (9.5.22) is equal to

$$-\sigma^2\left(UP^{-1} - U^2P^{-1}\right) = -\sigma^2\left(UP^{-1} - UP^{-1}\right) = 0,$$

which proves (9.5.18).

Further, $\tilde{V}$ is a q-dimensional vector, because the matrix U has rank q (see theorem 2.3.1). To prove that $\tilde{L} - Y$ is a $(N-q)$-dimensional vector, is sufficient to show that the rank of $E-U$ is equal to $N-q$.

We put $W = P^{\frac{1}{2}}UP^{-\frac{1}{2}}$; $W^2 = W$; W is a symmetric matrix. We choose an orthogonal matrix such that the matrix $FWF^T = D$ is diagonal; then $D^2 = D$, so that

$$D = \begin{Vmatrix} d_1 & 0 & \dots & 0 \\ 0 & d_2 & \dots & 0 \\ \cdot & \cdot & \cdot & \cdot \\ 0 & 0 & \dots & d_N \end{Vmatrix},$$

where $d_i^2 = d_i$; $d_i = 0$; 1.

Since rank $(U) =$ rank $(D) = q$, the number of d_i's, equal to unity, is q, and the number of d_i's equal to zero is $N - q$. Further the matrix

$$FP^{\frac{1}{2}}(E - U)P^{-\frac{1}{2}}F^T = E - D$$

has the same rank as $E - U$ and rank $(E - D)$ is, evidently, equal to $N - q$, which it was required to prove.

We will also find the correlation matrix $B_{\tilde{V}}$ of the vector $\tilde{V}$.

Theorem 9.5.4.

$$B_{\tilde{V}} = \sigma^2 P^{-1} X^T G^{-1} X P^{-1}. \qquad (9.5.23)$$

Proof. From (9.5.19) we have

$$\tilde{V} = -U\Delta; \quad U = P^{-1}X^T G^{-1} X; \quad E\tilde{V} = 0.$$

Hence

$$B_{\tilde{V}} = UB_\Delta U^T = \sigma^2 UP^{-1}PUP^{-1} = \sigma^2 U^2 P^{-1} =$$
$$= \sigma^2 UP^{-1} = \sigma^2 P^{-1}X^T G^{-1} X P^{-1}.$$

We introduce one more formula, which is useful in checking calculations.

Theorem 9.5.5.

$$\sum_{i=1}^{N} p_i D(\tilde{l}_i) = [pD(\tilde{l})] = (N - q)\sigma^2. \qquad (9.5.24)$$

Proof. From (9.4.5) we have (denoting the correlation matrix $\tilde{L}$ by $B_{\tilde{L}}$)

$$B_{\tilde{L}} = \sigma^2 (P^{-1} - P^{-1}X^T G^{-1} X P^{-1}),$$

$$D(\tilde{l}_i) = \sigma^2 \{P^{-1} - P^{-1}X^T G^{-1} X P^{-1}\}_{ii}; \qquad i = 1, 2, \dots, N. \quad (9.5.25)$$

$$\sum_{i=1}^{N} p_i D(\tilde{l}_i) = [pD(\tilde{l})] = \sigma^2 \sum_{i=1}^{N} \{E - P^{-1}X^T G^{-1} X\}_{ii} = \sigma^2\, \mathrm{Sp}\,(E - U),$$
(9.5.26)

where $U=P^{-1}X^{T}G^{-1}X$.

As in the proof of theorem (9.5.2), we note that, by using the non-singular matrix $Q=FP^{\frac{1}{2}}$, we can transform the matrix U to the diagonal form

$$D=\begin{Vmatrix} d_1 & 0 & \dots & 0 \\ \cdot & \cdot & \cdot & \cdot \\ 0 & 0 & \dots & d_N \end{Vmatrix},$$

where the d_i's are equal to zero or unity and the number of units among the d_i's is q.

Therefore

$$Q(E-U)Q^{-1}=E-D=\begin{Vmatrix} 1-d_1 & 0 & \dots & 0 \\ \cdot & \cdot & \cdot & \cdot \\ 0 & 0 & \dots & 1-d_N \end{Vmatrix}$$

is a diagonal matrix with exactly $N-q$ units and q zeros. Hence, from section 3 of chapter I

$$\mathrm{Sp}\,(E-U)=\mathrm{Sp}\,(E-D)=N-q.$$

This proves (9.5.24).

We have

$$\sigma(\tilde{l}_i)=\sqrt{(P^{-1}-P^{-1}X^{T}G^{-1}XP^{-1})_{ii}}\;\sigma. \qquad (9.5.27)$$

Since $\frac{1}{\sigma^2}[p\tilde{v}\tilde{v}]=\chi^2_q$, evidently

$$E\,[p\tilde{v}\tilde{v}]=q\sigma^2; \quad E\,\frac{[p\tilde{v}\tilde{v}]}{q}=\sigma^2,$$

i.e. $\frac{[p\tilde{v}\tilde{v}]}{q}$ is an unbiased estimator of σ^2. As q increases, an asymptotically unbiased estimator of σ is the estimator

$$s=\sqrt{\frac{[p\tilde{v}\tilde{v}]}{q}}. \qquad (9.5.28)$$

Also, for large q, $\sigma(s)\approx\frac{\sigma}{\sqrt{2q}}$.

Thus, we obtain the asymptotically unbiased estimator of $\sigma(\tilde{l}_i)$ for large q:

$$\sigma(\tilde{l}_i)\approx\sqrt{(P^{-1}-P^{-1}X^{T}G^{-1}XP^{-1})_{ii}}\cdot\sqrt{\frac{[p\tilde{v}\tilde{v}]}{q}}. \qquad (9.5.29)$$

As in chapter VIII, theorem 9.5.5 makes it possible to conceive of the overall accuracy of the estimators $\tilde{l}_i$. We see from (9.5.24) that

$$\frac{1}{N}\sum p_i D(\tilde{l}_i) = \left(1 - \frac{q}{N}\right)\sigma^2, \qquad (9.5.30)$$

so that it is convenient to have the number of independent equations of condition as great as possible, and the number of free parameters as small as possible, relative to N. It should be understood that this agrees with the corresponding results in chapter VIII, because $N-q$ corresponds to the number of elements.

To estimate σ by confidence intervals we make use of the relation

$$\frac{[p\tilde{v}\tilde{v}]}{\sigma^2} = \chi_q^2.$$

From Table III, with q degrees of freedom, we find γ_1 and γ_2. The confidence interval

$$I = \left[\gamma_1\sqrt{\frac{[p\tilde{v}\tilde{v}]}{q}},\quad \gamma_2\sqrt{\frac{[p\tilde{v}\tilde{v}]}{q}}\right]$$

covers σ with probability p_0.

6. Estimation of y_i and σ by Confidence Intervals

We have seen (theorem 9.5.3) that the normal vector $\tilde{V}$ is independent of $\tilde{L}$, so that $[p\tilde{v}\tilde{v}]$ is also independent of $\tilde{L}$. Further, $\frac{1}{\sigma^2}[p\tilde{v}\tilde{v}] = \chi_q^2$, therefore

$$\frac{1}{\sigma}\sqrt{\frac{[p\tilde{v}\tilde{v}]}{q}} = \frac{1}{\sigma}s = \sqrt{\frac{\chi_q^2}{q}}. \qquad (9.6.1)$$

We consider the quantity $\tilde{l}_i - y_i$. According to (9.5.27) we have

$$\frac{\tilde{l}_i - y_i}{\sigma\sqrt{(P^{-1} - P^{-1}X^T G^{-1} X P^{-1})_{ii}}} \in N(0,\ 1). \qquad (9.6.2)$$

This random variable is independent of $\frac{1}{\sigma}s$. According to the definition of Student's distribution the ratio

$$t_q = \frac{\tilde{l}_i - y_i}{s\sqrt{(P^{-1} - P^{-1}X^T G^{-1} X P^{-1})_{ii}}} \qquad (9.6.3)$$

has Student's distribution $S_q(t)$. To construct a confidence interval for estimation of y_i, with given confidence coefficient p and degrees of freedom q, we find the value γ_0. The confidence interval

$$J_\gamma^{(i)} = \left[\tilde{l}_i - \gamma_0 s \sqrt{(P^{-1} - P^{-1}X^TG^{-1}XP^{-1})_{ii}},\right.$$
$$\left.\tilde{l}_i + \gamma_0 s \sqrt{(P^{-1} - P^{-1}X^TG^{-1}XP^{-1})_{ii}}\right] \quad (9.6.4)$$

covers y_i with probability p.

The length of the confidence interval, $J_\gamma^{(i)}$ is a random variable equal to

$$d_\gamma^{(i)} = 2\gamma_0 s \sqrt{(P^{-1} - P^{-1}X^TG^{-1}XP^{-1})_{ii}}. \quad (9.6.5)$$

As before, we can estimate the weighted mean square of the lengths of these intervals

$$\frac{1}{N} E\left[\sum p_i (d_\gamma^{(i)})^2\right] = \left(1 - \frac{q}{N}\right)\sigma^2.$$

For a given confidence coefficient, the confidence intervals are, on the average, relatively worse, the smaller q is in comparison with N.

7. Estimation of a Linear Function of Measurable Parameters from Indirect Observations

As we will see from examples, it is often necessary to estimate a function of measurable quantities from indirect measurements. Also, many non-linear functions can be treated as linear ones, as was explained in section 1 of chapter VII.

For example, suppose that a triangle ABC, is given in which we measure the angles A, B, C and the side BC, and, after reduction of the measurements of the angles, we estimate the sides CA and BA. This is a problem of estimating a linear function of measurable quantities.

Suppose we have a linear function of the observations

$$y = h_1 y_1 + h_2 y_2 + \ldots + h_N y_N = [hy]. \quad (9.7.1)$$

We put

$$H = \| h_1, \ldots, h_N \|, \quad (9.7.2)$$

$$Y = \begin{Vmatrix} y_1 \\ \vdots \\ y_N \end{Vmatrix}. \qquad (9.7.3)$$

Then

$$y = HY. \qquad (9.7.4)$$

We have to estimate y. As in the case of unconditioned indirect observations (chapter VI) we take, as the estimator of y,

$$\tilde{y} = h_1\tilde{l}_1 + h_2\tilde{l}_2 + \ldots + h_N\tilde{l}_N = [h\tilde{l}] = H\tilde{L}. \qquad (9.7.5)$$

We will not discuss here the qualities of this estimator, but will only find its variance and construct confidence intervals. We have

$$E(\tilde{y}) = HY = y, \qquad (9.7.6)$$

i.e. $\tilde{y}$ is an unbiased estimator. Further, from theorem 2.3.1 we have

$$\begin{aligned} D(\tilde{y}) &= HB_{\tilde{L}}H^T = \sigma^2 H(P^{-1} - P^{-1}X^TG^{-1}XP^{-1})H^T = \\ &= \sigma^2\left[\sum_{i=1}^{N}\frac{h_i^2}{p_i} - HP^{-1}X^TG^{-1}XP^{-1}H^T\right]. \end{aligned} \qquad (9.7.7)$$

Putting $H_1 = HP^{-1} = \begin{Vmatrix} \frac{h_1}{p_1}, & \frac{h_2}{p_2}, & \ldots, & \frac{h_N}{p_N} \end{Vmatrix}$,

we have

$$HP^{-1}X^TG^{-1}XP^{-1}H^T = H_1X^TG^{-1}XH_1^T. \qquad (9.7.8)$$

We can construct a confidence interval for y. In fact, the random vector $\tilde{L}$ is independent of $\frac{1}{\sigma^2}[p\tilde{v}\tilde{v}] = \chi_q^2$. Therefore, $\tilde{y}$ is also independent of this quantity. The ratio

$$t_q = \frac{\tilde{y} - y}{s\sqrt{\left(\sum_{i=1}^{N}\frac{h_i^2}{p_i} - H_1X^TG^{-1}XH_1^T\right)}} \qquad (9.7.9)$$

has Student's distribution with q degrees of freedom. Choosing the confidence coefficient p, and with number of degrees of freedom q, we find the value γ and construct the confidence interval

$$J_\gamma^{(i)} = [\tilde{y} - \gamma sh,\ \tilde{y} + \gamma sh], \text{ where } h = \sqrt{\sum_{i=1}^{N} \frac{h_i^2}{p_i} - H_1 X^T G^{-1} X H_1^T}.$$

This interval covers y with probability p.

8. Comparison of Reduction by Means of Elements and by Means of Correlates

In reduction by means of elements the basic difficulty of calculations is in the solution of the normal equations, i.e. in the inversion of the matrix $C = C_{nn} = X^T P X$, of order n. In reduction by means of correlates the basic calculating difficulty is in the solution of the normal equations for correlates, i.e. in the inversion of the matrix $G = G_{qq} = X P^{-1} X^T$, of order q; the calculation of the apparent corrections $\tilde{V}$, with known correlates, requires the not very difficult operation of multiplying by the given matrix $P^{-1} X^T$. Here the number of elements is equal to $n = N - q$.

If the construction of the equations of condition, and of the fundamental equations in the elements, are of approximately the same difficulty (or, in general, not very difficult), then we see that for $N - q > q$, i.e. for $q < \frac{N}{2}$, we should normally prefer to use reduction by means of correlates, and for $q > \frac{N}{2}$, i.e. for $q > N - q$ we should prefer to use reduction by means of elements.

9. Summary of Formulae. Rules for Reduction by Means of Correlates

a) Point Estimation

The equations of condition are

$$x_{j0} + y_1 x_{j1} + y_2 x_{j2} + \ldots + y_N x_{jN} = 0 \quad (j = 1, 2, \ldots, q). \quad (9.9.1)$$

From the observations, l_i, of y_i, with weights p_i, we form

$$m_i = x_{i0} + x_{i1} l_1 + x_{i2} l_2 + \ldots + x_{iN} l_N = x_{i0} + [x_i l], \quad (9.9.2)$$

where

$$x_i = (x_{i1}, x_{i2}, \ldots, x_{iN}) \quad (i = 1, 2, \ldots, q). \quad (9.9.3)$$

Further, we form the normal equations for correlates $k_1, k_2, \ldots, k_q$:

$$\left[\frac{x_\nu x_1}{p}\right] k_1 + \left[\frac{x_\nu x_2}{p}\right] k_2 + \ldots + \left[\frac{x_\nu x_q}{p}\right] k_q + [x_\nu l] + x_{\nu 0} = 0,$$
$$\nu = 1, 2, \ldots, q. \quad (9.9.4)$$

Solving these normal equations for the correlates we find the apparent corrections by the formula

$$\tilde{v}_r = \frac{1}{p_r}(x_{1r}k_1 + x_{2r}k_2 + \ldots + x_{qr}k_q). \qquad (9.9.5)$$

Estimators of the quantities y_i are given by the formulae

$$\tilde{l}_i = l_i + \tilde{v}_i. \qquad (9.9.6)$$

Next, we calculate the quantity $[p\tilde{v}\tilde{v}]$. For calculating this, or for checking the calculations, we can use the formula (see (9.5.2)):

$$-[p\tilde{v}\tilde{v}] = m_1k_1 + m_2k_2 + \ldots + m_qk_q = [mk]. \qquad (9.9.7)$$

σ is estimated from the formula

$$\sigma \approx s = \sqrt{\frac{[p\tilde{v}\tilde{v}]}{q}}, \qquad (9.9.8)$$

where s is an asymptotically unbiased estimator of σ as q increases. Its standard deviation is equal to

$$\sigma(s) \approx \frac{\sigma}{\sqrt{2q}}. \qquad (9.9.9)$$

To calculate the standard deviations $\sigma(\tilde{l}_i)$ of the estimators $\tilde{l}_i$ it is necessary to find the i-th diagonal element of the matrix

$$P^{-1}X^TGXP^{-1}, \qquad (9.9.10)$$

where

$$G = XP^{-1}X^T = \begin{Vmatrix} \left[\frac{x_1x_1}{p}\right] & \left[\frac{x_1x_2}{p}\right] & \ldots & \left[\frac{x_1x_q}{p}\right] \\ \cdot & \cdot & \cdot & \cdot \\ \left[\frac{x_qx_1}{p}\right] & \left[\frac{x_qx_2}{p}\right] & \ldots & \left[\frac{x_qx_q}{p}\right] \end{Vmatrix}$$

is the matrix of the system of normal equations for the correlates,

$$X = \begin{Vmatrix} x_{11} & x_{12} & \ldots & x_{1N} \\ \cdot & \cdot & \cdot & \cdot \\ x_{q1} & x_{q2} & \ldots & x_{qN} \end{Vmatrix}; \quad X^T = \begin{Vmatrix} x_{11} & \ldots & x_{q1} \\ x_{12} & \ldots & x_{q2} \\ \cdot & \cdot & \cdot \\ x_{1N} & \ldots & x_{qN} \end{Vmatrix}; \quad P^{-1} = \begin{Vmatrix} \frac{1}{p_1} & 0 & \ldots & 0 \\ 0 & \frac{1}{p_2} & \ldots & 0 \\ \cdot & \cdot & \cdot & \cdot \\ 0 & 0 & \ldots & \frac{1}{p_N} \end{Vmatrix}.$$

Then

$$\sigma(\tilde{l}_i) \approx s\sqrt{\left(\frac{1}{p_i} - \{P^{-1}X^TGXP^{-1}\}_{ii}\right)}. \qquad (9.9.11)$$

The formula

$$\sum_{i=1}^{N} p_i\left(\frac{1}{p_i} - \{P^{-1}X^T GXP^{-1}\}_{ii}\right) = N - q, \qquad (9.9.12)$$

is useful for checking.

It is convenient to have the number of independent equations of condition as great as possible.

b) Estimation by Confidence Intervals

We use Table 1 of Student's distribution.

We choose a confidence coefficient p_0 and, for q degrees of freedom, find γ_0. We construct the confidence interval

$$J_{\gamma_0}^{(i)} = [\tilde{l}_i - \gamma_0 s\sqrt{\{P^{-1} - P^{-1}X^T G^{-1}XP^{-1}\}_{ii}},$$
$$\tilde{l}_i + \gamma_0 s\sqrt{\{P^{-1} - P^{-1}X^T G^{-1}XP^{-1}\}_{ii}}],$$

where $s = \frac{[p\tilde{v}\tilde{v}]}{q}$. It covers $\tilde{l}_i$ with probability p_0. To estimate σ by confidence intervals we choose from Table 1, with confidence coefficient p_0 and degrees of freedom q, values γ_1 and γ_2 such that the confidence interval $[\gamma_1 s, \gamma_2 s]$ covers σ with probability p_0.

10. Examples

Example 1. On a cross-section of land (Fig. 5) the differences of heights of five points are measured (the arrows in the figure indicate the directions of decreasing height) *). The measured values (in metres) are equal to

$$L = \begin{Vmatrix} l_1 \\ l_2 \\ l_3 \\ l_4 \\ l_5 \\ l_6 \\ l_7 \end{Vmatrix} = \begin{Vmatrix} 20,21 \\ 40,07 \\ 34,17 \\ 35,84 \\ 60,40 \\ 5,87 \\ 69,99 \end{Vmatrix}.$$

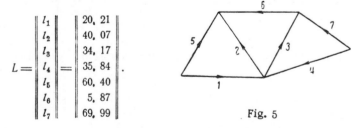

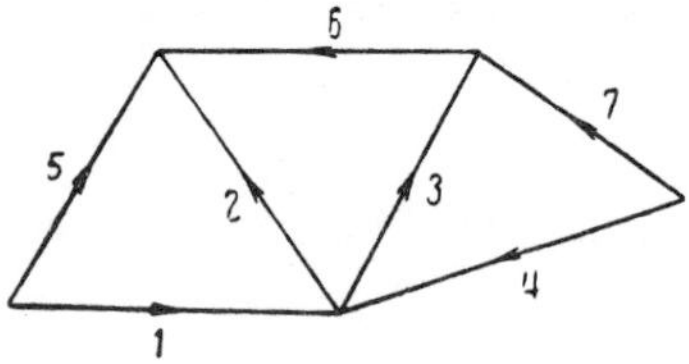

Fig. 5

We assume that the weights are reciprocal to the corresponding distances. The matrix of the weights is of the form

---

* The data are taken from the book [2], p. 204

$$P=\begin{Vmatrix} 1 & 0 & 0 & 0 & 0 & 0 & 0 \\ 0 & 0{,}9 & 0 & 0 & 0 & 0 & 0 \\ 0 & 0 & 1{,}1 & 0 & 0 & 0 & 0 \\ 0 & 0 & 0 & 0{,}8 & 0 & 0 & 0 \\ 0 & 0 & 0 & 0 & 1 & 0 & 0 \\ 0 & 0 & 0 & 0 & 0 & 0{,}9 & 0 \\ 0 & 0 & 0 & 0 & 0 & 0 & 1 \end{Vmatrix}.$$

Taking the first four differences between the heights as elements we find the best estimates for differences between heights using the method of reduction by means of elements.

The fundamental equations can, evidently, be written in the form

$$\lambda_1=\xi_1, \qquad \lambda_5=\xi_1+\xi_2$$
$$\lambda_2=\xi_2, \qquad \lambda_6=\xi_2-\xi_3,$$
$$\lambda_3=\xi_3, \qquad \lambda_7=\xi_3+\xi_4.$$
$$\lambda_4=\xi_4,$$

Or, if λ_r is changed into y_r and ξ_i is changed into a_i, then, in matrix notation, the fundamental equations are written in the form

$$Y=XA$$

(see (8.2.1); $X_0=0$).

We have

$$Y=\begin{Vmatrix} y_1 \\ y_2 \\ y_3 \\ y_4 \\ y_5 \\ y_6 \\ y_7 \end{Vmatrix}, \quad X=\begin{Vmatrix} 1 & 0 & 0 & 0 \\ 0 & 1 & 0 & 0 \\ 0 & 0 & 1 & 0 \\ 0 & 0 & 0 & 1 \\ 1 & 1 & 0 & 0 \\ 0 & 1 & -1 & 0 \\ 0 & 0 & 1 & 1 \end{Vmatrix}, \quad A=\begin{Vmatrix} a_1 \\ a_2 \\ a_3 \\ a_4 \end{Vmatrix}.$$

According to formula (8.2.4) the normal equations for unbiased estimators $\tilde{A}$ of A are of the form

$C\tilde{A}=X^TPL$, where $C=X^TPX$, or $\tilde{A}=C^{-1}X^TPL$.

We have

$$C=X^TPX=\begin{Vmatrix} 1 & 0 & 0 & 0 & 1 & 0 & 0 \\ 0 & 1 & 0 & 0 & 1 & 1 & 0 \\ 0 & 0 & 1 & 0 & 0 & -1 & 1 \\ 0 & 0 & 0 & 1 & 0 & 0 & 1 \end{Vmatrix}\times$$

$$\times\begin{Vmatrix} 1 & 0 & 0 & 0 & 0 & 0 & 0 \\ 0 & 0{,}9 & 0 & 0 & 0 & 0 & 0 \\ 0 & 0 & 1{,}1 & 0 & 0 & 0 & 0 \\ 0 & 0 & 0 & 0{,}8 & 0 & 0 & 0 \\ 0 & 0 & 0 & 0 & 1 & 0 & 0 \\ 0 & 0 & 0 & 0 & 0 & 0{,}9 & 0 \\ 0 & 0 & 0 & 0 & 0 & 0 & 1 \end{Vmatrix}\cdot X=\begin{Vmatrix} 1 & 0 & 0 & 0 & 1 & 0 & 0 \\ 0 & 0{,}9 & 0 & 0 & 1 & 0.9 & 0 \\ 0 & 0 & 1{,}1 & 0 & 0 & -0{,}9 & 1 \\ 0 & 0 & 0 & 0{,}8 & 0 & 0 & 1 \end{Vmatrix}\times$$

$$\times\begin{Vmatrix} 1 & 0 & 0 & 0 \\ 0 & 1 & 0 & 0 \\ 0 & 0 & 1 & 0 \\ 0 & 0 & 0 & 1 \\ 1 & 1 & 0 & 0 \\ 0 & 1 & -1 & 0 \\ 0 & 0 & 1 & 1 \end{Vmatrix}=\begin{Vmatrix} 2 & 1 & 0 & 0 \\ 1 & 2{,}8 & -0{,}9 & 0 \\ 0 & -0{,}9 & 3 & 1 \\ 0 & 0 & 1 & 1{,}8 \end{Vmatrix}$$

We now find the matrix C^{-1}. The elements of the reciprocal matrix can be calculated by the formula

$$(C^{-1})_{sr}=\frac{D_{rs}}{\det(C)},$$

where D_{rs} is the cofactor of the element c_{rs} in $\det(C)$. We have

$$\det(C)=\begin{vmatrix} 2 & 1 & 0 & 0 \\ 1 & 2{,}8 & -0{,}9 & 0 \\ 0 & -0{,}9 & 3 & 1 \\ 0 & 0 & 1 & 1{,}8 \end{vmatrix}=17{,}324.$$

Further, the matrix of cofactors of the elements of the determinant C is of the form

$$D=\begin{Vmatrix} 10{,}862 & -4{,}4 & -1{,}62 & 0{,}9 \\ -4{,}4 & 8{,}8 & 3{,}24 & -1{,}8 \\ -1{,}62 & 3{,}24 & 8{,}28 & -4{,}6 \\ 0{,}9 & -1{,}8 & -4{,}6 & 12{,}18 \end{Vmatrix},$$

which means that

$$C^{-1}=\begin{Vmatrix} 0{,}626991 & -0{,}253983 & -0{,}093512 & 0{,}051951 \\ -0{,}253983 & 0{,}507966 & 0{,}187024 & -0{,}103902 \\ -0{,}093512 & 0{,}187024 & 0{,}477950 & -0{,}265528 \\ 0{,}051951 & -0{,}103902 & -0{,}265528 & 0{,}703071 \end{Vmatrix}.$$

We have

$$X^T PL = \begin{Vmatrix} 1 & 0 & 0 & 0 & 1 & 0 & 0 \\ 0 & 0{,}9 & 0 & 0 & 1 & 0{,}9 & 0 \\ 0 & 0 & 1{,}1 & 0 & 0 & -0{,}9 & 1 \\ 0 & 0 & 0 & 0{,}8 & 0 & 0 & 1 \end{Vmatrix} \begin{Vmatrix} 20{,}21 \\ 40{,}07 \\ 34{,}17 \\ 35{,}84 \\ 60{,}40 \\ 5{,}87 \\ 69{,}99 \end{Vmatrix} = \begin{Vmatrix} 80{,}610 \\ 101{,}746 \\ 102{,}294 \\ 98{,}662 \end{Vmatrix}.$$

Consequently, the matrix $\tilde{A}$ is of the form

$$\tilde{A} = C^{-1} \cdot \begin{Vmatrix} 80{,}610 \\ 101{,}746 \\ 102{,}294 \\ 98{,}662 \end{Vmatrix} = \begin{Vmatrix} 20{,}260 \\ 40{,}090 \\ 34{,}185 \\ 35{,}821 \end{Vmatrix}.$$

Then, the estimators $\tilde{l}_r$ of the differences between heights are written, in accordance with formula (8.2.7), in the matrix form

$$\tilde{L} = X\tilde{A} = \begin{Vmatrix} 1 & 0 & 0 & 0 \\ 0 & 1 & 0 & 0 \\ 0 & 0 & 1 & 0 \\ 0 & 0 & 0 & 1 \\ 1 & 1 & 0 & 0 \\ 0 & 1 & -1 & 0 \\ 0 & 0 & 1 & 1 \end{Vmatrix} \cdot \begin{Vmatrix} 20{,}260 \\ 40{,}090 \\ 34{,}185 \\ 35{,}821 \end{Vmatrix} = \begin{Vmatrix} 20{,}260 \\ 40{,}090 \\ 34{,}185 \\ 35{,}821 \\ 60{,}350 \\ 5{,}905 \\ 70{,}006 \end{Vmatrix}.$$

Example 2. Measurements of the four angles of a quadrangle gave the following results *):

$$L = \begin{Vmatrix} l_1 \\ l_2 \\ l_3 \\ l_4 \end{Vmatrix} = \begin{Vmatrix} 50^\circ\, 12'\, 37'' \\ 112^\circ\, 17'\, 19'' \\ 120^\circ\, 47'\, 26'' \\ 76^\circ\, 46'\, 18'' \end{Vmatrix},$$

with a matrix of weights of the form

$$P = \begin{Vmatrix} 3 & 0 & 0 & 0 \\ 0 & 4 & 0 & 0 \\ 0 & 0 & 2 & 0 \\ 0 & 0 & 0 & 2 \end{Vmatrix}.$$

* The data are taken from the book [2], p. 237

Taking the first three angles as elements we will find the best estimators of the angles by the method of reduction by means of elements.

The fundamental equations are here written in the form

$$
\begin{aligned}
y_1 &= a_1, \\
y_2 &= a_2, \\
y_3 &= a_3, \\
y_4 &= 360^\circ - a_1 - a_2 - a_3.
\end{aligned}
$$

Or, in matrix form

$$Y = X_0 + XA,$$

where

$$Y = \begin{Vmatrix} y_1 \\ y_2 \\ y_3 \\ y_4 \end{Vmatrix}, \quad X_0 = \begin{Vmatrix} 0 \\ 0 \\ 0 \\ 360^\circ \end{Vmatrix}, \quad X = \begin{Vmatrix} 1 & 0 & 0 \\ 0 & 1 & 0 \\ 0 & 0 & 1 \\ -1 & -1 & -1 \end{Vmatrix}, \quad A = \begin{Vmatrix} a_1 \\ a_2 \\ a_3 \end{Vmatrix}.$$

According to formula (8.2.4) the normal equations for unbiased estimators $\tilde{A}$ of A are of the form

$$C\tilde{A} = X^T P (L - X_0), \quad C = X^T P X,$$

or

$$\tilde{A} = C^{-1} X^T P (L - X_0).$$

We have

$$C = X^T P X = \begin{Vmatrix} 1 & 0 & 0 & -1 \\ 0 & 1 & 0 & -1 \\ 0 & 0 & 1 & -1 \end{Vmatrix} \cdot \begin{Vmatrix} 3 & 0 & 0 & 0 \\ 0 & 4 & 0 & 0 \\ 0 & 0 & 2 & 0 \\ 0 & 0 & 0 & 2 \end{Vmatrix} \cdot X =$$

$$= \begin{Vmatrix} 3 & 0 & 0 & -2 \\ 0 & 4 & 0 & -2 \\ 0 & 0 & 2 & -2 \end{Vmatrix} \cdot \begin{Vmatrix} 1 & 0 & 0. \\ 0 & 1 & 0 \\ 0 & 0 & 1 \\ -1 & -1 & -1 \end{Vmatrix} = \begin{Vmatrix} 5 & 2 & 2 \\ 2 & 6 & 2 \\ 2 & 2 & 4 \end{Vmatrix}.$$

We will find the matrix C^{-1} (see example 1)

$$\det(C) = \begin{vmatrix} 5 & 2 & 2 \\ 2 & 6 & 2 \\ 2 & 2 & 4 \end{vmatrix} = 76.$$

The matrix of cofactors of the elements of C is of the form

$$K=\begin{Vmatrix} 20 & -4 & -8 \\ -4 & 16 & -6 \\ -8 & -6 & 26 \end{Vmatrix}.$$

Then

$$C^{-1}=\begin{Vmatrix} 0,26315790 & -0,05263158 & -0,10526316 \\ -0,05263158 & 0,21052632 & -0,07894737 \\ -0,10526316 & -0,07894737 & 0,34210527 \end{Vmatrix}.$$

Further, we calculate

$$\tilde{A}=C^{-1}X^TP(L-X_0)=C^{-1}X^TP\begin{Vmatrix} 50^\circ\,12'\,37'' \\ 112^\circ\,17'\,19'' \\ 120^\circ\,47'\,26'' \\ -283^\circ\,13'\,42'' \end{Vmatrix}=\begin{Vmatrix} 50^\circ\,11'\,50'',7 \\ 112^\circ\,16'\,44'',3 \\ 120^\circ\,46'\,16'',5 \end{Vmatrix}.$$

The estimators of the angles can be written in matrix form (the estimator of the fourth angle is, of course, the supplement to 360° of the calculated value 283° 14' 51''.5):

$$\tilde{L}=\begin{Vmatrix} 50^\circ\,11'\,50'',7 \\ 112^\circ\,16'\,44'',3 \\ 120^\circ\,46'\,16'',5 \\ 76^\circ\,45'\;\;8'',5 \end{Vmatrix}.$$

Example 3. We now solve example 1, applying reduction by means of correlates. The true values of the difference between the heights of the points are connected by three relationships:

$$\lambda_1+\lambda_2-\lambda_5=0,$$
$$\lambda_2-\lambda_3-\lambda_6=0,$$
$$\lambda_3+\lambda_4-\lambda_7=0.$$

For convenience we will, as before, use the matrix form. Then, the estimators of y, according to (9.2.27) are equal to

$$\tilde{L}=L+\tilde{V},$$

where L is a single-column matrix of observed values of differences between heights, $\tilde{V}$ is the matrix of apparent corrections determined by formula (9.2.21): i.e.

$$\tilde{V}=-P^{-1}X^TG^{-1}M=P^{-1}X^TK,$$

where $G=XP^{-1}X^T$, $K=-G^{-1}M$ is the matrix of correlates, and

$$M = X_0 + XL.$$

We have

$$X_0 = 0,$$

$$X = \begin{Vmatrix} 1 & 1 & 0 & 0 & -1 & 0 & 0 \\ 0 & 1 & -1 & 0 & 0 & -1 & 0 \\ 0 & 0 & 1 & 1 & 0 & 0 & -1 \end{Vmatrix}.$$

This means that

$$M = XL = \begin{Vmatrix} 1 & 1 & 0 & 0 & -1 & 0 & 0 \\ 0 & 1 & -1 & 0 & 0 & -1 & 0 \\ 0 & 0 & 1 & 1 & 0 & 0 & -1 \end{Vmatrix} \cdot \begin{Vmatrix} 20.21 \\ 40,07 \\ 34,17 \\ 35,84 \\ 60,40 \\ 5,87 \\ 69,99 \end{Vmatrix} = \begin{Vmatrix} -0,12 \\ 0,03 \\ 0,02 \end{Vmatrix}.$$

Evidently, $\det(P) = 0{,}7128$ and

$$P^{-1} = \begin{Vmatrix} 1 & 0 & 0 & 0 & 0 & 0 & 0 \\ 0 & 1{,}11111 & 0 & 0 & 0 & 0 & 0 \\ 0 & 0 & 0{,}90909 & 0 & 0 & 0 & 0 \\ 0 & 0 & 0 & 1{,}25 & 0 & 0 & 0 \\ 0 & 0 & 0 & 0 & 1 & 0 & 0 \\ 0 & 0 & 0 & 0 & 0 & 1{,}11111 & 0 \\ 0 & 0 & 0 & 0 & 0 & 0 & 1 \end{Vmatrix}.$$

We have

$$G = XP^{-1}X^T = \begin{Vmatrix} 1 & 1{,}11111 & 0 & 0 & -1 & 0 & 0 \\ 0 & 1{,}11111 & -0{,}90909 & 0 & 0 & -1{,}11111 & 0 \\ 0 & 0 & 0{,}90909 & 1{,}25 & 0 & 0 & -1 \end{Vmatrix} \times$$

$$\times \begin{Vmatrix} 1 & 0 & 0 \\ 1 & 1 & 0 \\ 0 & -1 & 1 \\ 0 & 0 & 1 \\ -1 & 0 & 0 \\ 0 & -1 & 0 \\ 0 & 0 & -1 \end{Vmatrix} = \begin{Vmatrix} 3{,}11111 & 1{,}11111 & 0 \\ 1{,}11111 & 3{,}13131 & -0{,}90909 \\ 0 & -0{,}90909 & 3{,}15909 \end{Vmatrix}$$

and $\det(G)=24{,}3041$; the matrix D of cofactors of the elements of G is equal to

$$D=\begin{Vmatrix} 9{,}06565 & -3{,}51010 & -1{,}01010 \\ -3{,}51010 & 9{,}82828 & 2{,}82828 \\ -1{,}01010 & 2{,}82828 & 8{,}50728 \end{Vmatrix},$$

therefore

$$G^{-1}=\begin{Vmatrix} 0{,}37301 & -0{,}14442 & -0{,}04156 \\ -0{,}14442 & 0{,}40439 & 0{,}11637 \\ -0{,}04156 & 0{,}11637 & 0{,}35003 \end{Vmatrix}.$$

We now write down the matrix of correlates

$$K=-G^{-1}M=-G^{-1}\cdot\begin{Vmatrix} -0{,}12 \\ 0{,}03 \\ 0{,}02 \end{Vmatrix}=\begin{Vmatrix} 0{,}04993 \\ -0{,}03179 \\ -0{,}01548 \end{Vmatrix}.$$

Further, we find the matrix of apparent corrections (we calculate them to three decimal figures),

$$\tilde{V}=P^{-1}X^TK=\begin{Vmatrix} 1 & 0 & 0 \\ 1{,}11111 & 1{,}11111 & 0 \\ 0 & -0{,}90909 & 0{,}90909 \\ 0 & 0 & 1{,}25 \\ -1 & 0 & 0 \\ 0 & -1{,}11111 & 0 \\ 0 & 0 & -1 \end{Vmatrix}\cdot\begin{Vmatrix} 0{,}04993 \\ -0{,}03179 \\ -0{,}01548 \end{Vmatrix}=\begin{Vmatrix} 0{,}050 \\ 0{,}020 \\ 0{,}015 \\ -0{,}019 \\ -0{,}050 \\ 0{,}035 \\ 0{,}015 \end{Vmatrix},$$

whence

$$\tilde{L}=L+\tilde{V}=\begin{Vmatrix} 20{,}260 \\ 40{,}090 \\ 34{,}185 \\ 35{,}821 \\ 60{,}350 \\ 5{,}905 \\ 70{,}004 \end{Vmatrix}.$$

CHAPTER X

SOME EXAMPLES OF THE ANALYSIS OF OBSERVATIONS IN GEODESY

1. Reduction of a Single Level Circuit *)

Suppose we have a single level circuit through n stations between the points A and B with known readings of position, H_A and H_B (Fig. 6). We want to find the position of the point E (at the kth station, starting from A). For this there are available readings at the point E relative to point A and relative to point B:

$$H'_E = H_A + \sum_{i=1}^{k} h_i; \quad H''_E = H_B - \sum_{i=k+1}^{n} h_i. \tag{10.1.1}$$

It is required to produce an estimate of H_E on the basis of the available data.

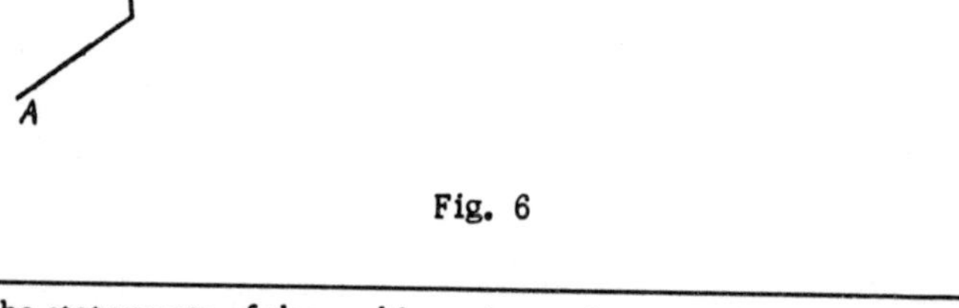

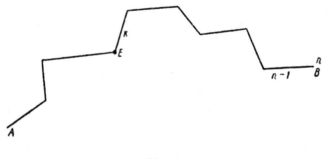

Fig. 6

* The statements of the problems in sections 1 and 2 are taken from Chebotariev's book [51], and Shalayevsky took part in the composition of section 1 and 2.

Formally, this is a problem in the conditional reduction of measurements, since the sum of the expected values of the approximations should be equal to $H_B - H_A$. But in this case it is simpler to reduce the problem to direct measurements. We assume that $h_i = y_i + \Delta_i$, where the y_i's are the true increments and the Δ_i's are the random errors, independent and normal $N(0,1)$. Thus, we suppose that systematic errors are absent, which is itself a hypothesis which must be tested. Problems of testing hypotheses belong to mathematical statistics, and are treated in the corresponding courses. Some cases of such tests are given in section 6 of chapter IV and in section 3 of chapter XII.

Denoting the true position of E by y_E, we have

$$H'_E = y_E + \Delta_1 + \Delta_2 + \ldots + \Delta_k, \tag{10.1.2}$$

$$H''_E = y_E - \Delta_{k+1} - \ldots - \Delta_n. \tag{10.1.3}$$

Further, by virtue of the independence of the Δ_i (see (2.1.18)) we have

$$\left.\begin{aligned} D(\Delta_1 + \ldots + \Delta_k) &= k\sigma^2, \\ D(-\Delta_{k+1} - \ldots - \Delta_n) &= (n-k)\sigma^2. \end{aligned}\right\} \tag{10.1.4}$$

Now equations (10.1.2) and (10.1.3) bring us back to the situation of chapter V. Putting $x_1 = H'_E$, $x_2 = H''_E$, we see that, for the estimation of the y_E's, we have direct measurements of unequal accuracy with weights $p_1 = \frac{1}{k}$ and $p_2 = \frac{1}{n-k}$.

From formula (5.2.3) we find, immediately, the estimator for y_E:

$$\tilde{y} = \frac{p_1 x_1 + p_2 x_2}{p_1 + p_2} = \frac{(n-k) H'_E + k H''_E}{n}. \tag{10.1.5}$$

Further, according to formula (5.2.7), we have

$$D(\tilde{y}) = \frac{\sigma^2}{p_1 + p_2} = \frac{k(n-k)\sigma^2}{n}. \tag{10.1.6}$$

These formulae are suitable for any station ($k = 1, 2, \ldots, n$). We now find the value of k, for which $D(\tilde{y})$ is maximum. If n is even, it is the station $k = \frac{n}{2}$, if n is odd, there are two stations:

$$k = \frac{n+1}{2} \text{ and } k = \frac{n-1}{2}.$$

In fact,

$$k(n-k) = \frac{n^2}{4} - \left(\frac{n}{2} - k\right)^2,$$

from which our assertion follows. Thus, the least accurate results of estimation are obtained in the middle of the level circuit. In this case, for even n, we have

$$D(\tilde{y}) = \frac{n}{4}\sigma^2;\quad \sigma(\tilde{y}) = \frac{\sigma\sqrt{n}}{2}. \tag{10.1.7}$$

The quantity $f_h = H'_E - H''_E$ is the 'discrepancy' for the given level circuit. From (10.1.5) we see that

$$\tilde{y} = H'_E + \frac{k(H'_E - H''_E)}{n} = H'_E + \frac{k}{n} f_h. \tag{10.1.8}$$

This formula applies for arbitrary values of k and is, in itself, the distribution law of the discrepancies at stations of a level circuit. To estimate σ, if there are no previous data, we can use the reversed level circuit. Suppose that, together with the increments $h_1, h_2, \ldots, h_n$ of the direct circuit, the reversed circuit gives the following measurements: $h'_n, h'_{n-1}, \ldots, h'_1$ (h'_k corresponds to the $(k-1)^{\text{th}}$ station, etc.) Assuming the absence of systematic error, we put $h'_i = -y_i + \delta_i$, where we can assume the quantities δ_i $(i = 1, 2, \ldots, n)$ to be statistically mutually independent and independent of the Δ_j's. They are also distributed as Δ_i, i.e. normal $N(0, \sigma)$. Then we have

$$h_i + h'_i = \Delta_i + \delta_i.$$

The quantities $\Delta_i + \delta_i$ are normal $N(0, \sigma\sqrt{2})$ by virtue of the independence of Δ_i and δ_i. We have

$$E\frac{1}{n}\sum_{i=1}^{n}(h_i + h'_i)^2 = E\frac{1}{n}[(h + h')^2] = 2\sigma^2. \tag{10.1.9}$$

Then the quantity

$$\frac{1}{2n}\sum_{i=1}^{n}(h_i + h'_i)^2 = \frac{1}{2n}[(h + h')^2] = q^2 \tag{10.1.10}$$

is an unbiased estimator of σ^2, and

$$\frac{n}{4}q^2 = \frac{1}{8}[(h + h')^2] \tag{10.1.11}$$

is an unbiased estimator of $D(\tilde{y})$. The corresponding standard deviations have the asymptotically unbiased estimators

$$q = \sqrt{\frac{1}{2n}[(h + h')^2]}, \tag{10.1.12}$$

$$\sqrt{\frac{1}{8}[(h + h')^2]} \quad \text{(the estimator for } \sigma(\tilde{y})\text{)}. \tag{10.1.13}$$

Further, in view of the fact that the quantities $\Delta_i + \delta_i$ are normal $N(0, \sigma\sqrt{2})$, the quantity $\frac{nq^2}{\sigma^2}$ is distributed as χ^2_n. From this it follows that, for large n

$$\sigma(q) \approx \frac{\sigma}{\sqrt{2n}}. \tag{10.1.14}$$

To estimate σ, we can construct confidence intervals as in chapter VI, using

$$\frac{nq^2}{\sigma^2} = \chi^2_n.$$

Hence, to construct the confidence interval we can use Table III of the Appendix. For a given confidence coefficient p_0 and degrees of freedom $k = n$, we find γ_1 and γ_2 such that $P(\gamma_1 q < \sigma < \gamma_2 q) = p_0$. The confidence interval $[\gamma_1 q, \gamma_2 q]$ covers σ with probability p_0.

The information provided by the reversed level circuit, together with the information from the direct circuit, can be used for estimating the position, y, of the kth station more accurately, and for constructing confidence intervals. Thus, we add to the equations (10.1.1) the equations

$$x_3 = H_B + h'_n + h'_{n-1} + \ldots + h'_{k+1}, \tag{10.1.15}$$

$$x_4 = H_A - h'_1 - h'_2 - \ldots - h'_k. \tag{10.1.16}$$

We can consider them as values of y with errors having weights $\frac{1}{n-k}$ and $\frac{1}{k}$ respectively, and on the basis of the theory of estimation for direct measurements of unequal accuracy (chapter V), we can introduce a new estimator, $\approx y$, for y:

$$\overset{\approx}{y} = \frac{\frac{1}{k}(x_1 + x_4) + \frac{1}{n-k}(x_2 + x_3)}{\frac{2}{k} + \frac{2}{n-k}} = \frac{(n-k)(x_1 + x_4) + k(x_2 + x_3)}{2n}. \tag{10.1.17}$$

We have (see (5.2.7))

$$D(\overset{\approx}{y}) = \frac{\sigma^2}{[p]} = \frac{k(n-k)\sigma^2}{2n}, \tag{10.1.18}$$

i.e. the variance of the new estimator is twice as small as that of the old, which is to be expected. The construction of the confidence intervals is rather complicated and we will not give it. We can obtain a compact level circuit $(H_A = H_B)$ using the same rules of reduction.

2. Reduction of Level Circuits Based on Station-points

Suppose that we have level circuits to the point E from some points $A_1, \ldots, A_k$ with known positions $H_{A_1}, \ldots, H_{A_k}$ (Fig. 7), and also that the circuit from the point A_i contains n_i stations. Then, for the circuit from the point A_i, we obtain the reading at the point E:

$$x_i = H_{A_i} + h_1 + h_2 + \ldots + h_{n_i}. \tag{10.2.1}$$

In the absence of systematic error we have, as in section 1,

$$x_i = y + \delta_{1i} + \ldots + \delta_{n_i i}, \tag{10.2.2}$$

where the δ_{ji} are a mutually independent set ($i = 1, 2, \ldots, k$; $j = 1, 2, \ldots, n_i$), the δ_{ji} are normal $N(0, \sigma)$ and y is the true value of the position of the point E.

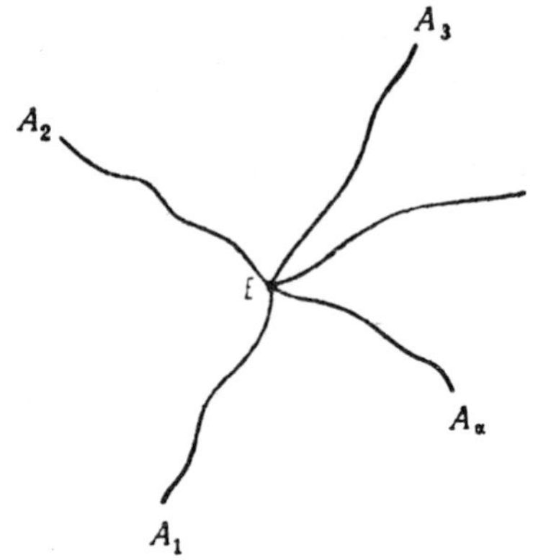

Fig. 7

We choose

$$\tilde{y} = \frac{\sum_{i=1}^{k} \frac{1}{n_i} x_i}{\sum_{i=1}^{k} \frac{1}{n_i}}. \tag{10.2.3}$$

as an estimator of y, following chapter V, section 2. We also have

$$D(\tilde{y}) = \frac{\sigma^2}{\sum_{i=1}^{k} \frac{1}{n_i}}; \quad \sigma(\tilde{y}) = \frac{\sigma}{\sqrt{\sum_{i=1}^{k} \frac{1}{n_i}}}. \tag{10.2.4}$$

To estimate σ we should either have preliminary information about the precision of the instruments under given conditions, or introduce reversed level circuits; then we must proceed as in section 1.

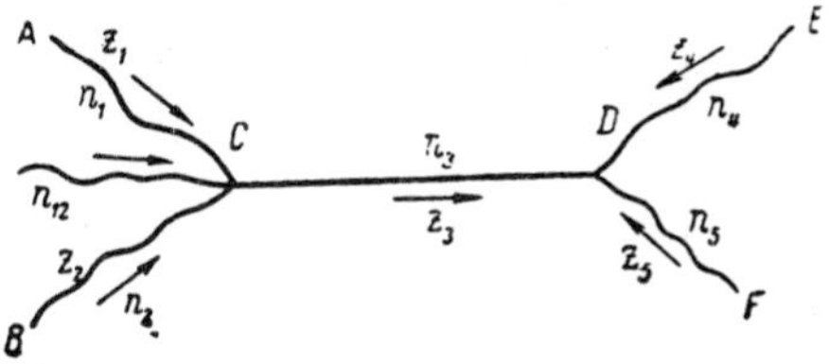

Fig. 8

We consider also the case of two points, which is illustrated in Fig. 8. The numbers of the stations are shown on the corresponding circuits. We could construct an estimator of the position of C from the circuits passing through it and then, starting from this point and using the weight obtained for it, estimate the position of the point D from the three available circuits.

It often happens that we do not get complicated estimators, and as we will see, the results are optimal.

We will study this problem as a problem of reduction by means of elements; in this way we will establish the optimal method of procedure (in the sense of chapter VII).

Let H_C and H_D be the true increments at C and D over the station-point A; H_B, H_E, H_F are the true increments at the points B, E, F over the point A. We denote the true increments in the following way: $(C, A)=\xi_1$,

$$(C, B)=\xi_2; \quad (D, C)=\xi_3; \quad (E, D)=\xi_4; \quad (F, D)=\xi_5.$$

We have the equations, in terms of elements

$$H_C=\xi_1=H_B+\xi_2,$$
$$H_D=\xi_1+\xi_3=H_E+\xi_4=H_F+\xi_5.$$

We introduce the new notation $\xi_1=\eta_1$, $\xi_3=\eta_2$. We have two independent elements η_1 and η_2 in terms of which the others are expressed, and the five measurements

$$\begin{aligned} l_1+\Delta_1&=\eta_1,\\ l_2+\Delta_2&=\eta_1,\\ l_3+\Delta_3&=\eta_2,\\ l_4+\Delta_4&=\eta_1+\eta_2,\\ l_5+\Delta_5&=\eta_1+\eta_2. \end{aligned} \tag{10.2.5}$$

The matrix X will have the form (see chapter VI)

$$X = X_{52} = \begin{Vmatrix} 1 & 0 \\ 1 & 0 \\ 0 & 1 \\ 1 & 1 \\ 1 & 1 \end{Vmatrix}; \quad X^T = \begin{Vmatrix} 1 & 1 & 0 & 1 & 1 \\ 0 & 0 & 1 & 1 & 1 \end{Vmatrix}. \tag{10.2.6}$$

The matrix of weights is:

$$P = \begin{Vmatrix} \frac{1}{n_1} & 0 & 0 & 0 & 0 \\ 0 & \frac{1}{n_2} & 0 & 0 & 0 \\ 0 & 0 & \frac{1}{n_3} & 0 & 0 \\ 0 & 0 & 0 & \frac{1}{n_4} & 0 \\ 0 & 0 & 0 & 0 & \frac{1}{n_5} \end{Vmatrix}; \tag{10.2.7}$$

$$X^TP = \begin{Vmatrix} \frac{1}{n_1} & \frac{1}{n_2} & 0 & \frac{1}{n_4} & \frac{1}{n_5} \\ 0 & 0 & \frac{1}{n_3} & \frac{1}{n_4} & \frac{1}{n_5} \end{Vmatrix}.$$

$$C = X^TPX = \begin{Vmatrix} \frac{1}{n_1} + \frac{1}{n_2} + \frac{1}{n_4} + \frac{1}{n_5}, & \frac{1}{n_4} + \frac{1}{n_5} \\ \frac{1}{n_4} + \frac{1}{n_5}, & \frac{1}{n_3} + \frac{1}{n_4} + \frac{1}{n_5} \end{Vmatrix},$$

$$X^TPL = \begin{Vmatrix} \frac{l_1}{n_1} + \frac{l_2}{n_2} + \frac{l_4}{n_4} + \frac{l_5}{n_5} \\ \frac{l_3}{n_3} + \frac{l_4}{n_4} + \frac{l_5}{n_5} \end{Vmatrix}.$$

The normal equations for η_1 and η_2 are of the form

$$\eta_1\left(\frac{1}{n_1} + \frac{1}{n_2} + \frac{1}{n_4} + \frac{1}{n_5}\right) + \eta_2\left(\frac{1}{n_4} + \frac{1}{n_5}\right) = \frac{l_1}{n_1} + \frac{l_2}{n_2} + \frac{l_4}{n_4} + \frac{l_5}{n_5},$$

$$\eta_1\left(\frac{1}{n_4} + \frac{1}{n_5}\right) + \eta_2\left(\frac{1}{n_3} + \frac{1}{n_4} + \frac{1}{n_5}\right) = \frac{l_3}{n_3} + \frac{l_4}{n_4} + \frac{l_5}{n_5}.$$

We put $p_i = \frac{1}{n_i}$ $(i = 1, 2, 3, 4, 5)$. We have

$$d = \det(C) = (p_1 + p_2 + p_4 + p_5)(p_3 + p_4 + p_5) - (p_4 + p_5)^2,$$

$$C^{-1} = \frac{1}{d} \begin{Vmatrix} (p_3 + p_4 + p_5) & -(p_4 + p_5) \\ -(p_4 + p_5) & (p_1 + p_2 + p_4 + p_5) \end{Vmatrix}.$$

From here we obtain estimators $\tilde{\eta}_1$ and $\tilde{\eta}_2$ of the elements η_1 and η_2:

$$\tilde{\eta}_1 = \frac{1}{d}[(p_3 + p_4 + p_5)(p_1 l_1 + p_2 l_2 + p_4 l_4 + p_5 l_5) - \\ -(p_4 + p_5)(p_3 l_3 + p_4 l_4 + p_5 l_5)] = \frac{1}{d}[(p_3 + p_4 + p_5)(p_1 l_1 + p_2 l_2) - \\ -(p_4 + p_5) p_3 l_3 + p_3 (p_4 l_4 + p_5 l_5)], \quad (10.2.8)$$

$$\tilde{\eta}_2 = \frac{1}{d}[-(p_4 + p_5)(p_1 l_1 + p_2 l_2 + p_4 l_4 + p_5 l_5) + \\ + (p_1 + p_2 + p_4 + p_5)(p_3 l_3 + p_4 l_4 + p_5 l_5)] = \\ = \frac{1}{d}[-(p_4 + p_5)(p_1 l_1 + p_2 l_2) + \\ + (p_1 + p_2 + p_4 + p_5) p_3 l_3 + (p_1 + p_2)(p_4 l_4 + p_5 l_5)]. \quad (10.2.9)$$

The quantity $\tilde{\eta}_1$ is an estimator of the position of the point C; for the point D we have the estimator $\tilde{\eta}_1 + \tilde{\eta}_2$:

$$\tilde{\eta}_1 + \tilde{\eta}_2 = \frac{1}{d}[p_3(p_1 l_1 + p_2 l_2) + \\ + (p_1 + p_2) p_3 l_3 + (p_1 + p_2 + p_3)(p_4 l_4 + p_5 l_5)]. \quad (10.2.10)$$

As is to be expected, there is a certain symmetry in the estimators of the increments of C and D over A; making the interchanges: $(p_4, p_5) \longleftrightarrow (p_1, p_2)$, $(l_4, l_5) \longleftrightarrow (l_1, l_2)$, $p_1 \longleftrightarrow p_3$, $l_1 \longleftrightarrow l_3$ one estimator is transformed into the other.

We find also the variance of the estimator $\tilde{\eta}_1$; according to formula (8.2.5) we have

$$D(\tilde{\eta}_1) = \sigma^2 \{C^{-1}\}_{11} = \sigma^2 \frac{p_3 + p_4 + p_5}{d} = \\ = \sigma^2 \frac{p_3 + p_4 + p_5}{p_3(p_1 + p_2 + p_4 + p_5) + (p_1 + p_2)(p_4 + p_5)}. \quad (10.2.11)$$

And, because of the symmetry noted above, we obtain

$$D(\tilde{\eta}_1 + \tilde{\eta}_2) = \sigma^2 \frac{p_1 + p_2 + p_3}{p_3(p_1 + p_2 + p_4 + p_5) + (p_1 + p_2)(p_4 + p_5)}. \quad (10.2.12)$$

It may be noted that the combination of the data of the two circuits from A and B to C, with the information from the other circuits, improves the accuracy of the estimators. In the estimation of the position of point C from two circuits only, we would have obtained the estimator η'_1 with variance

$$D(\eta'_1)=\frac{\sigma^2}{p_1+p_2}, \tag{10.2.13}$$

(see previous chapter).

We will show that

$$D(\tilde{\eta}_1)<D(\eta'_1). \tag{10.2.14}$$

We have

$$\frac{p_3+p_4+p_5}{p_3(p_1+p_2+p_4+p_5)+(p_1+p_2)(p_4+p_5)}-\frac{1}{p_1+p_2}=$$
$$=\frac{(p_3+p_4+p_5)(p_1+p_2)-p_3(p_1+p_2+p_4+p_5)-(p_1+p_2)(p_4+p_5)}{(p_1+p_2)\{p_3(p_1+p_2+p_4+p_5)+(p_1+p_2)(p_4+p_5)\}}.$$

The numerator is equal to $-p_3(p_4+p_5)<0$, which proves (10.2.14). As was explained in section 2 of chapter VIII, the results obtained are optimal, in a certain sense. We will show that another method, very often used by geodesists and described by Chebotariev [51], leads, in this case and in the same sense, to the same estimators and is also optimal.*)

We use the following notation (see Fig. 8)

l_1 observed reading at point C in circuit z_1,

l_2 observed reading at point C in circuit z_2,

l_3 observed increment of the point D over the point C in circuit z_3,

l_4 observed reading at point D in circuit z_4,

l_5 observed reading at point D in circuit z_5.

We calculate the preliminary estimator for station-point C from circuits z_1 and z_2

$$l_{12}=\frac{l_1p_1+l_2p_2}{p_1+p_2}. \tag{10.2.15}$$

The weight for l_{12} is $p_{12}=p_1+p_2$.

* This remark was communicated to the author by Shaleyevsky

In the place of the two circuits z_1 and z_2 we take one circuit z_{12} through C with the same weight p_{12}. This circuit has

$$n_{12}=\frac{1}{p_{12}}=\frac{1}{p_1+p_2}$$

stations.

We assume that at the point D there is one combined circuit z_{123}, consisting of circuits z_{12} and z_3, with the number of stations equal to $n_{12}+n_3$.

The circuit z_{123} gives an observed reading, at D, equal to

$$l_{123}=l_{12}+l_3.$$

The weight of the circuit z_{123} is

$$p_{123}=\frac{1}{n_{12}+n_3}=\frac{1}{\frac{1}{p_1+p_2}+\frac{1}{p_3}}=\frac{(p_1+p_2)\,p_3}{p_1+p_2+p_3}. \tag{10.2.16}$$

Now we determine the final estimator of the reading at D from the three circuits z_{123}, z_4, z_5 by the usual rule

$$\tilde{l}_D=\frac{l_{123}p_{123}+l_4p_4+l_5p_5}{p_{123}+p_4+p_5}. \tag{10.2.17}$$

We will write this in more detailed form. Since

$$l_{123}=l_{12}+l_3=\frac{l_1p_1+l_2p_2}{p_1+p_2}+l_3=\frac{l_1p_1+l_2p_2+l_3(p_1+p_2)}{p_1+p_2},$$

then

$$\tilde{l}_D=\frac{\frac{[l_1p_1+l_2p_2+l_3(p_1+p_2)]}{(p_1+p_2)}\,\frac{(p_1+p_2)\,p_3}{(p_1+p_2+p_3)}+l_4p_4+l_5p_5}{\frac{(p_1+p_2)\,p_3}{p_1+p_2+p_3}+p_4+p_5}=$$

$$=\frac{(l_1p_1+l_2p_2)\,p_3+l_3(p_1+p_2)\,p_3+(l_4p_4+l_5p_5)(p_1+p_2+p_3)}{(p_1+p_2)\,p_3+(p_1+p_2+p_3)(p_4+p_5)}=$$

$$=\frac{(l_1p_1+l_2p_2)\,p_3+(p_1+p_2)\,p_3l_3+(p_1+p_2+p_3)(l_4p_4+l_5p_5)}{(p_1+p_2)(p_4+p_5)+p_3(p_1+p_2+p_4+p_5)}.$$

This is identical with formula (10.2.10). We find the final estimator of the position in C in the following way.

We consider the circuit z_{123} and the discrepancy of this circuit, $l_{123}-\tilde{l}_D$.

The quantity

$$-\frac{l_{123}-\bar{l}_D}{n_{12}+n_3} \tag{10.2.18}$$

is a correction for one station of the circuit z_{123}, consequently

$$\bar{l}_C = l_{12} - \frac{l_{123} - \bar{l}_D}{n_{12} + n_3} n_{12}.$$

We write this in the more detailed form

$$\bar{l}_C = \frac{l_1 p_1 + l_2 p_2}{p_1 + p_2} - $$

$$- \frac{\dfrac{l_1 p_1 + l_2 p_2 + (p_1 + p_2) l_3}{p_1 + p_2} - \dfrac{(l_1 p_1 + l_2 p_2) p_3 + (p_1 + p_2) p_3 l_3 + (p_1 + p_2 + p_3)(l_4 p_4 + l_5 p_5)}{(p_1 + p_2) p_3 + (p_1 + p_2 + p_3)(p_4 + p_5)}}{\dfrac{(p_1 + p_2 + p_3)}{p_3 (p_1 + p_2)}} \quad \frac{1}{(p_1 + p_2)} =$$

$$= \frac{l_1 p_1 + l_2 p_2 + l_3 p_3}{p_1 + p_2 + p_3} + \frac{(l_1 p_1 + l_2 p_2) p_3^2 + (p_1 + p_2) p_3^2 l_3 + p_3 (p_1 + p_2 + p_3)(l_4 p_4 + l_5 p_5)}{(p_1 + p_2 + p_3)[(p_1 + p_2) p_3 + (p_1 + p_2 + p_3)(p_4 + p_5)]} =$$

$$= \frac{(p_1 + p_2 + p_3)(p_3 + p_4 + p_5)(l_1 p_1 + l_2 p_2) - (p_1 + p_2 + p_3)(p_4 + p_5) p_3 l_3 + p_3 (p_1 + p_2 + p_3)(l_4 p_4 + l_5 p_5)}{(p_1 + p_2 + p_3)[(p_1 + p_2) p_3 + (p_1 + p_2 + p_3)(p_4 + p_5)]} =$$

$$= \frac{(p_3 + p_4 + p_5)(l_1 p_1 + l_2 p_2) - p_3 (p_4 + p_5) l_3 + p_3 (l_4 p_4 + l_5 p_5)}{(p_1 + p_2)(p_4 + p_5) + p_3 (p_1 + p_2 + p_4 + p_5)}$$

This also is identical with formula (10.2.8). In view of the coincidence of the estimators, the accuracies of these estimators are equal.

The problem of reduction of angular circuits may be stated and solved in an exactly similar manner.

3. Measurement of Horizontal Angles by the Gauss-Schreiber Method

Suppose that from the point O, k angles are measured between the directions A_1, A_2, ..., A_k and the oriented line OA_0 (Fig. 9).

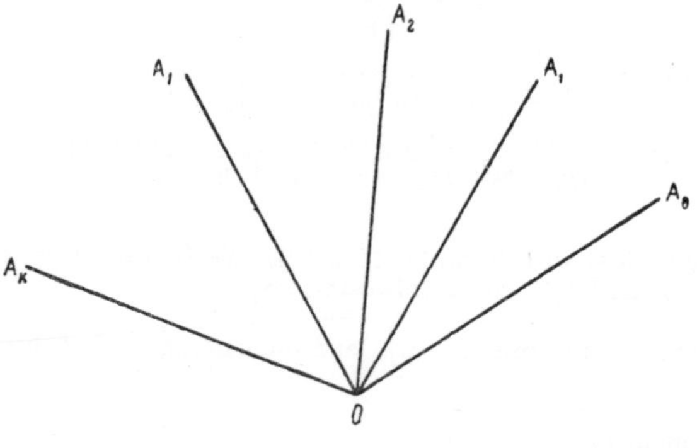

Fig. 9

Here the method suggested by Gauss, and worked out by the German officer Schreiber, is often used. In this method the angles between OA_0 and remaining directions $OA_1, OA_2, \ldots, OA_k$ are measured first, then the angles between OA_1 and the directions $OA_2, \ldots, OA_k$, etc.; altogether $\frac{k(k+1)}{2}$ angles. Among them we pick out k independent angles:

$$\alpha_1 = \angle A_0OA_1, \quad \alpha_2 = \angle A_0OA_2, \ldots, \alpha_k = \angle A_0OA_k;$$

these angles can be used as elements in reduction by means of elements. For simplicity, we assume that the measurements of the angles are of equal accuracy.

We obtain $\frac{k(k+1)}{2}$ fundamental equations in terms of the elements. These equations can be divided, in a natural way, into k systems, of $k, k-1, \ldots, 1$ equations respectively. We assign to these systems the numbers $0, 1, 2, \ldots, (k-1)$ respectively.

The zero system is of the form

$$l_1^{(0)} + \Delta_1^{(0)} = \alpha_1,$$
$$l_2^{(0)} + \Delta_2^{(0)} = \alpha_2,$$
$$\cdots\cdots$$
$$l_k^{(0)} + \Delta_k^{(0)} = \alpha_k,$$

the first system:

$$l_1^{(1)} + \Delta_1^{(1)} = \alpha_2 - \alpha_1,$$
$$\cdots\cdots$$
$$l_{k-1}^{(1)} + \Delta_{k-1}^{(1)} = \alpha_k - \alpha_1,$$

the jth system:

$$l_1^{(j)} + \Delta_1^{(j)} = \alpha_{j+1} - \alpha_j,$$
$$\cdots\cdots$$
$$l_{k-j}^{(j)} + \Delta_{k-j}^{(j)} = \alpha_k - \alpha_j,$$
$$j = 1, 2, \ldots, (k-1).$$

We denote the matrix corresponding to the zero system for the elements $\alpha_1, \ldots, \alpha_k$, by $R_{kk}^{(0)}$ We have

$$R_{kk}^{(0)}=\begin{Vmatrix}1 & 0 & \dots & 0\\ 0 & 1 & \dots & 0\\ \cdot & \cdot & \cdot & \cdot\\ 0 & 0 & \dots & 1\end{Vmatrix}=E_{kk}. \tag{10.3.1}$$

For the jth system $(j=1, 2, \dots, k-1)$ we have

$$R_{k-j,k}^{(j)}=\left.\begin{Vmatrix}\overbrace{0 \ \dots \ 0}^{(j-1)} & \overbrace{-1}^{j} & \overbrace{1 \ 0 \ \dots \ 0}^{(k-j)}\\ 0 \ \dots \ 0 & -1 & 0 \ 1 \ \dots \ 0\\ \cdot \ \cdot \ \cdot & \cdot & \cdot \ \cdot \ \cdot \ \cdot\\ 0 \ \dots \ 0 & -1 & 0 \ \dots\dots \ 1\end{Vmatrix}\right\}(k-j) \tag{10.3.2}$$

The matrix of all systems of observations is of the form

$$X=X_{\frac{k(k+1)}{2},\,k}=\begin{Vmatrix}R_{kk}^{(0)}\\ \dots\\ R_{k-1,k}^{(1)}\\ \dots\\ R_{k-2,k}^{(2)}\\ \dots\\ \dots\\ R_{1,k}^{(k-1)}\end{Vmatrix} \tag{10.3.3}$$

(see section 2 of chapter I).

The matrix of the system of k normal equations for estimators of the elements $\tilde{\alpha}_1, \tilde{\alpha}_2, \dots, \tilde{\alpha}_k$ is $C=C_{kk}=X^TX$ (see chapter VIII). From the fundamental equation, written in the form (8.3.1), it is easy to see that this matrix is of the form

$$C=C_{kk}=X^TX=(R_{kk}^{(0)})^T R_{kk}^{(0)}+(R_{k-1,k}^{(1)})^T R_{k-1,k}^{(1)}+\dots+ \\ +(R_{k-j,k}^{(j)})^T R_{k-j,k}^{(j)}+\dots+(R_{1,k}^{(k-1)})^T R_{1,k}^{(k-1)}. \tag{10.3.4}$$

The products of matrices given above are calculated immediately.

We have

$$(R_{kk}^{(0)})^T R_{kk}^{(0)}=E_{kk}=\left.\begin{Vmatrix}\overbrace{1 \ 0 \ \dots \ 0}^{(k)}\\ 0 \ 1 \ \dots \ 0\\ \cdot \ \cdot \ \cdot \ \cdot\\ 0 \ 0 \ \dots \ 1\end{Vmatrix}\right\}(k), \tag{10.3.5}$$

$$(R_{k-j,k}^{(j)})^T R_{k-j,k}^{(j)} = \begin{matrix} \\ (j-1)\left\{\begin{matrix} \\ \\ \\ \\ \end{matrix}\right. \\ (k-j+1)\left\{\begin{matrix} \\ \\ \\ \\ \end{matrix}\right. \end{matrix} \left\| \begin{matrix} \overbrace{0\dots 0}^{(j-1)} & \overbrace{0}^{j} & \overbrace{0\dots\ 0}^{(k-j)} \\ 0\dots 0 & 0 & 0\dots\ 0 \\ \dots & \dots & \dots \\ 0\dots 0 & 0 & 0\dots\ 0 \\ 0\dots 0 & k-j & -1\dots -1 \\ 0\dots 0 & -1 & 1\dots\ 0 \\ \dots & \dots & \dots \\ 0\dots 0 & -1 & 0\dots\ 1 \end{matrix} \right\|, \quad j = 1, 2, \dots, k-1 \qquad (10.3.6)$$

(evidently, this is a symmetric matrix). Hence, using (10.3.4), we obtain

$$C = C_{kk} = \left\| \begin{matrix} k & -1 & \dots & -1 \\ -1 & k & \dots & -1 \\ \dots & \dots & \dots & \dots \\ -1 & -1 & \dots & k \end{matrix} \right\|.$$

This simple form of the matrix C gives simple expressions for the estimators $\tilde{\alpha}_1, \dots, \tilde{\alpha}_k$ and allows us to construct confidence intervals for them. We need only to take note of the right-hand sides of the normal equations (see (8.3.2)), which in (8.3.2) are of the form $[x_i l]$ ($i = 1, 2, \dots, k$. $p_i = 1$). Using (10.3.2) and (10.3.3) we find

$$\left.\begin{aligned} &[x_i l] = d_i = \\ &= l_i^{(0)} + l_{i-1}^{(1)} + l_{i-2}^{(2)} + \dots + l_1^{(i-1)} - (l_1^{(i)} + l_2^{(i)} + \dots + l_{k-i}^{(i)}), \\ &\qquad i = 1, 2, \dots, k-1, \\ &[x_k l] = d_k = l_k^{(0)} + l_{k-1}^{(1)} + \dots + l_1^{(k-1)}. \end{aligned}\right\} \quad (10.3.7)$$

We will consider the geometrical meaning of the expressions we have obtained.

From the determination of $l_\gamma^{(\delta)}$, we have $l_\gamma^{(\delta)} = \alpha_{\delta+\gamma} - \alpha_\gamma$. Simultaneously we denote the difference of the angles α_μ and α_ν by (μ, ν): $\alpha_\mu - \alpha_\nu = (\mu, \nu)$ $(\mu > \nu > 1)$. We also put $\alpha_0 = 0$, so that $(\mu, 0) = \alpha_\mu$. Then

$$\left.\begin{aligned} &d_1 = (1, 0) - (2, 1) - (3, 1) - \dots - (k, 1); \\ &d_i = (i, 0) + (i, 1) + (i, 2) + \dots \\ &\qquad \dots + (i, i-1) - (i+1, i) - \dots - (k, i), \\ &\qquad i = 2, 3, \dots, k-1, \\ &d_k = (k, 0) + (k, 1) + \dots + (k, k-1). \end{aligned}\right\} \quad (10.3.8)$$

We have

$$\sum_{i=1}^{k} d_i = (1, 0) + (2, 0) + \ldots + (k, 0). \qquad (10.3.9)$$

In fact, each expression $(\mu, 0)$ in the sum $\sum_{i=1}^{k} d_i$ appears once with the sign + and never with the sign -. Further, for $\nu > 0$ the expression (μ, ν) $(\mu > \nu)$ is encountered once with the sign + and once with the sign -. For it to have the sign +, is necessary and sufficient that $i = \mu$, $d_i = d_\mu$; this is the expression (i, ν). For the sign - to enter, we must have $i = \nu$, $d_i = d_\nu$; this is the expression (μ, i), by what we proved in (10.3.9).

Writing $S = \sum_{i=1}^{k} d_i$, we also obtain

$$S + d_j = 2(j, 0) + \sum_{\substack{\mu=1 \\ j>1}}^{j-1} \big((j, \mu) + (\mu, 0)\big) - \sum_{\nu=j+1}^{k} \big((\nu, j) - (\nu, 0)\big). \qquad (10.3.10)$$

We construct the normal equations

$$\begin{array}{l} k\tilde{\alpha}_1 - \tilde{\alpha}_2 - \tilde{\alpha}_3 - \ldots - \tilde{\alpha}_k = d_1 \\ -\tilde{\alpha}_1 + k\tilde{\alpha}_2 - \tilde{\alpha}_3 - \ldots - \tilde{\alpha}_k = d_2 \\ \cdots\cdots\cdots\cdots\cdots \\ -\tilde{\alpha}_1 - \tilde{\alpha}_2 - \ldots\ldots + k\tilde{\alpha}_k = d_k. \end{array} \qquad (10.3.11)$$

To solve them, we need not seek the reciprocal matrix C^{-1} (although the diagonal elements $\{C^{-1}\}_{ii}$ are necessary for the calculation of the variances of the estimators), but apply the following method. We add the 2nd, 3rd. . . . kth equations to the first and obtain the new system

$$\begin{array}{l} \tilde{\alpha}_1 + \tilde{\alpha}_2 + \ldots + \tilde{\alpha}_k = d_1 + d_2 + \ldots + d_k \\ -\tilde{\alpha}_1 + k\tilde{\alpha}_2 - \ldots - \tilde{\alpha}_k = d_2 \\ \cdots\cdots\cdots\cdots\cdots \\ -\tilde{\alpha}_1 - \tilde{\alpha}_2 - \ldots + k\tilde{\alpha}_k = d_k. \end{array} \qquad (10.3.12)$$

Now, we add the first equation to each of the remainder and we get

$$\begin{array}{l} \tilde{\alpha}_1 + \tilde{\alpha}_2 + \ldots + \tilde{\alpha}_k = d_1 + d_2 + \ldots + d_k \\ (k+1)\tilde{\alpha}_2 = d_1 + 2d_2 + d_3 + \ldots + d_k \\ (k+1)\tilde{\alpha}_3 = d_1 + d_2 + 2d_3 + d_4 + \ldots + d_k \\ \cdots\cdots\cdots\cdots\cdots \\ (k+1)\tilde{\alpha}_k = d_1 + d_2 + \ldots + d_{k-1} + 2d_k. \end{array} \qquad (10.3.13)$$

We further put $S = d_1 + d_2 + \ldots + d_k$, and then we have

$$\tilde{\alpha}_j = \frac{S + d_j}{k+1}, \quad j = 2, 3, \ldots, k. \tag{10.3.14}$$

Hence

$$\tilde{\alpha}_1 = S - \sum_{i=2}^{k} \frac{S + d_i}{k+1} = \frac{S + d_1}{k+1}, \tag{10.3.15}$$

so that formula (10.3.14) is applicable also for $j = 1$. On the basis of (10.3.10) we obtain explicit expressions for the estimators

$$\tilde{\alpha}_j = \frac{1}{k+1}\left(2\,(j, 0) + \sum_{\substack{\mu=1 \\ j>1}}^{j-1}\big((j, \mu) + (\mu, 0)\big) - \sum_{\nu=j+1}^{k}\big((\nu, j) - (\nu, 0)\big)\right). \tag{10.3.16}$$

We will find the variances of the estimators $\tilde{\alpha}_j$. We have (see (8.2.5))

$$D(\tilde{\alpha}_j) = \sigma^2 \{C^{-1}\}_{jj}. \tag{10.3.17}$$

Further,

$$C = \begin{Vmatrix} k & -1 & \ldots & -1 \\ -1 & k & \ldots & -1 \\ \cdot & \cdot & \cdot & \cdot \\ -1 & -1 & \ldots & k \end{Vmatrix}.$$

The quantity $\{C^{-1}\}_{jj}$ is equal to the j th diagonal minor of the matrix C divided by $\det(C)$.

To calculate $\det(C)$ we add the 2nd, . . . , kth rows to the first row and we obtain

$$\begin{Vmatrix} 1 & 1 & \ldots\ldots & 1 \\ -1 & k & \ldots\ldots & -1 \\ \cdot & \cdot & \cdot & \cdot \\ -1 & -1 & \ldots\ldots & k \end{Vmatrix},$$

and now we add the first row to each of the remainder. Then

$$\det(C) = \begin{Vmatrix} 1 & 1 & \ldots\ldots & & 1 \\ 0 & k+1 & 0 & \ldots & 0 \\ 0 & 0 & k+1 & \ldots & 0 \\ \cdot & \cdot & \cdot & \cdot & \cdot \\ 0 & \ldots & \ldots & \ldots & k+1 \end{Vmatrix} = (k+1)^{k-1}. \tag{10.3.18}$$

Further, all diagonal minors are equal to each other. The first of them is equal to the determinant

$$\overbrace{\left\| \begin{matrix} k & -1 & \dots & -1 \\ -1 & k & \dots & -1 \\ \dots & \dots & \dots & \dots \\ -1 & \dots & \dots & k \end{matrix} \right\|}^{(k-1)} \Bigg\} (k-1).$$

Adding the 2nd, . . . , $(k-1)$th row to the first we get

$$\left\| \begin{matrix} 2 & 2 & \dots & 2 \\ -1 & k & \dots & -1 \\ \dots & \dots & \dots & \dots \\ -1 & \dots & \dots & k \end{matrix} \right\| = 2 \left\| \begin{matrix} 1 & \dots & \dots & 1 \\ -1 & k & \dots & -1 \\ \dots & \dots & \dots & \dots \\ -1 & -1 & \dots & k \end{matrix} \right\| = 2(k+1)^{k-2}. \tag{10.3.19}$$

We can obtain the last equation by adding the first row to each of the remainder. Hence, dividing (10.3.19) by (10.3.18) we find

$$\{C^{-1}\}_{jj} = \frac{2}{k+1} \tag{10.3.20}$$

$$D(\tilde{\alpha}_j) = \frac{2\sigma^2}{k+1}; \quad \sigma(\tilde{\alpha}_j) = \sigma\sqrt{\frac{2}{k+1}}, \quad j = 1, 2, \dots, k. \tag{10.3.21}$$

We see that the standard error of each of the obtained estimators is proportional to σ - the standard deviation of a single observation and reciprocal to $\sqrt{k+1}$, where k is the number of directions from the oriented line.

Now we construct confidence intervals from the estimators $\tilde{\alpha}_j$. For this we must form the expression $[p\tilde{v}\tilde{v}]$. From (8.3.5) we see that

$$[p\tilde{v}\tilde{v}] = [\tilde{v}\tilde{v}] = [ll] - [x_1 l]\,\tilde{\alpha}_1 - \dots - [x_k l]\,\tilde{\alpha}_k.$$

Further, from (9.3.7)

$$[x_i l] = d_i,$$
$$[ll] = \sum_{\substack{i,j=0 \\ i>j}}^{k} ((i,j))^2. \tag{10.3.22}$$

Thus, after finding the estimators $\tilde{\alpha}_1, \dots, \tilde{\alpha}_k$, we calculate $[p\tilde{v}\tilde{v}]$ from the formula

$$[p\tilde{v}\tilde{v}] = \sum_{\substack{i,j=0 \\ i>j}}^{k} ((i,j))^2 - \sum_{i=1}^{k} d_i \tilde{\alpha}_i. \tag{10.3.23}$$

Then, we can construct confidence intervals $I_{\gamma}^{(i)}$ for estimating the α_i's, using formula (8.3.14). In this formula we should put

$$n=k; \quad N=\frac{k(k+1)}{2}; \quad N-n=\frac{k(k-1)}{2}, \qquad (10.3.24)$$
$$\{C^{-1}\}_{ii}=\frac{2}{k+1}.$$

Using Table I, of Student's distribution, for a given confidence coefficient p_0 and degrees of freedom $N-n=\frac{k(k-1)}{2}$ we find γ_0. The confidence interval

$$I_{\gamma_0}^{(i)}=\left[\tilde{\alpha}_i-2\gamma_0\sqrt{\frac{[p\tilde{v}\tilde{v}]}{k(k^2-1)}}, \quad \tilde{\alpha}_i+2\gamma_0\sqrt{\frac{[p\tilde{v}\tilde{v}]}{k(k^2-1)}}\right] \qquad (10.3.25)$$

covers the measured angle α_i with probability p_0. To estimate σ by confidence intervals we use Table III. For a given confidence coefficient p_0 we find the values γ_1 and γ_2. The confidence interval

$$I=\left[\gamma_1\sqrt{\frac{2[p\tilde{v}\tilde{v}]}{k(k-1)}}, \quad \gamma_2\sqrt{\frac{2[p\tilde{v}\tilde{v}]}{k(k-1)}}\right] \qquad (10.3.26)$$

covers σ with probability p_0.

Besides the angles $\alpha_1, \ldots, \alpha_k$, we want to know the angles $\alpha_\mu-\alpha_\nu$ $(\mu>\nu)$ between the directions of the lines. The estimator of $\alpha_\mu-\alpha_\nu$ is of the form $\tilde{\alpha}_\mu-\tilde{\alpha}_\nu$ (see chapter VII). We will find its variance and construct confidence intervals for it, using the results of chapter VII.

Let $\tilde{\alpha}=\tilde{\alpha}_\mu-\tilde{\alpha}_\nu$. We must first of all find $D(\tilde{\alpha})$. We have

$$\begin{aligned} D(\tilde{\alpha}) &= E\left(\tilde{\alpha}_\mu-\alpha_\mu-(\tilde{\alpha}_\nu-\alpha_\nu)\right)^2= \\ &= D(\tilde{\alpha}_\mu)+D(\tilde{\alpha}_\nu)-2E(\tilde{\alpha}_\mu-\alpha_\mu)(\tilde{\alpha}_\nu-\alpha_\nu)= \\ &= \sigma^2\left(\{C^{-1}\}_{\mu\mu}+\{C^{-1}\}_{\nu\nu}-2\cdot\{C^{-1}\}_{\mu\nu}\right). \end{aligned} \qquad (10.3.27)$$

Thus, we must find all elements of the reciprocal matrix C^{-1}, except the diagonal elements, which have already been found.

The matrix C is of the form

$$C=\begin{Vmatrix} k & -1 & \ldots & -1 \\ -1 & k & \ldots & -1 \\ \cdot & \cdot & \cdot & \cdot \\ -1 & -1 & \ldots & k \end{Vmatrix}.$$

We calculate the element $\{C^{-1}\}_{ji}$. Let i be less than j. We put all the elements of the j th column in C equal to zero except the element of i th row of this column, which is put equal to one, and consider the matrix

$$
\begin{array}{c}
\\ \\ \\ i \rightarrow \\ \\ \\ \\ \\ \\ \\
\end{array}
\begin{array}{c}
\begin{array}{cccccccccc}
 & & & i\downarrow & & & j\downarrow & & & \\
\end{array}\\
\begin{Vmatrix}
k & -1 & \ldots & -1 & \ldots & -1 & 0 & -1 & \ldots & -1 \\
-1 & k & \ldots & -1 & \ldots & -1 & 0 & -1 & \ldots & -1 \\
\cdot & \cdot & \cdot & \cdot & \cdot & \cdot & \cdot & \cdot & \cdot & \cdot \\
-1 & -1 & \ldots & k & \ldots & -1 & 1 & -1 & \ldots & -1 \\
\cdot & \cdot & \cdot & \cdot & \cdot & \cdot & \cdot & \cdot & \cdot & \cdot \\
-1 & -1 & \ldots & -1 & \ldots & k & 0 & -1 & \ldots & -1 \\
-1 & -1 & \ldots & -1 & \ldots & -1 & 0 & -1 & \ldots & -1 \\
-1 & -1 & \ldots & -1 & \ldots & -1 & 0 & k & \ldots & -1 \\
\cdot & \cdot & \cdot & \cdot & \cdot & \cdot & \cdot & \cdot & \cdot & \cdot \\
-1 & -1 & \ldots & -1 & \ldots & -1 & 0 & -1 & \ldots & k
\end{Vmatrix}
\end{array}
$$

We add the 2nd, . . . , k th row to the first row, and then the first row so obtained to all the remainder. We obtain

$$
\begin{array}{c}
\\ \\ \\ i \rightarrow \\ \\ \\ \\ \\ \\ \\
\end{array}
\begin{array}{c}
\begin{array}{cccccccccc}
 & & & i\downarrow & & & j\downarrow & & & \\
\end{array}\\
\begin{Vmatrix}
1 & 1 & \ldots & 1 & \ldots & 1 & 1 & 1 & \ldots & 1 \\
0 & k+1 & \ldots & 0 & \ldots & 0 & 1 & 0 & \ldots & 0 \\
\cdot & \cdot & \cdot & \cdot & \cdot & \cdot & \cdot & \cdot & \cdot & \cdot \\
0 & 0 & \ldots & k+1 & \ldots & 0 & 2 & 0 & \ldots & 0 \\
\cdot & \cdot & \cdot & \cdot & \cdot & \cdot & \cdot & \cdot & \cdot & \cdot \\
0 & 0 & \ldots & 0 & \ldots & k+1 & 1 & 0 & \ldots & 0 \\
0 & 0 & \ldots & 0 & \ldots & 0 & 1 & 0 & \ldots & 0 \\
0 & 0 & \ldots & 0 & \ldots & 0 & 1 & k+1 & \ldots & 0 \\
\cdot & \cdot & \cdot & \cdot & \cdot & \cdot & \cdot & \cdot & \cdot & \cdot \\
0 & 0 & \ldots & 0 & \ldots & 0 & 1 & 0 & \ldots & k+1
\end{Vmatrix}
\end{array}
$$

All the elements of the j th row, except (jj), are equal to zero; consequently, we can remove the j th column and the j th row. Then we obtain a determinant of order $(k-1)$, in which there are zeros below the diagonal and in the principal diagonal there are $(k-2)$ - elements equal to $(k+1)$. This determinant is equal to $(k+1)^{k-2}$, but

$$\det(C) = (k+1)^{k-1}.$$

Thus

$$\{C^{-1}\}_{ij} = \{C^{-1}\}_{ji} = \frac{1}{k+1}.$$

Using formulae (10.3.27) and (10.3.20) we find

$$D(\tilde{\alpha})=\frac{\sigma^2}{k+1}(2+2-2)=\frac{2\sigma^2}{k+1}, \quad (10.3.28)$$

$$\sigma(\tilde{\alpha})=\sigma\sqrt{\frac{2}{k+1}}. \quad (10.3.29)$$

Comparing with formula (10.3.21) we see that

$$D(\tilde{\alpha}_\mu-\tilde{\alpha}_\nu)=D(\tilde{\alpha}_\mu)=D(\tilde{\alpha}_\nu)=\frac{2\sigma^2}{k+1}\ (\mu>\nu),$$

i.e. the estimators of the angles are in such a statistical relationship that the variance of the estimator of the difference between the angles is equal to the variance of the estimator of each angle. Now, we construct a confidence interval. Using formula (7.4.5) we form the quantity

$$\tilde{S}^2=\frac{[p\tilde{v}\tilde{v}]}{N-n}\frac{D(\tilde{\alpha})}{\sigma^2}=\frac{4[p\tilde{v}\tilde{v}]}{k(k^2-1)}. \quad (10.3.30)$$

Formula (7.4.8) shows that if we choose γ_0, with confidence coefficient p_0 and $\frac{k(k-1)}{2}$ degrees of freedom from Table I, of Student's distribution, we determine the confidence interval

$$I_\gamma=\left[\tilde{\alpha}-2\gamma_0\sqrt{\frac{[p\tilde{v}\tilde{v}]}{k(k^2-1)}},\ \tilde{\alpha}+2\gamma_0\sqrt{\frac{[p\tilde{v}\tilde{v}]}{k(k^2-1)}}\right], \quad (10.3.31)$$

covering $\alpha_\mu-\alpha_\nu$ with probability p_0.

CHAPTER XI

ESTIMATION OF RESULTS OF DIRECT AND REVERSE BEARINGS

1. Direct Bearings From More Than Two Points. Confidence Regions *)

As was shown in the introduction, problems of estimation from results of direct bearings are very often encountered in practice. In problems of geodesy and of instrumental reconnaissance in artillery and in problems of phonometry and radiolocation, it is often necessary to determine a point by means of bearings on it from some fixed points (points with known co-ordinates).

Suppose there are n fixed points $A_1, A_2, \ldots, A_n$ with known co-ordinates (Fig. 10); we measure the angles between the lines A_1A_1', A_2A_2', ..., A_nA_n' (which have known angles of direction) and the direction to the required point O. Due to the random errors in measurements of the angles, these lines do not intersect in a single point and do not give a unique point O, so that there arises the problem of estimating the position of the point O from the observational data. Assuming the errors to be small, we can first calculate approximate co-ordinates (x_0', y_0') by elementary trigonometrical formulae, using any triangle, among the $n-1$ available triangles, which has no angle less than 30°. To make the problem linear we will assume the corrections $x_0' - x_0$, $y_0' - y_0$ to be small, so that their squares can be ignored in comparison to the chosen unit of length.

We can consider the point O', with co-ordinates (x_0', y_0'), as an auxiliary fixed point; we denote the lengths of the lines A_iO' by d_i', and their angles of direction, $\alpha_i^{(0)}$, can be assumed to be known exactly. If α_i is the true value of the angle of direction of A_iO, then,

$$\alpha_i = \alpha_i^{(0)} + \Delta\alpha_i. \qquad (11.1.1)$$

---

* The geometrical part of the problem of direct and reverse bearings is here treated as in Chebotariev's book 'Geodesy', part II, M.1949. Only the construction of confidence regions is added.

For the system of co-ordinates chosen in this way we have

$$\operatorname{tg} \alpha_i^{(0)} = \frac{y_0' - y_i}{x_0' - x_i}; \quad y_0 - y_0' = \Delta y_0, \quad x_0 - x_0' = \Delta x_0. \tag{11.1.2}$$

We will measure the angles in radians; then we obtain

$$\frac{\Delta \alpha_i}{\cos^2 \alpha_i^{(0)}} \approx \frac{(x_0' - x_i)\,\Delta y_0 - (y_0' - y_i)\,\Delta x_0}{(x_0' - x_i)^2} \tag{11.1.3}$$

(this equation is correct to quantities of the second order of smallness).

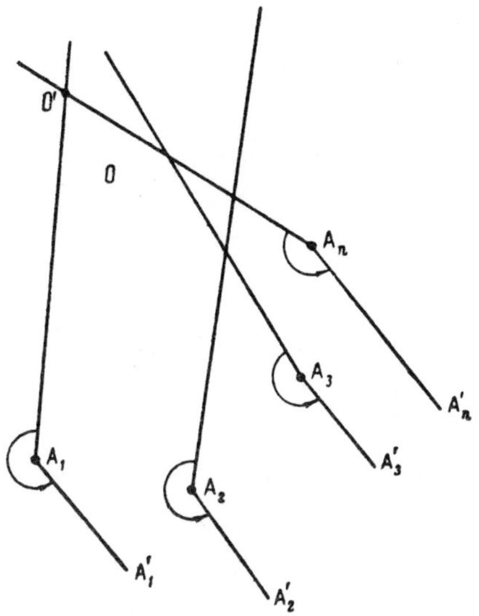

Fig. 10

Further, in the given system of co-ordinates

$$x_0' - x_i = d_i' \cos \alpha_i^{(0)}; \quad y_0' - y_i = d_i' \sin \alpha_i^{(0)}. \tag{11.1.4}$$

In view of (11.1.3), we obtain

$$\Delta \alpha_i \approx \frac{\cos \alpha_i^{(0)}}{d_i'} \Delta y_0 - \frac{\sin \alpha_i^{(0)}}{d_i'} \Delta x_0 . \tag{11.1.5}$$

However, we do not know the difference $\Delta \alpha_i = \alpha_i - \alpha_i^{(0)}$, but only the values $l_i = \alpha_i - \alpha_i^{(0)} + \Delta_i = \Delta\alpha_i + \Delta_i$ $(i = 1, 2, \ldots, n)$, because the observations contain the errors Δ_i. We assume these errors to be of equal accuracy, unbiased, independent and normal $N(0, \sigma)$.

We also write

$$-\frac{\sin \alpha_i^{(0)}}{d_i'} = a_i; \quad \frac{\cos \alpha_i^{(0)}}{d_i'} = b_i \quad (i = 1, 2, \ldots, n). \tag{11.1.6}$$

Then we obtain (with accuracy to quantities of the second order of smallness),

$$l_i - \Delta_i = a_i \Delta x_0 + b_i \Delta y_0 \quad (i = 1, 2, \ldots, n), \tag{11.1.7}$$

Thus, the task reduces to the problem considered in chapter VI (indirect, unconditional measurements). The fact that there are only two quantities, Δx_0 and Δy_0, allows us to give explicit expressions for point estimation; we will give them, and then we will construct confidence regions for the pair $(\Delta x_0, \Delta y_0)$.

The matrix of coefficients is of the form

$$X = \begin{Vmatrix} a_1 & b_1 \\ a_2 & b_2 \\ \vdots & \vdots \\ a_n & b_n \end{Vmatrix}. \tag{11.1.8}$$

We will assume, as usual, that $n > 2$, so that we have, at least, three fixed points.

We have: rank $(X) = 2$. In fact

$$\begin{vmatrix} a_1 & b_1 \\ a_2 & b_2 \end{vmatrix} = \begin{vmatrix} -\frac{\sin \alpha_1^{(0)}}{d_1'} & \frac{\cos \alpha_1^{(0)}}{d_1'} \\ -\frac{\sin \alpha_2^{(0)}}{d_2'} & \frac{\cos \alpha_2^{(0)}}{d_2'} \end{vmatrix} = \frac{1}{d_1' d_2'}\left(\sin \alpha_2^{(0)} \cos \alpha_1^{(0)} - \sin \alpha_1^{(0)} \cos \alpha_2^{(0)}\right) =$$

$$= \frac{1}{d_1' d_2'} \sin\left(\alpha_2^{(0)} - \alpha_1^{(0)}\right) \neq 0 .$$

To construct the normal equations we use the summary formulae of chapter VI, (section 11). From (6.11.2), remembering that $p_i = 1$, we obtain the normal equations

$$\left.\begin{aligned} [aa]\,\widetilde{\Delta x} + [ab]\,\widetilde{\Delta y} &= [al], \\ [ab]\,\widetilde{\Delta x} + [bb]\,\widetilde{\Delta y} &= [bl], \end{aligned}\right\} \tag{11.1.9}$$

where $\widetilde{\Delta x}$, $\widetilde{\Delta y}$ denote the estimators of Δx_0 and Δy_0 respectively. Hence we find immediately

$$\left.\begin{aligned}\widetilde{\Delta x}&=\frac{[bb][al]-[ab][bl]}{[aa][bb]-[ab]^2},\\ \widetilde{\Delta y}&=\frac{[aa][bl]-[ab][al]}{[aa][bb]-[ab]^2}.\end{aligned}\right\} \quad (11.1.10)$$

We have obtained the point estimators $(\widetilde{\Delta x}, \widetilde{\Delta y})$ for the true corrections Δx_0, Δy_0. We now find the correlation matrix of the vector of estimators $(\widetilde{\Delta x}, \widetilde{\Delta y})$, which is equal to $\sigma^2 C^{-1}$. We have

$$C=\begin{Vmatrix}[aa] & [ab]\\ [ab] & [bb]\end{Vmatrix}. \quad (11.1.11)$$

We put $D=[aa][bb]-]ab]^2$.

The required correlation matrix is

$$B=\sigma^2 C^{-1}=\frac{\sigma^2}{D}\begin{Vmatrix}[bb] & -[ab]\\ -[ab] & [aa]\end{Vmatrix}. \quad (11.1.12)$$

Hence

$$D(\widetilde{\Delta x})=\frac{\sigma^2[bb]}{D};\quad \sigma(\widetilde{\Delta x})=\sigma\sqrt{\frac{[bb]}{D}}; \quad (11.1.13)$$

$$D(\widetilde{\Delta y})=\frac{\sigma^2[aa]}{D};\quad \sigma(\widetilde{\Delta y})=\sigma\sqrt{\frac{[aa]}{D}}. \quad (11.1.14)$$

From these formulae, characterizing the accuracy of estimation, we see that for a finite number n of fixed points $A_1, \ldots, A_n$ we have greater accuracy the smaller the standard error of measurement of the angles, σ.

For later work we must obtain an expression for $[p\tilde{v}\tilde{v}]$. Using formula (6.11.3) we find

$$[p\tilde{v}\tilde{v}]=[\tilde{v}\tilde{v}]=[ll]-[al]\widetilde{\Delta x}-[bl]\widetilde{\Delta y}, \quad (11.1.15)$$

where $\tilde{v}$ has the same meaning as in chapter VI, and $\widetilde{\Delta x}$ and $\widetilde{\Delta y}$ are defined by formulae (11.1.10).

Further, we have (see chapter VI, section 9).

$$E\left(\frac{[p\tilde{v}\tilde{v}]}{n-2}\right)=\sigma^2, \quad (11.1.16)$$

so that $\frac{[p\tilde{v}\tilde{v}]}{n-2}$ is an unbiased estimator of σ^2. As was shown in chapter VI, section 9, we can use $[p\tilde{v}\tilde{v}]$ in the estimation of σ by confidence intervals; however, it hardly appears to be expedient to do this in the case of bearings, when it is more natural to estimate the accuracy of the measuring instruments from previous knowledge of their work under similar conditions. It would appear to be more appropriate to consider the problem of constructing confidence regions covering the required true corrections $(\Delta x_0, \Delta y_0)$. Here we will present two constructions for such confidence regions. We start by constructing confidence intervals separately for Δx_0 and Δy_0, using formula (6.11.10).

Table I of Student's distribution, with $k=n-2$ degrees of freedom, is used here. From (11.1.15), using also (11.1.10), we calculate $[p\tilde{v}\tilde{v}]=[\tilde{v}\tilde{v}]$. With confidence coefficient p, we find the value γ for $n-2$ degrees of freedom. Further,

$$C^{-1}=\frac{1}{D}\begin{Vmatrix} [bb] & -[ab] \\ -[ab] & [aa] \end{Vmatrix}. \tag{11.1.17}$$

Thus, we obtain the confidence interval for Δx_0

$$I_\gamma^{(\Delta x_0)}=\left[\widetilde{\Delta x}-\gamma\sqrt{\frac{[bb]}{D}\frac{[\tilde{v}\tilde{v}]}{n-2}},\quad \widetilde{\Delta x}+\gamma\sqrt{\frac{[bb]}{D}\frac{[\tilde{v}\tilde{v}]}{n-2}}\right]. \tag{11.1.18}$$

For Δy_0, the confidence interval is of the form

$$I_\gamma^{(\Delta y_0)}=\left[\widetilde{\Delta y}-\gamma\sqrt{\frac{[aa]}{D}\frac{[\tilde{v}\tilde{v}]}{n-2}},\quad \widetilde{\Delta y}+\gamma\sqrt{\frac{[aa]}{D}\frac{[\tilde{v}\tilde{v}]}{n-2}}\right]. \tag{11.1.19}$$

Let $\mathfrak{A}$ be the event that the interval $I_\gamma^{(\Delta x_0)}$ covers Δx_0 (which we will write: $\Delta x_0 \in I_\gamma^{(\Delta x_0)}$) and let $\mathfrak{B}$ be the event $\Delta y_0 \in I_\gamma^{(\Delta y_0)}$.

The probabilities of each event separately are equal to p:

$$P(\mathfrak{A})=p; \quad P(\mathfrak{B})=p.$$

The product of the events $\mathfrak{A}$ and $\mathfrak{B}$ means that the point $(\Delta x_0, \Delta y_0)$ is covered by the rectangle Q_γ, projections of which on the coordinate axes are $I_\gamma^{(\Delta x)}$ and $I_\gamma^{(\Delta y)}$ (by which it is therefore determined). However, the product of the events, i.e. the event ($\mathfrak{A}$ and $\mathfrak{B}$), does not have probability equal to the product of $P(\mathfrak{A})$ and $P(\mathfrak{B})$, since the events $\mathfrak{A}$ and $\mathfrak{B}$ are dependent. Nevertheless, applying elementary theorems in probability, we can write

$$P(\mathfrak{A} \text{ and } \mathfrak{B})=1-P(\overline{\mathfrak{A}} \text{ or } \overline{\mathfrak{B}})=$$
$$=1-P(\overline{\mathfrak{A}})-P(\overline{\mathfrak{B}})+P(\overline{\mathfrak{A}} \text{ and } \overline{\mathfrak{B}})\geqslant 1-P(\mathfrak{A})-P(\mathfrak{B}), \tag{11.1.20}$$

where $\bar{\mathfrak{A}}$ and $\bar{\mathfrak{B}}$ are the events contrary to the events $\mathfrak{A}$ and $\mathfrak{B}$ respectively.

Further, we have

$$P(\bar{\mathfrak{A}}) = 1 - P(\mathfrak{A}) = 1 - p;\quad P(\bar{\mathfrak{B}}) = 1 - p.$$

Thus, from (11.1.20), we obtain

$$P(\mathfrak{A} \text{ and } \mathfrak{B}) \geqslant 1 - (1-p) - (1-p) = 2p - 1. \quad \textbf{(11.1.21)}$$

For example, if $p = 0{,}9$, then $P(\mathfrak{A}$ and $\mathfrak{B}) \geqslant 0{,}8$, and if $p = 0{,}95$, then $P(\mathfrak{A}$ and $\mathfrak{B}) \geqslant 0{,}9$.

Hence we can formulate the following theorem.

Theorem 1.1.1.

The rectangular region Q_γ, determined by its projections on the co-ordinate axes, i.e. by the confidence intervals (11.1.8) and (11.1.9), covers the point $(\Delta x_0, \Delta y_0)$ with probability not less than $2p - 1$, where p is the confidence coefficient for each interval.

We will call the region Q_γ a confidence rectangle.

As can be seen from formulae (11.1.18) and (11.1.19), the breadth and length of the confidence rectangle are equal to

$$2\gamma\sqrt{\frac{[bb]}{D}\frac{[\tilde{v}\tilde{v}]}{n-2}} \text{ and } 2\gamma\sqrt{\frac{[aa]}{D}\frac{[\tilde{v}\tilde{v}]}{n-2}}. \quad \textbf{(11.1.22)}$$

respectively.

We note that, for confidence coefficient $p = 0{,}95$ and finite number of degrees of freedom, $n-2$ the value γ can be comparatively large. Since $E\left(\frac{[\tilde{v}\tilde{v}]}{n-2}\right) = \sigma^2$, then from (11.1.22) we see that, for this value of p, the application of confidence rectangle Q_γ will be useful only for sufficiently good accuracy of the original measurements (sufficiently small σ^2).

We will also describe one further form of confidence region, covering the point $(\Delta x_0, \Delta y_0)$ with probability p. As follows from theorem 6.6.3, the random vector $(\widetilde{\Delta x}, \widetilde{\Delta y})$ is statistically independent of the vector $[\tilde{v}\tilde{v}]$, determined by the formula (11.1.15). The correlation matrix of this vector is equal to $\sigma^2 C^{-1}$. We will find the density function of the normal vector $(\widetilde{\Delta x} - \Delta x_0, \widetilde{\Delta y} - \Delta y_0)$. According to formula (2.3.10), this density function $f(\xi, \eta)$ is of the form

$$f(\xi, \eta)=\frac{\sqrt{D}}{2\pi\sigma^2}\exp\left\{-\frac{1}{2\sigma^2}\left[[aa]\xi^2+2[ab]\xi\eta+[bb]\eta^2\right]\right\}. \quad (11.1.23)$$

We put $Q(\xi, \eta)=([aa]\xi^2+2[ab]\xi\eta+[bb]\eta^2)$ and prove that the quantity $\frac{1}{\sigma^2}Q(\xi, \eta)$ is distributed according to the χ_2^2 law. We have

$$\varphi(x)=P\left(\frac{1}{\sigma^2}Q(\xi, \eta)<x\right)=\iint_{\frac{1}{\sigma^2}Q(\xi, \eta)<x} f(\xi, \eta)\,d\xi\,d\eta=$$

$$=\frac{\sqrt{D}}{2\pi\sigma^2}\iint_{\frac{1}{\sigma^2}Q(\xi, \eta)<x}\exp\left\{-\frac{1}{2\sigma^2}Q(\xi, \eta)\right\}d\xi\,d\eta. \quad (11.1.24)$$

Putting $\frac{\xi}{\sigma}=u_1$, $\frac{\eta}{\sigma}=u_2$, we have

$$\varphi(x)=\frac{\sqrt{D}}{2\pi}\iint_{Q(u_1, u_2)<x}\exp\left\{-\frac{1}{2}Q(u_1, u_2)\right\}du_1\,du_2. \quad (11.1.25)$$

We introduce the matrix $U=U_{21}=\left\|\begin{matrix}u_1\\ u_2\end{matrix}\right\|$; then, (see chapter II, section 3), we obtain

$$\varphi(x)=\frac{\sqrt{D}}{2\pi}\iint_{U^TCU<x}\exp\left\{-\frac{1}{2}U^TCU\right\}du_1\,du_2. \quad (11.1.26)$$

We introduce an orthogonal transformation F, putting

$$U'=\left\|\begin{matrix}u_1'\\ u_2'\end{matrix}\right\|=FU \quad \text{so that} \quad F^TCF=\left\|\begin{matrix}d_1 & 0\\ 0 & d_2\end{matrix}\right\|$$

is a diagonal matrix. Also $d_1d_2=D$. We obtain

$$\varphi(x)=\frac{\sqrt{D}}{2\pi}\iint_{d_1u_1'^2+d_2u_2'^2<x}\exp\left\{-\frac{1}{2}\left(d_1u_1'^2+d_2u_2'^2\right)\right\}du_1'\,du_2'.$$

We also put $w_1=u_1'\sqrt{d_1}$; $w_2=u_2'\sqrt{d_2}$; then

$$\varphi(x)=\frac{1}{2\pi}\iint\limits_{w_1^2+w_2^2<x}\exp\left\{-\frac{1}{2}\left(w_1^2+w_2^2\right)\right\}dw_1\,dw_2. \qquad (11.1.27)$$

But on the right-hand side there is a quantity equal, by definition, to $P\left(\chi_2^2<x\right)$ (see chapter II, section 6). Thus

$$\varphi(x)=P\left(\chi_2^2<x\right)$$

and

$$\frac{1}{\sigma^2}Q(\xi,\eta)=\chi_2^2, \qquad (11.1.28)$$

which it was required to prove.

Now we can construct the confidence region for $(\Delta x_0, \Delta y_0)$. We have

$$\frac{1}{\sigma^2}Q(\xi,\eta)=\chi_2^2 \quad \text{and} \quad \frac{[\tilde{v}\tilde{v}]}{\sigma^2}=\chi_{n-2}^2,$$

and these quantities are mutually independent. Thus the quantity

$$\frac{\frac{1}{\sigma^2}Q(\xi,\eta)}{\frac{[\tilde{v}\tilde{v}]}{\sigma^2}}=\frac{Q(\xi,\eta)}{[\tilde{v}\tilde{v}]} \qquad (11.1.29)$$

is distributed as Fisher's $F_{2,n-2}(x)$ (see chapter II, section 6). Writing the expressions $Q(\xi,\eta)$ and $[\tilde{v}\tilde{v}]$ in more detailed form we get the following theorem.

Theorem 11.1.2 *).

The quantity

$$\frac{Q(\xi,\eta)}{[\tilde{v}\tilde{v}]}=\frac{[aa]\left(\widetilde{\Delta x}-\Delta x_0\right)^2+2[ab]\left(\widetilde{\Delta x}-\Delta x_0\right)\left(\widetilde{\Delta y}-\Delta y_0\right)+[bb]\left(\widetilde{\Delta y}-\Delta y_0\right)^2}{[ll]-[al]\widetilde{\Delta x}-[bl]\widetilde{\Delta y}} \qquad (11.1.30)$$

has Fisher's $F_{2,n-2}(x)$ distribution.

This last distribution is of very simple form. From formula (2.6.13) we see that

* This theorem is probably new.

$$F'_{2, n-2}(x) = f_{2, n-2}(x) = \frac{\Gamma\left(\frac{n}{2}\right)}{\Gamma(1)\Gamma\left(\frac{n}{2}-1\right)} \cdot \frac{1}{(1+x)^{\frac{n}{2}}} = \frac{\frac{n}{2}-1}{(1+x)^{\frac{n}{2}}} \quad (x>0). \tag{11.1.31}$$

Thus, for $\gamma > 0$, we have

$$F_{2, n-2}(\gamma) = \left(\frac{n-2}{2}\right) \int_0^{\gamma} \frac{dx}{(1+x)^{\frac{n}{2}}} = 1 - \frac{1}{(1+\gamma)^{\frac{n-2}{2}}}. \tag{11.1.32}$$

Therefore

$$P\left(\frac{Q(\xi, \eta)}{[\tilde{v}\tilde{v}]} < \gamma\right) = P(Q(\xi, \eta) < \gamma[\tilde{v}\tilde{v}]) = 1 - \frac{1}{(1+\gamma)^{\frac{n-2}{2}}}. \tag{11.1.33}$$

If the confidence coefficient p_0 is chosen, then for $F_{2, n-2}(\gamma) = p_0$ we have

$$p_0 = 1 - \frac{1}{(1+\gamma)^{\frac{n-2}{2}}}; \qquad \gamma = \frac{1}{(1-p_0)^{\frac{2}{n-2}}} - 1. \tag{11.1.34}$$

The values of γ as a function of n are given in Table II of the Appendix.

The event $Q(\xi, \eta) < \gamma[\tilde{v}\tilde{v}]$ can be written in the form

$$Q(\Delta x_0 - \widetilde{\Delta x};\ \Delta y_0 - \widetilde{\Delta y}) < \gamma([ll] - [al]\widetilde{\Delta x} - [bl]\widetilde{\Delta y}) \tag{11.1.35}$$

and can be interpreted in the following way: for given $\widetilde{\Delta x}, \widetilde{\Delta y}$ the point $(\Delta x_0, \Delta y_0)$ lies inside a certain ellipse with centre $(\widetilde{\Delta x}, \widetilde{\Delta y})$ known semi-axes ratio and position in the plane, determined by the quadratic form $Q(\xi, \eta) = [aa]\xi^2 + 2[ab]\xi\eta + [bb]\eta^2$ with known coefficients and with major half-axis determined by the right-hand side of (11.1.35). This ellipse, which we will denote by $\mathcal{E}_{\gamma}$, and which has the equation

$$Q(\Delta x - \widetilde{\Delta x},\ \Delta y - \widetilde{\Delta y}) = \gamma([ll] - [al]\widetilde{\Delta x} - [bl]\widetilde{\Delta y}) \tag{11.1.36}$$

(Δx, Δy are current co-ordinates), does cover the point $(\Delta x_0, \Delta y_0)$ if (11.1.35) is valid. In the situation, which we are studying, where $(\widetilde{\Delta x}, \widetilde{\Delta y})$ is a random vector, this ellipse is random and covers the point $(\Delta x_0, \Delta y_0)$ with probability p_0, where p_0 and γ are related by (11.1.34). This leads to theorem 11.1.2.

We will also consider what happens as n increases. For large n we will have

$$\left(\frac{1}{1-p_0}\right)^{\frac{2}{n-2}} = \exp \frac{2}{n-2} \ln \frac{1}{1-p_0} = 1 + \frac{2}{n-2} \ln \frac{1}{1-p_0} + \delta_n,$$

where $\delta_n \leqslant \frac{K(p_0)}{n^2}$. Here $K(p_0)$ is a constant depending only on p_0. Thus

$$\gamma = \frac{-2}{n-2} \ln (1-p_0) + \delta_n \approx \frac{2}{n-2} \ln \frac{1}{1-p_0}$$

for large n.

In view of this, the confidence ellipse, for large n, is approximately of the form

$$Q(\Delta x - \widetilde{\Delta x},\ \Delta y - \widetilde{\Delta y}) \approx \frac{2}{n-2} \ln \frac{1}{1-p_0} [\tilde{v}\tilde{v}]. \qquad (11.1.37)$$

Theorem 11.1.3.

For a given confidence coefficient p_0, the confidence ellipse $\mathcal{E}_\gamma$ with the equation

$$Q(\Delta x - \widetilde{\Delta x},\ \Delta y - \widetilde{\Delta y}) = \gamma([ll] - [al]\widetilde{\Delta x} - [bl]\widetilde{\Delta y}), \qquad (11.1.38)$$

where Δx, Δy are the current co-ordinates, $Q(\xi, \eta) = [aa]\xi^2 + 2[ab]\xi\eta + [bb]\eta^2$ and $\gamma = \frac{1}{(1-p_0)^{\frac{2}{n-2}}} - 1$, covers the point $(\Delta x_0, \Delta y_0)$ with probability p_0.

We note that the ellipse $Q(\xi, \eta) = 1$ is the correlation ellipse of the random vector $(\widetilde{\Delta x}, \widetilde{\Delta y})$ (see chapter II, section 4). We will also make use of the following remark on the accuracy of working with the confidence ellipse $\mathcal{E}_\gamma$. Its dimensions are determined by the right-hand side of (11.1.38), which is equal to $\gamma[\tilde{v}\tilde{v}]$ and also

$$E\gamma[\tilde{v}\tilde{v}] = (n-2)\gamma\sigma^2. \qquad (11.1.39)$$

Thus, for given n, good accuracy is obtained (as in all other methods of estimation) only with small σ^2, i.e. with large initial weights; for example, with a sufficient number of repeated measurements of the angles.

We will also consider the problem of the most suitable choice of the points $A_1, \ldots, A_n$, if, of course, it is possible for us to choose them. From formulae (11.1.13) and (11.1.14) we see that $D(\widetilde{\Delta x})$ and $D(\widetilde{\Delta y})$ are proportional to the ratios of $[aa]$ and $[bb]$ to $D=[aa][bb]-([ab])^2$; the quantities a_i and b_i have a geometrical meaning, which is clear from formulae (11.1.6). If we take as the measure of the accuracy of the work the sum $D(\widetilde{\Delta x})+D(\widetilde{\Delta y})$, then we see that the most desirable choice of the $A_i (i=1, 2, \ldots, n)$, is that for which the quantity

$$\frac{[aa]+[bb]}{[aa][bb]-[ab]^2} \tag{11.1.40}$$

is as small as possible.

2. Direct Bearings from Two Points with Repeated Observations

We will consider the case of simple direct bearings from two fixed points A_1 and A_2, and we will also suppose, for simplicity, that at each point $n/2$ (n being even) observations of equal accuracy are made. We can make the same assertions as in section 1; formulae (11.1.1) - (11.1.6) will be satisfied with $i=1, 2$; in particular, a_i and $b_i (i=1, 2)$ will take the values given by equations (11.1.6). The fundamental equations for the elements Δx_0, Δy_0 are of the form

$$l_i-\Delta_i=a_1\Delta x_0+b_1\Delta y_0 \qquad \left(i=1, 2, \ldots, \frac{n}{2}\right),$$
$$l_i-\Delta_i=a_2\Delta x_0+b_2\Delta y_0 \qquad \left(i=\frac{n}{2}+1, \ldots, n\right).$$

Thus, the basic coefficient matrix X will be

$$X=\left\|\begin{matrix} a_1 & b_1 \\ a_1 & b_1 \\ \vdots & \vdots \\ a_1 & b_1 \\ a_2 & b_2 \\ \vdots & \vdots \\ a_2 & b_2 \end{matrix}\right\| \begin{matrix} \left.\vphantom{\begin{matrix}a\\a\\ \vdots\\a\end{matrix}}\right\}\frac{n}{2} \\ \left.\vphantom{\begin{matrix}a\\ \vdots\\a\end{matrix}}\right\}\frac{n}{2}\end{matrix} . \tag{11.2.1}$$

The normal equations for the estimators $\widetilde{\Delta x}$ and $\widetilde{\Delta y}$ of the quantities Δx_0, Δy_0 are of the form (11.1.9):

$$[aa]\widetilde{\Delta x} + [ab]\widetilde{\Delta y} = [al],$$
$$[ab]\widetilde{\Delta x} + [bb]\widetilde{\Delta y} = [bl], \tag{11.2.2}$$

where

$$\left.\begin{aligned}
&[aa] = \frac{n(a_1^2 + a_2^2)}{2}; \ [bb] = \frac{n(b_1^2 + b_2^2)}{2};\\
&[ab] = \frac{n(a_1 b_1 + a_2 b_2)}{2}; \ [al] = a_1\left(l_1 + \ldots + l_{\frac{n}{2}}\right) +\\
&\qquad + a_2\left(l_{\frac{n}{2}+1} + \ldots + l_n\right);\\
&[bl] = b_1\left(l_1 + \ldots + l_{\frac{n}{2}}\right) + b_2\left(l_{\frac{n}{2}+1} + \ldots + l_n\right).
\end{aligned}\right\} \tag{11.2.3}$$

In view of this,

$$D = [aa][bb] - [ab]^2 = \frac{n^2}{4}\left((a_1^2 + a_2^2)(b_1^2 + b_2^2) - (a_1 b_1 + a_2 b_2)^2\right) =$$
$$= \frac{n^2}{4}(a_1 b_2 - a_2 b_1)^2 = \left(\frac{n}{2} D_0\right)^2,$$

where

$$D_0 = \begin{vmatrix} a_1 & b_1 \\ a_2 & b_2 \end{vmatrix}. \tag{11.2.4}$$

We also write

$$l_1 + \ldots + l_{\frac{n}{2}} = l^{(1)}; \quad l_{\frac{n}{2}+1} + \ldots + l_n = l^{(2)}. \tag{11.2.5}$$

The solutions of the normal equations (11.1.10) are of the form

$$\left.\begin{aligned}
\widetilde{\Delta x} &= \frac{(b_1^2+b_2^2)(a_1 l^{(1)} + a_2 l^{(2)}) - (a_1 b_1 + a_2 b_2)(b_1 l^{(1)} + b_2 l^{(2)})}{D_0^2},\\
\widetilde{\Delta y} &= \frac{(a_1^2+a_2^2)(b_1 l^{(1)} + b_2 l^{(2)}) - (a_1 b_1 + a_2 b_2)(a_1 l^{(1)} + a_2 l^{(2)})}{D_0^2}.
\end{aligned}\right\} \tag{11.2.6}$$

Elementary calculations simplify these expressions:

$$\left.\begin{aligned}
\widetilde{\Delta x} &= \frac{b_2 l^{(1)} - b_1 l^{(2)}}{D_0},\\
\widetilde{\Delta y} &= \frac{-a_2 l^{(1)} + a_1 l^{(2)}}{D_0}.
\end{aligned}\right\} \tag{11.2.7}$$

Further, (11.1.13) and (11.1.14) give

$$D(\widetilde{\Delta x}) = \frac{\sigma^2 n}{2} \cdot \frac{b_1^2 + b_2^2}{D_0^2}, \tag{11.2.8}$$

$$D(\widetilde{\Delta y}) = \frac{\sigma^2 n}{2} \cdot \frac{a_1^2 + a_2^2}{D_0^2}, \tag{11.2.9}$$

$$\sigma(\widetilde{\Delta x}) = \frac{\sigma}{|D_0|} \sqrt{\frac{n(b_1^2 + b_2^2)}{2}}; \quad \sigma(\widetilde{\Delta y}) = \frac{\sigma}{|D_0|} \sqrt{\frac{n(a_1^2 + a_2^2)}{2}}. \tag{11.2.10}$$

Later, we will recall the geometrical meanings of some of the quantities used.

According to the formulae (11.1.15) and (11.2.3) we have

$$[\tilde{v}\,\tilde{v}] = [ll] - (a_1 l^{(1)} + a_2 l^{(2)})\,\widetilde{\Delta x} - (b_1 l^{(1)} + b_2 l^{(2)})\,\widetilde{\Delta y}, \tag{11.2.11}$$

where $\widetilde{\Delta x}$ and $\widetilde{\Delta y}$ are determined by formulae (11.2.7).

We have

$$\frac{1}{\sigma^2}[\tilde{v}\,\tilde{v}] = \chi^2_{N-2}; \quad E[\tilde{v}\,\tilde{v}] = (n-2)\sigma^2. \tag{11.2.12}$$

Estimation of σ can be effected in the way described in chapter V. For increasing n, the asymptotically unbiased estimate of σ is

$$\sqrt{\frac{[\tilde{v}\,\tilde{v}]}{n-2}}.$$

Estimation of σ by confidence intervals can be effected, using Table III. Choosing a confidence coefficient p, we find, for $n-2$ degrees of freedom, values γ_1 and γ_2 such that the confidence interval

$$\left[\gamma_1 \sqrt{\frac{[\tilde{v}\,\tilde{v}]}{n-2}},\ \gamma_2 \sqrt{\frac{[\tilde{v}\,\tilde{v}]}{n-2}}\right] \tag{11.2.13}$$

covers σ with probability p.

A confidence region for the point $(\Delta x_0, \Delta y_0)$ is constructed as in section 1. Confidence intervals for Δx_0 and Δy_0 separately, according to (11.1.17), (11.1.18), (11.2.3) are of the form

$$I_\gamma^{(\Delta x_0)} = \left[\widetilde{\Delta x} - \frac{\gamma}{|D_0|}\sqrt{\frac{2}{n(n-2)}(b_1^2 + b_2^2)[\tilde{v}\,\tilde{v}]},\right.$$
$$\left.\widetilde{\Delta x} + \frac{\gamma}{|D_0|}\sqrt{\frac{2}{n(n-2)}(b_1^2 + b_2^2)[\tilde{v}\,\tilde{v}]}\right], \tag{11.2.14}$$

$$I_\gamma^{(\Delta y)} = \left[\widetilde{\Delta y} - \frac{\gamma}{|D_0|}\sqrt{\frac{2}{n(n-2)}(a_1^2+a_2^2)[\tilde{v}\tilde{v}]},\right.$$
$$\left.\widetilde{\Delta y} + \frac{\gamma}{|D_0|}\sqrt{\frac{2}{n(n-2)}(a_1^2+a_2^2)[\tilde{v}\tilde{v}]}\right], \quad (11.2.15)$$

where γ is taken for confidence coefficient p and the number of degrees of freedom given in section 1.

The confidence rectangle Q_γ, determined by its projections, $I_\gamma^{(\Delta x)}$, $I_\gamma^{(\Delta y)}$, on the co-ordinate axes, covers the point $(\Delta x_0, \Delta y_0)$ with probability not less than $2p-1$. The length and the breadth of the rectangle Q_γ are the random variables

$$\frac{2\gamma}{|D_0|}\sqrt{\frac{2}{n(n-2)}(b_1^2+b_2^2)[\tilde{v}\tilde{v}]} \quad \text{and} \quad \frac{2\gamma}{|D_0|}\sqrt{\frac{2}{n(n-2)}(a_1^2+a_2^2)[\tilde{v}\tilde{v}]}. \quad (11.2.16)$$

The expected values of these quantities have the asymptotic expressions, for large n,

$$\frac{\gamma\sigma}{|D_0|}\frac{2}{\sqrt{n}}\sqrt{2(b_1^2+b_2^2)} \quad \text{and} \quad \frac{\gamma\sigma}{|D_0|}\frac{2}{\sqrt{n}}\sqrt{2(a_1^2+a_2^2)}, \quad (11.2.17)$$

whence it is clear that the average dimensions of the confidence rectangle Q_γ, for large numbers of observations, n, are proportional to σ and inversely proportional to $\sqrt{n}$.

We now construct the confidence ellipse $Э_\gamma$. All calculations are carried out as in section 1. Here the matrix C of normal equations has the form

$$C = \frac{n}{2}\begin{Vmatrix} (a_1^2+a_2^2) & (a_1b_1+a_2b_2) \\ (a_1b_1+a_2b_2) & (b_1^2+b_2^2) \end{Vmatrix}, \quad (11.2.18)$$

and the quadratic form corresponding to it is

$$Q(\xi,\eta) = \frac{n}{2}\left((a_1^2+a_2^2)\xi^2 + 2(a_1b_1+a_2b_2)\xi\eta + (b_1^2+b_2^2)\eta^2\right) =$$
$$= \frac{n}{2}\left((a_1\xi+b_1\eta)^2+(a_2\xi+b_2\eta)^2\right). \quad (11.2.19)$$

The equation for the confidence ellipse is (see (11.1.36))

$$Q(\Delta x - \widetilde{\Delta x}, \Delta y - \widetilde{\Delta y}) = \gamma[\tilde{v}\tilde{v}]\frac{2}{n-2}, \quad (11.2.20)$$

where Δx, Δy are current co-ordinates, $[\tilde{v}\tilde{v}]$ is calculated from formula (11.2.11), and γ is connected with the confidence coefficient

p by the simple formula

$$\gamma = \frac{1}{(1-p)^{\frac{2}{n-2}}} - 1. \tag{11.2.21}$$

The ellipse $Э_\gamma$ covers the required point $(\Delta x_0, \Delta y_0)$ with the probability p. Using the formulae: - (11.2.19), (11.2.11) and (11.2.5) - we can write the detailed equation for the confidence ellipse $Э_\gamma$:

$$(a_1^2+a_2^2)(\Delta x-\widetilde{\Delta x})^2+2(a_1b_1+a_2b_2)(\Delta x-\widetilde{\Delta x})(\Delta y-\widetilde{\Delta y})+ \\ +(b_1^2+b_2^2)(\Delta y-\widetilde{\Delta y})^2=\frac{4\gamma[\tilde{v}\tilde{v}]}{n^2}, \tag{11.2.22}$$

$$[\tilde{v}\tilde{v}]=[ll]-(a_1l^{(1)}+a_2l^{(2)})\widetilde{\Delta x}-(b_1l^{(1)}+b_2l^{(2)})\widetilde{\Delta y};$$
$$l^{(1)}=l_1+\ldots+l_{\frac{n}{2}};\quad l^{(2)}=l_{\frac{n}{2}+1}+\ldots+l_n.$$

Since $E[\tilde{v}\tilde{v}]=(n-2)\cdot\sigma^2$, the average sizes of semi-axes of the ellipse $Э_\gamma$ are proportional to σ, and asymptotically proportional to $\frac{1}{\sqrt{n}}$ as n increases.

We will also consider the geometrical meaning of the individual coefficients in our expressions.

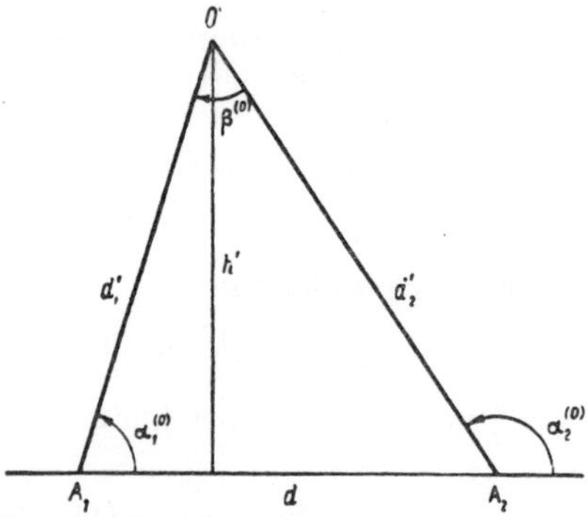

Fig. 11

We assume for simplicity that the fixed points A_1 and A_2 are lying on the same straight line, parallel to the line from which we measure off the angles of direction (for example, the meridian axis;

Fig. 11). From formulae (11.1.6), with $i=1, 2$, we find

$$D_0=\begin{vmatrix} a_1 & b_1 \\ a_2 & b_2 \end{vmatrix}=\frac{1}{d'_1 d'_2}\begin{vmatrix} -\sin\alpha_1^{(0)} & \cos\alpha_1^{(0)} \\ -\sin\alpha_2^{(0)} & \cos\alpha_2^{(0)} \end{vmatrix}=$$

$$=\frac{1}{d'_1 d'_2}(\sin\alpha_2^{(0)}\cos\alpha_1^{(0)}-\sin\alpha_1^{(0)}\cos\alpha_2^{(0)})=\frac{1}{d'_1 d'_2}\sin(\alpha_2^{(0)}-\alpha_1^{(0)}) \quad (11.2.23)$$

If we denote the angle to the auxiliary point by $\beta^{(0)}$, then

$$D_0=\frac{\sin\beta^{(0)}}{d'_1 d'_2}. \quad (11.2.24)$$

From Fig. 11 we see that $\alpha_2^{(0)}=\alpha_1^{(0)}+\beta^{(0)}$. Whence we have

$$a_1^2+a_2^2=\frac{\sin^2\alpha_1^{(0)}}{d_1'^2}+\frac{\sin^2(\alpha_1^{(0)}+\beta^{(0)})}{d_2'^2}, \quad (11.2.25)$$

$$b_1^2+b_2^2=\frac{\cos^2\alpha_1^{(0)}}{d_1'^2}+\frac{\cos^2(\alpha_1^{(0)}+\beta^{(0)})}{d_2'^2}. \quad (11.2.26)$$

The expressions for the variances of the estimators $\widetilde{\Delta x}$ and $\widetilde{\Delta y}$ (11.2.8) and (11.2.9), can be written in the following form

$$D(\widetilde{\Delta x})=\frac{\sigma^2 n}{2}\cdot\frac{d_1'^2\cos^2\alpha_1^{(0)}+d_2'^2\cos^2(\alpha_1^{(0)}+\beta^{(0)})}{\sin^2\beta^{(0)}},$$

$$D(\widetilde{\Delta y})=\frac{\sigma^2 n}{2}\cdot\frac{d_1'^2\sin^2\alpha_1^{(0)}+d_2'^2\sin^2(\alpha_1^{(0)}+\beta^{(0)})}{\sin^2\beta^{(0)}}.$$

Hence

$$D(\widetilde{\Delta x})+D(\widetilde{\Delta y})=\frac{\sigma^2 n}{2}\,\frac{d_1'^2+d_2'^2}{\sin^2\beta^{(0)}}. \quad (11.2.27)$$

If d is the distance between the points A_1 and A_2, then (Fig. 11)

$$\frac{d}{\sin\beta^{(0)}}=\frac{d'_1}{|\sin\alpha_2^{(0)}|}=\frac{d'_2}{|\sin\alpha_1^{(0)}|}, \quad (11.2.28)$$

therefore

$$D(\widetilde{\Delta x})+D(\widetilde{\Delta y})=\frac{\sigma^2 n}{2}\cdot d^2\cdot\frac{\sin^2\alpha_1^{(0)}+\sin^2(\alpha_1^{(0)}+\beta^{(0)})}{\sin^4\beta^{(0)}}$$

If we can choose the points A_1 and A_2 lying on the same straight line with given value of angle $\beta^{(0)}$ at the auxiliary point O', then we obtain the minimum of $D(\widetilde{\Delta x})+D(\widetilde{\Delta y})$, when $f\ \alpha_1^{(0)}=\sin^2\alpha_1^{(0)}+ +\sin^2(\alpha_1^{(0)}+\beta^{(0)})$ is a minimum. To calculate the minimum we form the equation

$$\frac{df(\alpha_1^{(0)})}{d\alpha_1^{(0)}}=\frac{1}{2}\left(\sin 2\,\alpha_1^{(0)}+\sin 2\,(\alpha_1^{(0)}+\beta^{(0)})\right)=0.$$

Further $\alpha_1^{(0)}+\beta^{(0)}=\alpha_2^{(0)}$, whence we see that we must have $\pi-\alpha_2^{(0)}=\alpha_1^{(0)}$, i.e. the minimum of $D(\widetilde{\Delta x})+D(\widetilde{\Delta y})$ is obtained, if the triangle $A_1O'A_2$ is isosceles. From the equation

$$f''(\alpha_1^{(0)})=\cos 2\alpha_1^{(0)}-\cos 2\,(\alpha_1^{(0)}+\beta^{(0)})=-\cos 2\alpha_1^{(0)}-\cos(2\pi-2\alpha_1^{(0)})= \\ =-2\cos 2\alpha_1^{(0)}>0,$$

it is clear that there is a minimum here if

$$\alpha_1^{(0)}<\frac{\pi}{4}.$$

We return once again to the equation for the confidence ellipse, $\mathcal{E}_\gamma$, (11.2.22). The expression (11.2.19) for $Q(\xi,\ \eta)$, using (11.1.6), can be written in the form

$$Q(\xi,\ \eta)=\frac{n}{2}\left((a_1\xi+b_1\eta)^2+(a_2\xi+b_2\eta)^2\right)= \\ =\frac{n}{2}\left(\frac{(-\xi\sin\alpha_1^{(0)}+\eta\cos\alpha_1^{(0)})^2}{d_1'^2}+\frac{(-\xi\sin\alpha_2^{(0)}+\eta\cos\alpha_2^{(0)})^2}{d_2'^2}\right). \quad (11.2.29)$$

Assuming $\alpha_1^{(0)}$ is acute, and $\alpha_2^{(0)}$ obtuse, introducing the angle $\pi-\alpha_2^{(0)}$ and using the formula (11.2.28) we obtain

$$Q(\xi,\ \eta)=\frac{n\sin^2\beta^{(0)}}{2d^2}\left((-\xi+\eta\operatorname{ctg}\alpha_1^{(0)})^2+[\xi-\eta\operatorname{ctg}(\pi-\alpha_2^{(0)})]^2\right). \quad (11.2.30)$$

This is a rather more convenient expression for the confidence ellipse $\mathcal{E}_\gamma$

3. Reverse Bearings on Many Points. Confidence Regions

Reverse bearings on more than two points are, as is well known, a very useful way of determining position; reverse bearings on three points is known as Potenot's *) problem; it was applied more than 300 years ago, and has not lost its practical importance (for example, in geodesy and navigation). Solution of Potenot's problem ('determination of the fourth point from three given points'), assuming the absence of errors of measurement, is attained by means of elementary trigonometry and is given in all text-books on geodesy (for example, Krasovski [26], p. 188-90).

Let the angles between the radius vectors to the fixed points $A_1, A_2, \ldots, A_n$ $(n \geqslant 3)$, from the required point O be measured, with some small errors. Selecting three appropriate points and solving Potentot's problem, we obtain an approximate (because of the existence of measurement errors) position O' for the point O; we assume the differences between co-ordinates of the points O and O' are such that their squares can be neglected in comparison with the chosen unit (Fig. 12).

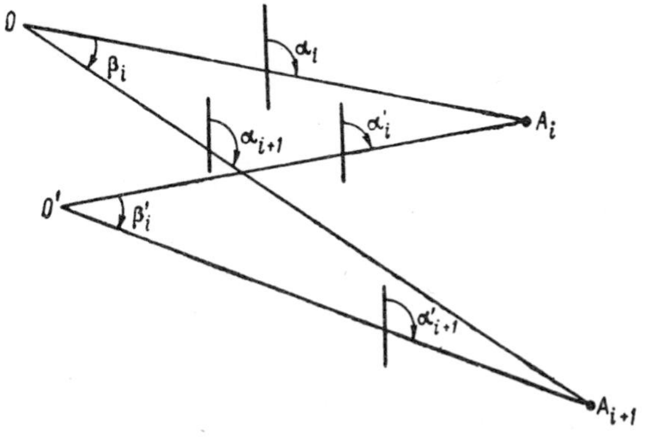

Fig. 12

Introducing the notation for angles given in Fig. 12 (α_i — direction angles; $i = 1, 2, \ldots, n$), we find

$$\beta_i = \alpha_{i+1} - \alpha_i, \quad \beta_i^{(0)} = \alpha_{i+1}^{(0)} - \alpha_i^{(0)}.$$

We put $\Delta\alpha_{i+1} = \alpha_{i+1} - \alpha_{i+1}^{(0)}$; $\Delta\alpha_i = \alpha_i - \alpha_i^{(0)}$. Hence

$$\Delta\beta_i = \beta_i - \beta_i^{(0)} = \Delta\alpha_{i+1} - \Delta\alpha_i. \tag{11.3.1}$$

We know, however, not the differences $\Delta\beta_i = \beta_i - \beta_i^{(0)}$, but

* Potenot (1660-1732) - French mathematician

$$l_i = \beta_i + \Delta_i - \beta_i^{(0)} = \Delta\beta_i + \Delta_i \qquad (i = 1, 2, \ldots, n), \quad (11.3.2)$$

where Δ_i are errors in the measurements of the angles. As before, in the case of direct line bearings (section 1), we assume them to be of equal accuracy, unbiased, independent and normal $N(0, \sigma)$. From formula (11.1.5), introducing the differences Δx_0, Δy_0 between the co-ordinates of the points O and O', we find:

$$\left.\begin{aligned} \Delta\alpha_i &\approx -\frac{\cos\alpha_i^{(0)}}{d_i'}\Delta y_0 + \frac{\sin\alpha_i^{(0)}}{d_i'}\Delta x_0, \\ \Delta\alpha_{i+1} &\approx \frac{\cos\alpha_{i+1}^{(0)}}{d_{i+1}'}\Delta y_0 + \frac{\sin\alpha_{i+1}^{(0)}}{d_{i+1}'}\Delta x_0 \end{aligned}\right\} \quad (11.3.3)$$

(the angles being measured in radians), where the equations are correct up to the second order of small quantities. In comparison with (11.1.5), the signs are changed, because here the sense of the angles has changed. Substituting in (11.3.1) and using (11.3.2), we obtain

$$l_i - \Delta_i = \left(\frac{\sin\alpha_{i+1}^{(0)}}{d_{i+1}'} - \frac{\sin\alpha_i^{(0)}}{d_i'}\right)\Delta x_0 + \left(-\frac{\cos\alpha_{i+1}^{(0)}}{d_{i+1}'} + \frac{\cos\alpha_i^{(0)}}{d_i'}\right)\Delta y_0,$$
$$i = 1, 2, \ldots, n. \quad (11.3.4)$$

Further, we write

$$a_i = \frac{\sin\alpha_{i+1}^{(0)}}{d_{i+1}'} - \frac{\sin\alpha_i^{(0)}}{d_i'}; \quad b_i = -\frac{\cos\alpha_{i+1}^{(0)}}{d_{i+1}'} + \frac{\cos\alpha_i^{(0)}}{d_i'}. \quad (11.3.5)$$

Then, we obtain the following system of fundamental equations in the elements Δx_0, Δy_0:

$$l_i - \Delta_i = a_i \Delta x_0 + b_i \Delta y_0 \qquad (i = 1, 2, \ldots, n-1). \quad (11.3.6)$$

This system has exactly the same form as (11.1.7); only the quantities a_i and b_i have different meanings.

Of course, all the statements made in section 1 about the estimators $\widetilde{\Delta x}$ and $\widetilde{\Delta y}$, remain valid. All formulae for the point estimators $\widetilde{\Delta x}$ and $\widetilde{\Delta y}$ given in section 1 are valid, replacing $n-1$ by n, and (11.1.6) by (11.3.5). The confidence rectangle, Q_γ, and confidence ellipse $Э_\gamma$ are constructed in the same way as in section 1.

4. Confidence Regions in Potenot's Problem with Repeated Measurements

Let the number of fixed points for reverse bearings be equal to three, so that Potenot's problem is solved uniquely (the three fixed points and the required point not lying on or near to some circle). Let the angles between the three points A_1, A_2, A_3 from the required point O, be measured $\frac{n}{2}$ times (n even). Then, we obtain fundamental equations of the form (11.2.2), where a_i and b_i must be taken from formula (11.3.5). The confidence ellipse, $\mathcal{E}_{\gamma_0}$, is of the form (11.2.22), where a_i and b_i are taken from (11.3.5). For given p_0 and $\gamma_0 = \frac{1}{(1-p_0)^{\frac{2}{n-2}}} - 1$ it covers $(\Delta x_0, \Delta y_0)$ with probability p_0.

CHAPTER XII

PARABOLIC INTERPOLATION BY THE METHOD OF LEAST SQUARES

1. Statement of the Problem

Curves having equations of the form

$$y = a_0 + a_1 x + a_2 x^2 + \dots + a_n x^n. \tag{12.1.1}$$

in Cartesian co-ordinates are called n^{th} order parabolas. According to a theorem of Weierstrass (see, for example, Fichtenholz [47]), any arbitrary continuous function can be approximated, over a finite interval, to any desired accuracy by such an nth order parabola; hence it is possible to represent any continuous experimental curve, with sufficient practical accuracy, in the same way. Suppose x takes values x_i $(i = 1, 2, \dots, N)$ and, for each $x = x_i$ values $y = y_i$ are observed, with errors Δ_i, which we assume to be mutually independent and, for simplicity, of equal accuracy and normal $N(0, \sigma)$. Here the problem of estimating the coefficients from N observations $(N > n+1)$ will be a special case of the problem, already known to us, of estimation by the method of least squares using elements; here $x_{ij} = x_i^j$ $\quad (j = 1, 2, \dots, n)$,

$$X = \begin{Vmatrix} 1 & x_1 & \dots & x_1^n \\ 1 & x_2 & \dots & x_2^n \\ \cdot & \cdot & \cdot & \cdot \\ 1 & x_N & \dots & x_N^n \end{Vmatrix} \tag{12.1.2}$$

and rank $(X) = n+1$ for $N > n+1$. In fact, if the points x_i are all different (as has been supposed) then, from courses in algebra, we know that Vandermonde's determinant cannot be zero, i.e.

$$\begin{vmatrix} 1 & x_1 & \dots & x_1^n \\ \cdot & \cdot & \cdot & \cdot \\ 1 & x_{n+1} & \dots & x_{n+1}^n \end{vmatrix} = \prod_{j<i} (x_i - x_j) \neq 0.$$

For the stated conditions, estimation of the coefficients $a_0, a_1, \dots a_n$, by the method of least squares, will have a real, definite probabilistic meaning as described above. This mode of estimation is then called fitting a curvilinear regression line of parabolic interpolation by the method of least squares. Even if it is not assumed that the error vector

$\Delta = \begin{Vmatrix} \Delta_1 \\ \vdots \\ \Delta_N \end{Vmatrix}$ is normal, the rules for calculating the estimates by the method of least squares are just the same.

Cases are often encountered in which we do not know, initially, what order of parabola it will be necessary to take so that, having found the coefficients by the method of least squares, it would represent the empirical series of observations well. Thus, in examples 2 and 3 of the introduction (the distance travelled by a car after a signal to stop; content of vitreous kernels in wheat grains) we can start by smoothing the series of observations by a straight line $a_0 + a_1 x$, then try smoothing by a parabola of 2nd order $a_0 + a_1 x + a_2 x^2$, then, if necessary, proceed to a 3rd order parabola $a_0 + a_1 x + a_2 x^2 + a_3 x^3$ and so on.

From this there naturally arises the question of how to decide that a parabola of n th order describes our series of observations adequately, while a parabola of $(n-1)$ th order is not satisfactory in this respect. This question, which belongs to the theory of testing hypotheses and the study of mathematical statistics, will be discussed later.

2. Normal Equations. Chebyshev's Orthogonal Polynominals

To form the system of normal equations with matrix X, we use formula (6.11.2). Putting

$$X_0 = (1, \dots, 1); \quad X_j = (x_1^j, x_2^j, \dots, x_N^j) \qquad (j = 1, \dots, n)$$

and

$$\alpha_\nu = \sum_{i=1}^{N} x_i^\nu = [x^\nu], \quad \nu = 0, 1, \dots, n \qquad (\alpha_0 = N + 1),$$

$$\alpha_{\nu 1} = \sum_{i=1}^{N} x_i^\nu l_i = [x^\nu l] \qquad (\nu = 0, 1, \dots, n),$$

we can write the system of normal equations

$$\sum_{\nu=0}^{n} [X_i x_\nu]\,\tilde{a}_\nu = [X_i l] \qquad (i=0,\ 1,\ \ldots,\ n) \qquad (12.2.1)$$

in the form

$$\left.\begin{array}{r} a_0\alpha_0 + a_1\alpha_1 + \ldots + \ a_n\alpha_n = \alpha_{01} \\ a_0\alpha_1 + a_1\alpha_2 + \ldots + a_n\alpha_{n+1} = \alpha_{11} \\ \cdot\ \cdot\ \cdot\ \cdot\ \cdot\ \cdot\ \cdot\ \cdot\ \cdot\ \cdot\ \cdot\ \cdot\ \cdot\ \cdot\ \cdot \\ a_0\alpha_n + a_1\alpha_{n+1} + \ldots + \ a_n\alpha_{2n} = \alpha_{n1}. \end{array}\right\} \qquad (12.2.2)$$

Since rank $(X) = n+1$, we have

$$\Delta_{n+1} = \begin{vmatrix} \alpha_0 & \alpha_1 & \ldots & \alpha_n \\ \alpha_1 & \alpha_2 & \ldots & \alpha_{n+1} \\ \cdot & \cdot & \cdot & \cdot \\ \alpha_n & \alpha_{n+1} & \ldots & \alpha_{2n} \end{vmatrix} \neq 0$$

(see section 3, chapter 1). The solution of system (12.2.1) can be found by well-known rules, given in any course of algebra. We have

$$a_j = \frac{\Delta_{j,\,n+1}}{\Delta_{n+1}} \qquad (j=0,\ 1,\ 2,\ \ldots,\ n), \qquad (12.2.3)$$

where $\Delta_{j,\,n+1}$ is the minor obtained by replacing the $(j+1)$-st column of Δ_{n+1} by $\begin{matrix}\alpha_{01}\\ \vdots \\ \alpha_{n1}\end{matrix}$. If the equation of the fitted curve be written

$$\tilde{y} = \tilde{a}_0 + \tilde{a}_1 x + \ldots + \tilde{a}_n x_n^n, \qquad (12.2.4)$$

differing from (12.1.1) in that the coefficients a_i are replaced by their estimators obtained by the method of least squares, $\tilde{a}_i$, then by virtue of (12.2.3) this equation takes the form

$$\begin{vmatrix} \tilde{y} & 1 & x & \ldots & x^n \\ \alpha_{01} & \alpha_0 & \alpha_1 & \ldots & \alpha_n \\ \alpha_{11} & \alpha_1 & \alpha_2 & \ldots & \alpha_{n+1} \\ \cdot & \cdot & \cdot & \cdot & \cdot \\ \alpha_{n1} & \alpha_n & \alpha_{n+1} & \ldots & \alpha_{2n} \end{vmatrix} = 0. \qquad (12.2.5)$$

For $n=1, 2, 3, 4$ this equation can be used directly; beyond this, the calculations become heavier. However, with such methods of calculation, all the estimators $\tilde{a}_0, \ldots, \tilde{a}_n$ must be calculated for each value of n. There naturally arises a desire for a type of scheme for estimating the coefficients of parabolas of successive orders, fitted to a given series of observations, in which the estimators of coefficients already obtained would be unchanged in progressing from an $(n-1)^{\text{st}}$ order parabola to an nth order parabola, so that it will only be necessary to add the calculations of the estimator of the coefficient a_n. In order to bring this about, in place of the fundamental system of monomials $1, x, x^2, \ldots, x^n, \ldots$ we are led to use a suitable system of polynomials $\varphi_0(x)=\text{const}, \varphi_1(x), \ldots, \varphi_n(x)$ where $\varphi_n(x)$ is a polynomial of order n, and instead of (12.1.1) an expression of form

$$y=c_0\varphi_0(x)+c_1\varphi_1(x)+\ldots+c_n\varphi_n(x) \qquad (12.2.6)$$

is used.

Suppose that the observations corresponding to the values $x=x_1, x_2, \ldots, x_N$ have values $l=l_1, l_2, \ldots, l_N$. (In the case, when the stochastic model, considered earlier, is realized exactly, $l_i=y_i+\Delta_i$, where the Δ_i's are random errors, mutually independent and normal $N(0, \sigma)$). If such a scheme is not precisely realized, the rules of estimation still remain the same and lead to unique results, the real meaning of which will depend on the nature of the errors ($\Delta_1, \ldots, \Delta_N$). Let the sequence of polynomials

$$\varphi_0(x), \varphi_1(x), \ldots, \varphi_n(x), \ldots \qquad (12.2.7)$$

be an orthogonal system of functions with respect to the system of points $x_1, x_2, \ldots, x_N$. This means that

$$\sum_{i=1}^{N}\varphi_\mu(x_i)\varphi_\nu(x_i)=[\varphi_\mu(x)\cdot\varphi_\nu(x)]=0 \text{ for } \mu\neq\nu. \qquad (12.2.8)$$

These relationships lead to great simplification in the system of normal equations for estimators of the coefficients $c_0, c_1, \ldots, c_n$ in (12.2.6). A system of type (12.2.1) takes the form

$$[\varphi_i(x)\varphi_i(x)]\tilde{c}_i=[\varphi_i(x)l] \qquad (i=0, 1, \ldots, n), \qquad (12.2.9)$$

whence

$$\tilde{c}_i=\frac{[\varphi_i(x)l]}{[\varphi_i(x)\varphi_i(x)]}. \qquad (12.2.10)$$

We will show how to form a system of orthogonal polynomials with respect to the system of points $x_1, \ldots, x_N$, which is called a system of Chebyshev polynomials. We put $\varphi_0(x) = 1$. We can regard $\varphi_1(x)$ as a linear combination of x and $\varphi_0(x)$, so that: $\varphi_1(x) = x + b\varphi_0(x)$, where b is chosen so that $[\varphi_0(x)\varphi_1(x)] = [x] + b[1] = 0$. Hence, from the equation $[1] = N$, we have

$$b = -\frac{[x]}{N} = -\bar{x},$$

$$\varphi_1(x) = x - \bar{x} = x - \frac{[x]}{N}. \qquad (12.2.11)$$

Now we put

$$\varphi_2(x) = x^2 + b_1\varphi_1(x) + b_0\varphi_0(x) = x^2 + b_1(x - \bar{x}) + b_0.$$

For the determination of the coefficients b_1 and b_0 we use the orthogonality conditions $[\varphi_2(x)\varphi_0(x)] = 0$, $[\varphi_2(x)\varphi_1(x)] = 0$. We get

$$[x^2] + b_0[1] = 0, \qquad [x^2\varphi_1(x)] + b_1[(\varphi_1(x))^2] = 0;$$

whence

$$b_0 = -\frac{[x^2]}{N}; \qquad b_1 = -\frac{[x^2\varphi_1(x)]}{[(x - \bar{x})^2]}$$

and

$$\varphi_2(x) = x^2 - \frac{[x^2(x - \bar{x})]}{[(x - \bar{x})^2]}(x - \bar{x}) - \frac{[x^2]}{N}.$$

We can proceed further in this way, determining $\varphi_3(x)$, $\varphi_4(x)$, ... It is possible to find a formula giving the general form of $\varphi_m(x)$.

Theorem 12.2.1.

$$\varphi_m(x) = x^m - \frac{[x^m\varphi_{m-1}(x)]}{[\varphi_{m-1}(x)\varphi_{m-1}(x)]}\varphi_{m-1}(x) - \ldots - \frac{[x^m]}{N}. \qquad (12.2.12)$$

Proof. We put

$$\varphi_m(x) = x^m + b_{m-1}\varphi_{m-1}(x) + b_{m-2}\varphi_{m-2}(x) + \ldots + \varphi_0(x).$$

Multiplying by $\varphi_k(x)$ $(k = m-1, \ldots, 0)$ and summing over $x = x_1, x_2, \ldots, x_N$, we make use of the condition $[\varphi_m(x)\varphi_k(x)] = 0$. We obtain

$$[x^m\varphi_k(x)] = b_k[\varphi_k(x)\varphi_k(x)],$$

$$b_k = -\frac{[x^m\varphi_k(x)]}{[\varphi_k(x)\varphi_k(x)]},$$

which proves the theorem. We see that it is not necessary for all the points to be different. For the coefficients to be determined uniquely it is only necessary that $[\varphi_k(x)\varphi_k(x)] \neq 0$ for all values of k employed.

It is easy to see that every power x^k, and so every polynomial, $P(x)$, can be written in the form of a linear combination of Chebyshev polynomials. From formula (12.2.10), in which $\varphi_i(x)$ can be considered as a Chebyshev polynomial, it is seen that the use of these polynomials is very convenient; solutions $\tilde{c}_i$ of the normal equations are immediately expressed in terms of $[\varphi_i(x)l]$ and $[\varphi_i(x)\varphi_i(x)]$. It is true that the $\varphi_i(x)$'s themselves depend on the abscissae $x_1, \ldots, x_N$ and must be constructed in advance. It is also very important that as n is increased, i.e. introducing coefficients $c_{n+1}, c_{n+2}, \ldots$ it is only necessary (for the same set of observations $l_1, \ldots, l_N$), to calculate the estimates for the new coefficients $c_{n+1}, c_{n+2}, \ldots,$ since the estimates $\tilde{c}_0, \tilde{c}_1, \ldots, \tilde{c}_n$ for $c_0, \ldots, c_n$ remain the same, and it is not necessary to calculate them anew.

Further, comparatively simple expressions are obtained for the correlation matrix B_C of the estimators $\tilde{c}_0, \ldots, \tilde{c}_n$, for confidence intervals and confidence regions. By virtue of the orthogonality of the Chebyshev polynomials, the matrix of the normal equations

$$C = \| [\varphi_\mu(x)\varphi_\nu(x)] \|$$

can be expressed as the diagonal matrix

$$C = \begin{Vmatrix} [\varphi_0(x)\varphi_0(x)] & 0 & \ldots & 0 \\ 0 & [\varphi_1(x)\varphi_1(x)] & \ldots & 0 \\ \cdots & \cdots & \cdots & \cdots \\ 0 & 0 & \ldots & [\varphi_n(x)\varphi_n(x)] \end{Vmatrix}. \qquad (12.2.13)$$

Thus, (see (8.2.5))

$$B_C = \sigma^2 C^{-1} = \sigma^2 \begin{Vmatrix} \frac{1}{[\varphi_0(x)\varphi_0(x)]} & 0 & \ldots & 0 \\ 0 & \frac{1}{[\varphi_1(x)\varphi_1(x)]} & \ldots & 0 \\ \cdots & \cdots & \cdots & \cdots \\ 0 & 0 & \ldots & \frac{1}{[\varphi_n(x)\varphi_n(x)]} \end{Vmatrix}, \qquad (12.2.14)$$

from which there follows

Theorem 12.2.2.

The estimators $\tilde{c}_0, \tilde{c}_1, \ldots, \tilde{c}_n$ are normal and mutually independent (in the case of a normal error vector) and have variances

$$D(\tilde{c}_i) = \frac{\sigma^2}{[\varphi_i(x)\,\varphi_i(x)]}. \qquad (12.2.15)$$

If the condition of normality of the error vector Δ be omitted, it can only be asserted that the errors $\tilde{c}_i$ are uncorrelated. For the estimation of σ^2, and for the construction of confidence intervals and regions (the error vector Δ being assumed normal) we need to calculate $[p\tilde{v}\tilde{v}] = [\tilde{v}\tilde{v}]$. In the present case this can be done immediately. We have (see chapter VIII)

$$\tilde{V} = X \begin{Vmatrix} \tilde{c}_0 \\ \tilde{c}_1 \\ \vdots \\ \tilde{c}_n \end{Vmatrix} - L, \qquad (12.2.16)$$

where

$$X = \begin{Vmatrix} \varphi_0(x_1) & \varphi_1(x_1) & \ldots & \varphi_n(x_1) \\ \varphi_0(x_2) & \varphi_1(x_2) & \ldots & \varphi_n(x_2) \\ \ldots & \ldots & \ldots & \ldots \\ \varphi_0(x_N) & \varphi_1(x_N) & \ldots & \varphi_n(x_N) \end{Vmatrix}. \qquad (12.2.17)$$

Putting

$$\tilde{L} = X \begin{Vmatrix} \tilde{c}_0 \\ \vdots \\ \tilde{c}_n \end{Vmatrix},$$

so that

$$\tilde{l}_r = \varphi_0(x_r)\tilde{c}_0 + \varphi_1(x_r)\tilde{c}_1 + \ldots + \varphi_n(x_r)\tilde{c}_n \qquad (r = 1, 2, \ldots, N), \qquad (12.2.18)$$

we have $\tilde{V} = \tilde{L} - L$; $\tilde{v}_r = \tilde{l}_r - l_r$, therefore

$$[\tilde{v}\tilde{v}] = [(\tilde{l} - l)^2]. \qquad (12.2.19)$$

According to theorem 6.6.4

$$E\frac{[\tilde{v}\tilde{v}]}{N-n-1} = \sigma^2, \qquad (12.2.20)$$

so that $\frac{[\tilde{v}\tilde{v}]}{N-n-1}$ is an unbiased estimator of σ^2. Further, the quantity $\frac{1}{\sigma^2}[\tilde{v}\tilde{v}]$ has a χ^2 - distribution with $N-n$ degrees cf freedom; the method of constructing confidence intervals for $c_0, \ldots, c_n$ separately is laid down in section 3 of chapter VIII.

Analogously to the construction of confidence ellipses $\mathcal{E}_{\gamma_0}$ in chapter XI, we can construct a confidence ellipsoid $\mathcal{E}_{\gamma_0}$ for the set $c_0, \ldots, c_n$; in the present case such a construction is comparatively easy. As is known from the general theory of reduction by means of elements (see chapter VIII), the normal random vector $(\tilde{c}_0, \ldots, \tilde{c}_n)$ is stochastically independent of $[\tilde{v}\tilde{v}]$. We form a new normal vector

$$\left(\frac{\tilde{c}_0-c_0}{\sigma\sqrt{[\varphi_0(x)\varphi_0(x)]}}, \ldots, \frac{\tilde{c}_n-c_n}{\sigma\sqrt{[\varphi_n(x)\varphi_n(x)]}}\right).$$

This is also independent of $[\tilde{v}\tilde{v}]$ and has a zero vector of means and unit correlation matrix

$$B=E=\begin{Vmatrix} 1 & 0 & \ldots & 0 \\ \cdot & \cdot & \cdot & \cdot \\ 0 & 0 & \ldots & 1 \end{Vmatrix}.$$

Hence the quadratic form

$$\frac{1}{\sigma^2}Q(\tilde{c}_0-c_0, \ldots, \tilde{c}_n-c_n)=\frac{1}{\sigma^2}\sum_{i=0}^{n}\frac{(\tilde{c}_i-c_i)^2}{[\varphi_i(x)\varphi_i(x)]} \qquad (12.2.21)$$

will be distributed as χ^2_{n+1}, while the quantity

$$q=\frac{\frac{1}{\sigma^2}Q(\tilde{c}_0-c_0, \ldots, \tilde{c}_n-c_n)}{\frac{1}{\sigma^2}[\tilde{v}\tilde{v}]}=\frac{Q(\tilde{c}_0-c_0, \ldots, \tilde{c}_n-c_n)}{[\tilde{v}\tilde{v}]} \qquad (12.2.22)$$

will have Fisher's distribution $F_{n+1, N-n-1}(x)$. If we choose a confidence coefficient p_0 and select from tables of Fisher's distribution γ_0 such that $F_{n+1, N-n-1}(\gamma_0)=p_0$, then we can note (as in section 1, chapter XI) that the ellipsoid $\mathcal{E}_\gamma$ with equation

$$Q(z_0-\tilde{c}_0, \ldots, z_n-\tilde{c}_n)=\gamma_0[\tilde{v}\tilde{v}] \qquad (12.2.23)$$

will cover the point $(\tilde{c}_0, \tilde{c}_1, \ldots, \tilde{c}_n)$ with probability p_0.

The case when the abscissae of the observations $x_1, x_2, \ldots, x_N$ take equidistant values, i.e. $x_{i+1}-x_i=d$ $(i=1, 2, \ldots, N-1)$, was investigated by Chebyshev. For this case there are tables which lighten the technical calculations (see Nemchinov [39]). We give, without proof, Chebyshev's relationships

$$\varphi_{k+1}(x)=(x-\bar{x})\varphi_k(x)-\frac{k^2(N^2-k^2)}{4(4k^2-1)}\varphi_{k-1}(x). \quad (12.2.24)$$

The first four polynomials have the form

$$\varphi_1(x)=x-\bar{x},\quad \varphi_2(x)=(x-\bar{x})^2-\frac{N^2-1}{12},$$
$$\varphi_3(x)=(x-\bar{x})^3-\frac{3N^2-7}{20}(x-\bar{x}),$$
$$\varphi_4(x)=(x-\bar{x})^4-\frac{3N^2-13}{14}(x-\bar{x})^2+\frac{3(N^2-1)(N^2-9)}{560};$$
$$[\varphi_k(x)\varphi_k(x)]=\frac{(k!)^2N(N^2-1)(N^2-4)\dots(N^2-k^2)}{(1\cdot 3\cdot 5\dots(2k-1))^2\cdot 2^{2k}(2k+1)}.$$

Values of the first five polynomials, for $n \leqslant 52$, are given in the tables of Fisher and Yates [57] for the abscissae $x=0, 1, 2, \dots, \dots, n-1$ (to which the general case of equidistant abscissae is equivalent). The first six Chebyshev polynomials for these abscissae have the form (Kendall [20], p. 160),

$$\varphi_1=x-\frac{n-1}{2},\quad \varphi_2=\varphi_1^2-\frac{n^2-1}{12},$$
$$\varphi_3=\varphi_1^3-\frac{3n^2-7}{20}\varphi_1,$$
$$\varphi_4=\varphi_1^4-\frac{3n^2-13}{14}\varphi_1^2+\frac{3(n^2-1)(n^2-9)}{560},$$
$$\varphi_5=\varphi_1^5-\frac{5(n^2-7)}{18}\varphi_1^3+\frac{15n^4-230n^2+407}{1008}\varphi_1,$$
$$\varphi_6=\varphi_1^6-\frac{5(3n^2-31)}{44}\varphi_1^4+\frac{5n^4-110n^2+329}{176}\varphi_1^2-\frac{5(n^2-1)(n^2-9)(n^2-25)}{14784}.$$

The question of multiple correlation, when the fundamental equation has the form

$$l_r-\Delta_r=a_1z_1^{(r)}+a_2z_2^{(r)}+\dots+a_nz_n^{(r)} \qquad (r=1, 2, \dots, N)$$

(the linear case), is considered in a similar way. We have already encountered similar cases in chapter VII.

3. Tests of Hypotheses About the Existence of Parabolic Regression of a Given Order. Examples

We consider the problem of testing the hypothesis of the adequacy of the equations

$$l_r + \Delta_r = c_0\varphi_0(x_r) + \ldots + c_n\varphi_n(x_r) \qquad (r = 1, 2, \ldots, N), \quad (12.3.1)$$

where $\varphi_i(x)$ is an orthogonal Chebyshev polynomial and the error vector $\Delta = \begin{Vmatrix} \Delta_1 \\ \vdots \\ \Delta_N \end{Vmatrix}$ has normal and independent components with identical distributions. Such a hypothesis is called a hypothesis of the existence of parabolic regression of nth order.

The right hand side of (12.3.1) can represent any linear combination of arbitrary polynomials of degree less than, or equal to, n; as has been explained above, these can be expressed as a linear combination of Chebyshev polynomials, i.e. in the form of the right hand side of (12.3.1). To test the stated hypothesis it is desirable to have, for each abscissa x_r $(r = 1, 2, \ldots, N)$ not just one, but many observations $l_{r1}, l_{r2}, \ldots, l_{rm}$; for simplicity, we will assume that the number $m > 1$ is the same for all abscissae x_r. This is equivalent to having each abscissa x_r repeated m times, so that the total number, counting repetitions, will be $N_1 = mN$. All the rules of calculation given in section 2 remain valid. The expressions $[\varphi_i(x)\varphi_i(x)]$ and $[\varphi_i(x)l]$ occuring in formula (12.2.10) for calculating $\tilde{c}_i$, take the form

$$[\varphi_i(x)\varphi_i(x)] = m\sum_{r=1}^{N}(\varphi_i(x_r))^2, \quad (12.3.2)$$

$$[\varphi_i(x)l] = \sum_{r=1}^{N}\varphi_i(x_r)l^{(r)}, \quad (12.3.3)$$

where

$$l^{(r)} = l_{r1} + l_{r2} + \ldots + l_{rm}. \quad (12.3.4)$$

Putting

$$\bar{l}_r = \frac{1}{m}l^{(r)} = \frac{l_{r1} + \ldots + l_{rm}}{m}, \quad (12.3.5)$$

we obtain

$$\tilde{c}_i = \frac{\sum_{r=1}^{N}\varphi_i(x_r)\bar{l}_r}{\sum_{r=1}^{N}(\varphi_i(x_r))^2}. \quad (12.3.6)$$

Now we consider the expression

$$\tilde{l}_r = \tilde{c}_0\varphi_0(x_r) + \tilde{c}_1\varphi_1(x_r) + \ldots + \tilde{c}_n\varphi_n(x_r). \qquad (12.3.7)$$

Theorem 12.3.1.

If the hypothesis being tested is true then the normal random vectors

$$\begin{gathered}(l_{11}-\bar{l}_1, \ldots, l_{1m}-\bar{l}_1, l_{21}-\bar{l}_2, \ldots, l_{2m}-\bar{l}_2, \ldots \\ \ldots, l_{N1}-\bar{l}_N, \ldots, l_{Nm}-\bar{l}_N)\end{gathered} \qquad (12.3.8)$$

and

$$(\bar{l}_1-\tilde{l}_1, \bar{l}_2-\tilde{l}_2, \ldots, \bar{l}_N-\tilde{l}_N) \qquad (12.3.9)$$

are independent.

Proof. From theorem 2.3.3 it is sufficient to prove that

$$E\left((l_{\nu\mu}-\bar{l}_\nu)(\bar{l}_\rho-\tilde{l}_\rho)\right) = 0 \qquad (12.3.10)$$

for any $\nu, \rho = 1, 2, \ldots, N$ and $\mu = 1, 2, \ldots, m$.

We note that, for arbitrary μ, ν and ρ, we have the equation

$$E(l_{\nu\mu}-\bar{l}_\nu)\bar{l}_\rho = 0. \qquad (12.3.11)$$

In fact, $l_{\nu\mu}$ and $\bar{l}_\nu$ are independent of the set $l_{\rho 1}, l_{\rho 2}, \ldots, l_{\rho m}$ if $\rho \neq \nu$, since the errors of observations, $\Delta_1, \ldots, \Delta_N$ are assumed to be mutually independent. If $\rho = \nu$, then

$$E(l_{\nu\mu}-\bar{l}_\nu)\bar{l}_\rho = E(l_{\nu\mu}-\bar{l}_\nu)\bar{l}_\nu = E(\Delta_{\nu\mu}-\bar{\Delta}_\nu)\bar{\Delta}_\nu,$$

where Δ_i is the error corresponding to l_i. But

$$E(\Delta_{\nu\mu}\bar{\Delta}_\nu) = \frac{\sigma^2}{m}; \quad E(\bar{\Delta}_\nu^2) = \frac{\sigma^2}{m},$$

which proves (12.3.11).

It remains to prove that

$$E\tilde{l}_\rho(l_{\nu\mu}-\bar{l}_\nu) = 0. \qquad (12.3.12)$$

In view of (12.3.6) and (12.3.7) it is sufficient to demonstrate that, for all values of τ

$$E\left(\bar{l}_\tau(l_{\nu\mu}-\bar{l}_\nu)\right) = 0. \qquad (12.3.13)$$

This is equivalent to (12.3.11), and is therefore true. In the same way, (12.3.12) and (12.3.10) are true, which proves the theorem.

We draw attention to the fact that the vectors (12.3.8) and (12.3.9) give different unbiased estimators for the variance σ^2, if the hypothesis is true. To construct these estimators we consider first the random vector (12.3.9). We have from (12.3.6)

$$\tilde{c}_i = \frac{\sum \varphi_i(x_r)\bar{l}_r}{\sum (\varphi_i(x_r))^2}, \tag{12.3.14}$$

which can be interpreted as the solution of the normal equations for a system of fundamental equations of the form

$$\bar{l}_r - \bar{\Delta}_r = c_0\varphi_0(x_r) + \dots + c_n\varphi_n(x_r) \quad (r = 1, 2, \dots, N), \tag{12.3.15}$$

where the $\bar{\Delta}_r$'s are independent random errors, normal $N\left(0, \frac{\sigma}{\sqrt{m}}\right)$.

In this case $\bar{l}_r - \tilde{l}_r = \tilde{v}_r$ $(r = 1, 2, \dots, N)$ and $\frac{m}{\sigma^2}[\tilde{v}\tilde{v}]$ must be distributed as χ^2_{N-n-1} (see chapter VIII). Hence

$$q_1 = \frac{m}{N-n-1}[\tilde{v}\tilde{v}] \tag{12.3.16}$$

is an unbiased estimator of σ^2.

The vector (12.3.8) provides us with another unbiased estimator. The group $l_{r1}, l_{r2}, \dots, l_{rm}$, with the group mean $\bar{l}_r$ gives, immediately, an unbiased estimator of the variance σ^2 (see section 2, chapter III)

$$\frac{1}{m-1}\sum_{i=1}^{m}(l_{ri} - \bar{l}_r)^2.$$

Adding such estimators for $r = 1, 2, \dots, N$ and dividing by N, we get the unbiased estimator of σ^2:

$$q_2 = \frac{1}{N(m-1)}\sum_{r=1}^{N}\sum_{i=1}^{m}(l_{ri} - \bar{l}_r)^2. \tag{12.3.17}$$

Here the quantity $\frac{1}{\sigma^2}\sum_{i=1}^{m}(l_{ri} - \bar{l}_r)^2$ is distributed as χ^2_{m-1} (see chapter III) and for different r the quantities $l_{ri} - \bar{l}_r$ are independent. Thus, the quantity $\frac{1}{\sigma^2}N(m-1)q_2$ is distributed as the sum of N

independent χ^2_{m-1}'s and, from formula (2.6.4), we have $\frac{1}{\sigma^2} N(m-1) q_2 = \chi^2_{N(m-1)}$. Also q_1 is independent of q_2.

We note that the estimator (12.3.16) is obtained using only the observed values, l_r, without using the fundamental formula (12.3.1), while the estimator (12.3.17) makes use of the hypothesis tested and the fundamental equations. To construct a criterion for acceptance or rejection of the hypothesis tested, we form the ratio

$$w = \frac{m[\tilde{v}\tilde{v}]}{N(m-1)q_2} = \frac{\frac{m}{m-1}[\tilde{v}\tilde{v}]}{Nq_2} = \frac{\chi^2_{N-n-1}}{\chi^2_{N(m-1)}}. \qquad (12.3.18)$$

The numerator and denominator of this ratio are independent. Thus, we have Fisher's distribution $F_{N-n-1,\, N(m-1)}(x)$.

We form the auxiliary quantity $w_1 = \frac{N(m-1)}{N-n-1} w$ and, from Table II of the Appendix we find γ_0 such that

$$p_0 = 0{,}95 = P\left(\frac{1}{\gamma_0} < w_1 < \gamma_0\right) = P(|\log w_1| < \log \gamma_0) =$$
$$= P\left(\frac{N(m-1)}{N-n-1}\gamma_1 \leqslant w_1 \leqslant \frac{N(m-1)}{N-n-1}\gamma_2\right).$$

If we now obtain a value of w from (12.3.8) which does not satisfy the inequality

$$\gamma_1 < w < \gamma_2,$$

then we reject the hypothesis of the existence of an nth order parabolic regression. The reasons for chosing this, and not some other criteria, are given in detail in courses on mathematical statistics (see, for example, Kendall [20]). It should be noted that the improved Abbé criterion, described in section 6 of chapter IV, is a special case of the procedures put forward here.

We now turn to some examples.

Example 1. In table 28 (columns 1-3) are given data on the distribution of the ellipticity of cylinders before and after polishing *). Here x denotes ellipticity of a cylinder before polishing and $y(x)$ the mean value calculated from observations after polishing, for a fixed value of x (x and y are measured in hundredths of millimetres); n_i is the number of observations of x_i.

---

* Data are taken from the book [14], p. 429

TABLE 28

x_i	n_i	y_i	n_iy_i	x_i^2	x_i^3	$\varphi_1(x_i)$	$\varphi_1^2(x_i)$	$\varphi_2(x_i)$	$\varphi_2^2(x_i)$
1	21	0,10	2,10	1	1	−2,18	4,75	2,24	5,02
2	8	0,19	1,52	4	8	−1,18	1,39	−1,41	1,99
3	13	0,24	3,12	9	27	−0,18	0,03	−3,06	9,36
4	11	0,32	3,52	16	64	0,82	0,67	−2,71	7,34
5	11	0,39	4,29	25	125	1,82	3,31	−0,36	0,13
6	10	0,48	4,80	36	216	2,82	7,95	3,99	15,92

We will find the relationship between y and x in the form of the second order parabola

$$y = a_0 + a_1x + a_2x^2,$$

using the method of least squares.

We write the equation of the required parabola in the form

$$y = c_0\varphi_0(x) + c_1\varphi_1(x) + c_2\varphi_2(x),$$

where $\varphi_0(x)$, $\varphi_1(x)$ and $\varphi_2(x)$ are an orthogonal system of polynomials with respect to the system of points x_i, and we will estimate the coefficients c_0, c_1, c_2. The values of the orthogonal functions are calculated by the formulae

$$\varphi_0(x) = 1,$$

$$\varphi_1(x) = x - \frac{[x]}{N},$$

$$\varphi_2(x) = x^2 - \frac{[x^3] - \frac{[x][x^2]}{N}}{[x^2] - \frac{[x]^2}{N}}\left(x - \frac{[x]}{N}\right) - \frac{[x^2]}{N}.$$

In our case

$$N = \sum_{i=1}^{6} n_i = 74, \quad [x] = \sum_{i=1}^{6} n_ix_i = 235,$$

$$[x^2] = \sum_{i=1}^{6} n_ix_i^2 = 981, \quad [x^3] = 4675,$$

whence the Chebyshev polynomials are

$$\varphi_0(x)=1,$$
$$\varphi_1(x)=x-3{,}18,$$
$$\varphi_2(x)=x^2-6{,}65x+7{,}89.$$

The values of the polynomials $\varphi_i(x)$, and their squares, for different x_i, are shown in columns 7-10 of table 28.

The estimates $\tilde{c}_i$ of the coefficients c_i are calculated from the formula

$$\tilde{c}_i=\frac{[\varphi_i(x)\,y]}{[\varphi_i(x)\,\varphi_i(x)]}.$$

We have

$$\tilde{c}_0=\frac{[\varphi_0(x)\,y]}{[\varphi_0(x)\,\varphi_0(x)]}=\frac{\sum_{i=1}^{6} n_i y_i}{[\varphi_0^2(x)]}=\frac{19{,}35}{74}=0{,}261,$$

$$\tilde{c}_1=\frac{[\varphi_1(x)\,y]}{[\varphi_1(x)\,\varphi_1(x)]}=\frac{\sum_{i=1}^{6}\varphi_1(x_i)\,n_i y_i}{\sum_{i=1}^{6} n_i\varphi_1^2(x_i)}=\frac{17{,}30}{234{,}5}=0{,}074,$$

$$\tilde{c}_2=\frac{[\varphi_2(x)\,y]}{[\varphi_2(x)\,\varphi_2(x)]}=\frac{\sum_{i=1}^{6}\varphi_2(x_i)\,n_i y_i}{\sum_{i=1}^{6} n_i\varphi_2^2(x_i)}=\frac{1{,}082}{484{,}4}=0{,}0022.$$

Consequently, the equation of the required parabola is

$$y=0{,}26+0{,}074(x-3{,}18)+0{,}0022(x^2-6{,}65x+7{,}89)=$$
$$=0{,}042+0{,}059x+0{,}0022x^2.$$

Example 2. The data of table 29 exhibit the dependence between loss of weight, y, (in per cent) and temperature, t, (in degrees Celsius) for 16 samples of soil*).

It is required to find the regression of y on t, using the method of least squares.

---

* Data taken from the book [20], p. 150, the temperatures being changed to degrees Celsius

In order to avoid large numbers in the calculations we replace t by the quantity $x = \frac{t}{100}$.

TABLE 29

t_i	y_i	x_i	x_i^2	x_i^3	$\varphi_1(x)$	$\varphi_2(x)$	$\varphi_3(x)$
37,8	3,71	0,378	0,14288	0,05401	—0,36163	0,08383	—0,01997
40,6	3,81	0,406	0,16484	0,06692	—0,33363	0,06236	—0,01005
43,3	3,86	0,433	0,18749	0,08118	—0,30663	0,04313	—0,00217
46,1	3,93	0,461	0,21252	0,09797	—0,27863	0,02473	0,00435
49,4	3,96	0,494	0,24404	0,12055	—0,24563	0,00506	0,01004
55,6	4,20	0,556	0,30914	0,17188	—0,18363	—0,02600	0,01564
62,2	4,34	0,622	0,38688	0,24064	—0,11763	—0,05064	0,01574
67,2	4,51	0,672	0,45158	0,30346	—0,06763	—0,06349	0,01274
72,8	4,73	0,728	0,52998	0,38583	—0,01163	—0,07195	0,00731
81,7	5,35	0,817	0,66749	0,54534	0,07737	—0,07248	—0,00336
88,3	5,74	0,883	0,77969	0,68847	0,14337	—0,06265	—0,01070
95,0	6,14	0,950	0,90250	0,85728	0,21037	—0,04377	—0,01565
100,0	6,51	1,000	1,00000	1,00000	0,26037	—0,02382	—0,01669
107,8	6,98	1,078	1,16208	1,25273	0,33837	0,01728	—0,01174
113,9	7,44	1,139	1,29732	1,47765	0,39937	0,05790	—0,00071
121,7	7,76	1,217	1,48109	1,80249	0,47737	0,12069	0,02487
Sum .	82,97	11,834	9,91952	9,14650			

Starting the calculations by fitting the series of observations by a straight line, we will proceed to fit second order and third order parabolas. We write the straight line $y = c_0\varphi_0(x) + c_1\varphi_1(x)$, where $\varphi_0(x)$ and $\varphi_1(x)$ are orthogonal Chebyshev polynomials for the system of points x_i, $\varphi_0(x) = 1$, $\varphi_1(x) = x - \frac{[x]}{N}$, and estimates of c_i are calculated by the formula $\tilde{c}_i = \frac{[\varphi_i(x)\, y]}{[\varphi_i^2(x)]}$. In our case, $N = 16$, $[x] = 11{,}834$, whence $\varphi_1(x) = x - 0{,}73963$ (the values of $\varphi_1(x)$ are given in the sixth column of Table 29). Next, we calculate the sums $[\varphi_1(x)y] = 5{,}75522$, $[\varphi_1^2(x)] = 1{,}16680$. Consequently

$$\tilde{c}_0 = \frac{82\,97}{16} = 5{,}1856, \quad \tilde{c}_1 = \frac{5{,}75522}{1{,}1668} = 4{,}932,$$

and the equation of the required straight line is

$$y = 5{,}186 + 4{,}932\,(x - 0{,}73963) = 1{,}538 + 4{,}932x.$$

For fitting the parabolas of second and third order

$$y = c_0\varphi_0(x) + c_1\varphi_1(x) + c_2\varphi_2(x),$$
$$y = c_0\varphi_0(x) + c_1\varphi_1(x) + c_2\varphi_2(x) + c_3\varphi_3(x)$$

we find the polynomials $\varphi_2(x)$ and $\varphi_3(x)$ from the formulae

$$\varphi_2(x) = x^2 - \frac{[x^3] - \frac{[x][x^2]}{N}}{[x^2] - \frac{[x]^2}{N}}\left(x - \frac{[x]}{N}\right) - \frac{[x^2]}{N},$$
$$\varphi_3(x) = x^3 - \frac{[x^3\varphi_2(x)]}{[\varphi_2^2(x)]}\varphi_2(x) - \frac{[x^3\varphi_1(x)]}{[\varphi_1^2(x)]}\varphi_1(x) - \frac{[x^3]}{N}.$$

Inserting the appropriate values in the formula for $\varphi_2(x)$ we find

$$\varphi_2(x) = x^2 - 1,55107x + 0,52725.$$

The values of $\varphi_2(x_i)$ are shown in the seventh column of table 29. We calculate the sums $[x^3\varphi_2(x)] = 0,13229$, $[\varphi_2^2(x)] = 0,05574$, $[x^3\varphi_1(x)] = 2,24757$, $[\varphi_1^2(x)] = 1,16680$. We obtain the following expression for $\varphi_3(x)$;

$$\varphi_3(x) = x^3 - 2,373\ \varphi_2(x) - 1,9263\ \varphi_1(x) - 0,57166.$$

The values of $\varphi_3(x_i)$ are shown in the last column of Table 29.

We find the estimates of the coefficients c_2 and c_3:

$$\tilde{c}_2 = \frac{[\varphi_2(x)\,y]}{[\varphi_2^2(x)]} = \frac{0,1934}{0,05574} = 3,470,$$
$$\tilde{c}_3 = \frac{[\varphi_3(x)\,y]}{[\varphi_3^2(x)]} = \frac{-0,01624}{0,002738} = -5,931.$$

Hence the equations of the required parabolas of second and third orders are

$$y = 3,368 - 0,450x + 3,470x^2,$$
$$y = 5,73 - 10,86x + 17,54x^2 - 5,93x^3.$$

The absolute magnitude of the greatest deviation between the observed values and the values fitted by straight line, second and third order parabolas are, respectively, 0.40, 0.20, 0.11.

We note that in the successive calculation of the values of $\varphi_i(x)$

by recurrence formulae some significant figures may disappear, and therefore it is expedient to carry out the calculations with a larger number of significant figures, than we finally desire.

CHAPTER XIII

SOME INVESTIGATIONS OF A. WALD. LINE OF ORTHOGONAL REGRESSION AND ITS APPLICATIONS

1. Statement of the Problem. Consistent Estimators

In the introduction, and in chapter VII, the problem of estimation of the coefficients α and β in the linear regression $y=\alpha x+\beta$ on the basis of a sequence of observations l_r satisfying the fundamental equations

$$l_r-\Delta_r=\alpha x_r+\beta \qquad (r=1, 2, \ldots, N),$$

was considered in detail. This problem is an important special case of reduction by elements, with the matrix of coefficients

$$X=\begin{Vmatrix} x_1 & 1 \\ x_2 & 1 \\ \vdots & \vdots \\ x_N & 1 \end{Vmatrix}.$$

Here, as in the general scheme of reduction, the abscissae x_i are assumed to be known exactly, and the random errors, Δ_r, are assumed to occur only in measurements of the ordinates y_r.

Often, however, cases are encountered in which it is expedient to assume that the measurements of the abscissae also have errors.

In example 1 of the introduction (on Mendeléjev's data) this would be the case, for instance, if not only the measurements of solubility of $NaNO_3$, but also the measurements of temperature, had noticeable random errors. A model of this type was studied by Wald *) in 1940.

Wald pointed out that situations of this type are encountered, for

---

* Wald (1902-1950) - American mathematical statistician

example, in the problems of capitalist economics. Let $t_1, t_2, \ldots, t_n$ be the moments in time when the price, x_i, of a certain product, and the demand, y_i, for this product, are recorded. It can be assumed that, for each t_i, the mathematical expectations, $E(x_i)=X_i$ and $E(y_i)=Y_i$, exist. If X_i and Y_i are connected by the linear relation

$$Y_i=\alpha X_i+\beta,$$

we are then in the situation described above.

Here we give an account of Wald's work [5] in investigating a problem closely connected with the method of least squares. We give an exact statement of the problem.

We are given N pairs of observations $(x_1, y_1), \ldots, (x_N, y_N)$, which are regarded as different values of random vectors, for which $E(x_i)=X_i$ and $E(y_i)=Y_i$. We will call the quantities X_i and Y_i the <u>true values</u> of x_i and y_i, and the quantities $\delta_i=x_i-X_i$ and $\Delta_i=y_i-Y_i$ we will call <u>errors</u>. We will suppose that the following conditions are satisfied.

1. The random variables $\delta_1, \delta_2, \ldots, \delta_N$ have identical distributions and are uncorrelated; $E(\delta_i\delta_j)=0$ $(i \neq j)$; $E(\delta_i^2)$ exists $(i = 1, 2, \ldots, N)$.

2. $\Delta_1, \ldots, \Delta_N$ have identical distributions and are uncorrelated; $E(\Delta_i\Delta_j)=0$ $(i \neq j)$; $E(\Delta_i^2)$ exists $(i=1, 2, \ldots, N)$.

3. The random errors δ_i and Δ_j are uncorrelated: $E(\delta_i\Delta_j)=0$; $(i, j=1, 2, \ldots, N)$.

4. There is a linear relation

$$Y_i=\alpha X_i+\beta. \tag{13.1.1}$$

between the true values X_i and Y_i. Also, since $E(x_i)=X_i$; $E(y_i)=Y_i$, it follows that $E(\delta_i)=0$, $E(\Delta_i)=0$.

Let δ be a random variable distributed as δ_i and Δ a random variable distributed as Δ_i.

On the basis of the observations

$$(x_1, y_1), \ldots, (x_N, y_N) \tag{13.1.2}$$

it is required to obtain estimators of the coefficients of α and β, and of the standard errors $\sigma(\delta)=\sigma_\delta$, $\sigma(\Delta)=\sigma_\Delta$ of the random variables δ and Δ.

We start by finding estimators of α and β such that, as the number of observations increases without limit, the estimators will differ from the corresponding parameters by less than an arbitrarily chosen ε, with probability as near to unity as desired. (Such estimators are called consistent). For convenience we will assume that N is even, $N=2m$.

We introduce the statistics

$$\left.\begin{aligned} a_1 &= \frac{(x_1+\dots+x_m)-(x_{m+1}+\dots+x_N)}{N}, \\ a_2 &= \frac{(y_1+\dots+y_m)-(y_{m+1}+\dots+y_N)}{N}. \end{aligned}\right\} \tag{13.1.3}$$

For estimating α we will use the statistic

$$a=\frac{a_2}{a_1}=\frac{(y_1+\dots+y_m)-(y_{m+1}+\dots+y_N)}{(x_1+\dots+x_m)-(x_{m+1}+\dots+x_N)}. \tag{13.1.4}$$

We add one further (fifth)*) condition.

5.

$$\left|\frac{(X_1+\dots+X_m)-(X_{m+1}+\dots+X_N)}{N}\right|>c_0>0, \tag{13.1.5}$$

where c_0 is a positive constant. We note that this will be so, for example, if $X_i-X_{i+1}=c_0>0$. We will prove that, under the stated conditions, a is a consistent estimator for α, i.e.

$$P\{|a-\alpha|<\varepsilon\}\to 1 \tag{13.1.6}$$

as $N\to\infty$ for any $\varepsilon>0$

We denote $E(a_1)$ by α_1 and $E(a_2)$ by α_2. Evidently

$$\left.\begin{aligned} \alpha_1 &= \frac{(X_1+\dots+X_m)-(X_{m+1}+\dots+X_N)}{N}, \\ \alpha_2 &= \frac{(Y_1+\dots+Y_m)-(Y_{m+1}+\dots+Y_N)}{N}. \end{aligned}\right\} \tag{13.1.7}$$

---

* For simplicity of presentation this is rather stronger than the corresponding condition of Wald [5].

By virtue of (13.1.1) we have

$$\alpha_2 = \alpha\alpha_1; \quad \frac{\alpha_2}{\alpha_1} = \alpha. \tag{13.1.8}$$

Further,

$$D(a_1) = \frac{N}{N^2} D(x_1) = \frac{\sigma_\xi^2}{N},$$

and analogously

$$D(a_2) = \frac{\sigma_\Delta^2}{N}.$$

We will prove (13.1.6). Let $\varepsilon > 0$ be given. From Chebyshev's inequality,

$$\left.\begin{aligned} P\{|a_1 - \alpha_1| \leqslant \varepsilon\} \geqslant 1 - \frac{\sigma_\xi^2}{N\varepsilon^2}, \\ P\{|a_2 - \alpha_2| \leqslant \varepsilon\} \geqslant 1 - \frac{\sigma_\Delta^2}{N\varepsilon^2}. \end{aligned}\right\} \tag{13.1.9}$$

Hence, for the probability of the joint event (see (11.1.20)),

$$P\{|a_1 - \alpha_1| \leqslant \varepsilon, \ |a_2 - \alpha_2| \leqslant \varepsilon\} \geqslant 1 - \frac{\sigma_\delta^2 + \sigma_\Delta^2}{N\varepsilon^2}. \tag{13.1.10}$$

In view of this we have

$$\frac{\alpha_2 - \varepsilon}{\alpha_1 + \varepsilon} \leqslant \frac{a_2}{a_1} \leqslant \frac{\alpha_2 + \varepsilon}{\alpha_1 - \varepsilon} \tag{13.1.11}$$

with probability greater than or equal to $1 - \frac{\sigma_\xi^2 + \sigma_\Delta^2}{N\varepsilon^2}$. In view of the fifth condition, $\alpha_1 > c_0$. Since $\alpha = \frac{\alpha_2}{\alpha_1}$ we have

$$\left|\frac{a_2}{a_1} - \alpha\right| \leqslant \varepsilon' \tag{13.1.12}$$

with probability greater or equal to $1 - \frac{\sigma_\xi^2 + \sigma_\Delta^2}{N\varepsilon^2}$. Here $\varepsilon' = \varepsilon'(\varepsilon)$ is arbitrarily small together with ε. For given ε, and $N \to \infty$, the probability of the event (13.1.12) will be arbitrarily close to unity.

Next, we estimate the initial ordinate, β, of the straight line $Y = \alpha X + \beta$ in the following way:

$$b = \bar{y} - a\bar{x}, \tag{13.1.13}$$

where, as usual, $\bar{y}=\frac{[y]}{N}$; $\bar{x}=\frac{[x]}{N}$. By reason of the law of large numbers, $\bar{y}$ converges in probability to $\bar{Y}=\frac{[Y]}{N}$, $\bar{x}$ converges in probability to $\bar{X}=\frac{[X]}{N}$ and therefore, by the proof for a, the estimator b will converge in probability to $\bar{Y}-\alpha\bar{X}=\beta$ as $N\to\infty$, so that b will be a consistent estimator of β.

Now we want to find consistent estimators for σ_δ^2 and σ_Δ^2. We introduce the sample standard deviations

$$s_x=\sqrt{\frac{1}{N}\sum(x_i-\bar{x})^2}\ ;\quad s_y=\sqrt{\frac{1}{N}\sum(y_i-\bar{y})^2}\ ,$$

and the 'sample covariance'

$$s_{xy}=\sum\frac{(x_i-\bar{x})(y_i-\bar{y})}{N}\,.$$

We will denote the same functions for the true values $X_1, \ldots, X_N$; $Y_1, \ldots, Y_N$ by s_X, s_Y, s_{XY}.

We have

$$E\left(s_x^2\right)=s_X^2+\sigma_\delta^2\frac{N-1}{N}, \tag{13.1.14}$$

$$E\left(s_y^2\right)=s_Y^2+\sigma_\Delta^2\frac{N-1}{N}, \tag{13.1.15}$$

$$E(s_{xy})=s_{XY}. \tag{13.1.16}$$

We prove these formulae.

We have

$$(x_i-\bar{x})=(x_i-X_i)+(X_i-\bar{X})-(\bar{x}-\bar{X}),$$

whence

$$E\sum_{i=1}^{N}(x_i-\bar{x})^2=E\sum_{i=1}^{N}(x_i-X_i)^2+E\sum_{i=1}^{N}(X_i-\bar{X})^2+$$
$$+NE(\bar{x}-\bar{X})^2+2E\sum_{i=1}^{N}(X_i-\bar{X})(x_i-X_i)-2E\sum_{i=1}^{N}(X_i-\bar{X})(\bar{x}-\bar{X})-$$
$$-2E\sum_{i=1}^{N}(x_i-X_i)(\bar{x}-\bar{X}). \tag{13.1.17}$$

Also, $X_i-x_i=\delta_i$, $\bar{x}-\bar{X}=\bar{\delta}$, so that

$$E\sum_{i=1}^{N}\delta_i\bar{\delta}=N\frac{\sigma_\delta^2}{N}=\sigma_\delta^2;\quad E(\bar{\delta}^2)=\frac{\sigma_\delta^2}{N}.$$

Remembering that $X_i-\bar{X}$ are constant quantities and $E(x_i-X_i)=$ $=E(\delta_i)=0;\ E(\bar{x}-\bar{X})=0,$ we can rewrite (13.1.17) in the form

$$NE(s_x^2)=N\sigma_\delta^2+Ns_X^2+\sigma_\delta^2-2\sigma_\delta^2=(N-1)\,\sigma_\delta^2+Ns_X^2.$$

Division by N gives (13.1.14). Equation (13.1.15) is proved similarly.

To prove (13.1.16), we write

$$(x_i-\bar{x})(y_i-\bar{y})=\left((x_i-X_i)+(X_i-\bar{X})-(\bar{x}-\bar{X})\right)\times$$
$$\times\left[(y_i-Y_i)+(Y_i-\bar{Y})-(\bar{y}-\bar{Y})\right].$$

Taking mathematical expectations, and remembering that x_i and y_i are uncorrelated, we find

$$E(x_i-\bar{x})(y_i-\bar{y})=(X_i-\bar{X})(Y_i-\bar{Y}),$$

which leads to (13.1.16).

Since $Y_i=\alpha X_i+\beta$, then

$$s_Y=\alpha s_X, \tag{13.1.18}$$

$$s_{XY}=\alpha s_X^2. \tag{13.1.19}$$

From these formulae and (13.1.16) we find

$$s_X^2=\frac{E(s_{xy})}{\alpha}, \tag{13.1.20}$$

$$s_Y^2=\alpha E(s_{xy}). \tag{13.1.21}$$

Inserting these expressions in (13.1.14) and (13.1.15) we obtain

$$\sigma_\delta^2=\frac{N}{N-1}\left(E(s_x^2)-\frac{E(s_{xy})}{\alpha}\right), \tag{13.1.22}$$

$$\sigma_\Delta^2=\frac{N}{N-1}\left(E(s_y^2)-\alpha E(s_{xy})\right). \tag{13.1.23}$$

By the law of large numbers, s_x^2, s_y^2 and s_{xy} converge in probability to their mathematical expectations, and we obtain the consistent estimators for σ_δ^2 and σ_Δ^2,

$$\frac{N}{N-1}\left(s_x^2-\frac{s_{xy}}{a}\right), \tag{13.1.24}$$

$$\frac{N}{N-1}\left(s_y^2-as_{xy}\right). \tag{13.1.25}$$

respectively.

2. Confidence Intervals

We now assume that the errors δ_r and Δ_r are distributed according to the normal laws $N(0, \sigma_\delta)$ and $N(0, \sigma_\Delta)$. We will suppose that all the conditions of section 1, excluding condition 5, are satisfied. We introduce the statistics

$$\bar{x}_1=\frac{x_1+\ldots+x_m}{m};\qquad \bar{y}_1=\frac{y_1+\ldots+y_m}{m};$$

$$\bar{x}_2=\frac{x_{m+1}+\ldots+x_N}{m};\qquad \bar{y}_2=\frac{y_{m+1}+\ldots+y_N}{m};$$

$$(s_x')^2=\frac{\sum_{i=1}^{m}(x_i-\bar{x}_1)^2+\sum_{j=m+1}^{N}(x_j-\bar{x}_2)^2}{N};$$

$$(s_y')^2=\frac{\sum_{i=1}^{m}(y_i-\bar{y}_1)^2+\sum_{j=m+1}^{N}(y_j-\bar{y}_2)^2}{N};$$

$$s_{xy}'=\frac{\sum_{i=1}^{m}(x_i-\bar{x}_1)(y_i-\bar{y}_1)+\sum_{j=m+1}^{N}(x_j-\bar{x}_2)(y_j-\bar{y}_2)}{N};$$

and the quantities $\bar{X}_1, \bar{X}_2, \bar{Y}_1, \bar{Y}_2, (s_X')^2, (s_Y')^2, s_{XY}'$ denote similar functions of the true values $X_1, \ldots, X_N; Y_1, \ldots, Y_N$.

The expressions s_x', s_y', s_{xy}' differ a little from s_x, s_y, s_{xy}. They are introduced because they are independent of the slope coefficient $a=\frac{a_2}{a_1}=\frac{\bar{y}_2-\bar{y}_1}{\bar{x}_2-\bar{x}_1}$, while the earlier quantities s_x, s_y, s_{xy}, in general depend on a.

We will prove the mutual independence of s_x', s_y', s_{xy}' and a. It is sufficient to prove that $x_i-\bar{x}_1, y_i-\bar{y}_1$ $(i=1, 2, \ldots, m)$; $x_j-\bar{x}_2, y_j-\bar{y}_2$, $(j=m+1, \ldots, N)$ do not depend on $\bar{x}_2-\bar{x}_1$ and $\bar{y}_2-\bar{y}_1$.

We note that all the random variables defined are jointly normally distributed. It is sufficient to show that the mathematical expectations of the appropriate products in pairs are equal to zero. We have, for example,

$$E\left[\left(x_i-\bar{x}_1-E(x_i-\bar{x}_1)\right)\left(\bar{x}_2-\bar{x}_1-E(\bar{x}_2-\bar{x}_1)\right)\right]=$$
$$=E(x_i-\bar{x}_1)E(\bar{x}_2)-E(x_i\bar{x}_1)+E(\bar{x}_1^2)-(X_i-\bar{X}_1)(\bar{X}_2-\bar{X}_1)-$$
$$-(X_i-\bar{X}_1)(\bar{X}_2-\bar{X}_1)+(X_i-\bar{X}_1)(\bar{X}_2-\bar{X}_1)=(X_i-\bar{X}_1)\bar{X}_2-$$
$$-X_i\bar{X}_1-\frac{\sigma_\delta^2}{m}+X_1^2+\frac{\sigma_\delta^2}{m}-(X_i-\bar{X}_1)(\bar{X}_2-\bar{X}_1)=0.$$

Calculation, exactly similar to that leading to (13.1.22) and (13.1.23), gives

$$\sigma_\delta^2=\left[E(s_x')^2-\frac{E(s_{xy}')}{\alpha}\right]\frac{N}{N-2}. \tag{13.2.1}$$

$$\sigma_\Delta^2=\left[E(s_y')^2-\alpha E(s_{xy}')\right]\frac{N}{N-2}. \tag{13.2.2}$$

We note that these formulae differ from (13.1.22) and (13.1.23) only in the replacement of $N-1$ by $N-2$.

If α is known, then

$$\left[(s_x')^2-\frac{s_{xy}'}{\alpha}\right]\frac{N}{N-2}, \tag{13.2.3}$$

$$\left[(s_y')^2-\alpha s_{xy}'\right]\frac{N}{N-2} \tag{13.2.4}$$

are unbiased estimators for σ_δ^2 and σ_Δ^2 respectively.

Hence if α is known, we take, for an unbiased estimator of $\sigma_\Delta^2+\alpha^2\sigma_\delta^2$,

$$s^2=\left((s_y')^2+\alpha^2(s_x')^2-2\alpha s_{xy}'\right)\frac{N}{N-2}=$$
$$=\frac{1}{N-2}\left[\sum_{i=1}^{m}\left((y_i-\alpha x_i)-(\bar{y}_1-\alpha\bar{x}_1)\right)^2+\right.$$
$$\left.+\sum_{j=m+1}^{N}\left((y_j-\alpha x_j)-(\bar{y}_2-\alpha\bar{x}_2)\right)^2\right]. \tag{13.2.5}$$

We will now prove that the quantity

$$\frac{(N-2)s^2}{\sigma_\Delta^2+\alpha^2\sigma_\delta^2} \tag{13.2.6}$$

is distributed as χ^2_{N-2}.

In fact,

$$(y_i-\alpha x_i)-(\bar{y}_1-\alpha\bar{x}_1)=\Delta_i-\alpha\delta_i-(\bar{\Delta}_1-\alpha\bar{\delta}_1) \qquad (i=1, \ldots, m),$$

since

$$\bar{y}_1-\alpha\bar{x}_1=\bar{\Delta}_1-\alpha\bar{\delta}_1+\bar{Y}_1-\alpha\bar{X}_1=\bar{\Delta}_1-\alpha\bar{\delta}_1+\beta,$$

and analogously

$$(y_j-\alpha x_j)-(\bar{y}_2-\alpha\bar{x}_2)=\Delta_j-\alpha\delta_j-(\bar{\Delta}_2-\alpha\bar{\delta}_2), \quad (j=m+1, \ldots, N),$$

where

$$\bar{\Delta}_1=\frac{\Delta_1+\cdots+\Delta_m}{m}; \quad \bar{\Delta}_2=\frac{\Delta_{m+1}+\cdots+\Delta_N}{m};$$
$$\bar{\delta}_1=\frac{\delta_1+\cdots+\delta_m}{m}; \quad \bar{\delta}_2=\frac{\delta_{m+1}+\cdots+\delta_N}{m}.$$

Also, $D(\Delta_k-\alpha\delta_k)=\sigma_\Delta^2+\alpha^2\sigma_\delta^2$, and $\Delta_k-\alpha\delta_k$ does not depend on $\Delta_l-\alpha\delta_l$ $(k\neq l)$. Therefore the quantity

$$\frac{(N-2)s^2}{\sigma_\Delta^2+\alpha^2\sigma_\delta^2}=\frac{1}{\sigma_\Delta^2+\alpha^2\sigma_\delta^2}\left(\sum_{i=1}^{m}(\Delta_i-\alpha\delta_i-(\bar{\Delta}_i-\alpha\bar{\delta}_i))^2+\right.$$
$$\left.+\sum_{j=m+1}^{N}((\Delta_j-\alpha\delta_j)-(\bar{\Delta}_j-\alpha\bar{\delta}_j))^2\right)$$

is the sum of two independent quantities each distributed as χ^2_{m-1}, i.e. it is distributed as $\chi^2_{2m-2}=\chi^2_{N-2}$, which was required to be proved.

We will now prove that the quantity

$$\frac{\sqrt{N}\,a_1(a-\alpha)}{\sqrt{\sigma_\Delta^2+\alpha^2\sigma_\delta^2}}=\frac{\sqrt{N}\,(a_2-\alpha a_1)}{\sqrt{\sigma_\Delta^2+\alpha^2\sigma_\delta^2}} \tag{13.2.7}$$

is normal $N(0,\ 1)$.

In fact, from (13.1.3) - (13.1.7) it is seen that

$$a_1(a-\alpha)=a_2-\alpha a_1=\alpha_2+\frac{\bar{\Delta}_1-\bar{\Delta}_2}{2}-a_1\frac{\alpha_2}{\alpha_1}=$$

$$=\alpha_2+\frac{\bar{\Delta}_1-\bar{\Delta}_2}{2}-\left(\alpha_1+\frac{\bar{\delta}_1-\bar{\delta}_2}{2}\right)\frac{\alpha_2}{\alpha_1}=\frac{\bar{\Delta}_1-\bar{\Delta}_2}{2}-\alpha\,\frac{\bar{\delta}_1-\bar{\delta}_2}{2}.$$

The latter expression is normal, and its variance is equal to

$$\frac{1}{4}\left\{D(\bar{\Delta}_1-\bar{\Delta}_2)+\alpha^2 D(\bar{\delta}_1-\bar{\delta}_2)\right\}=\frac{1}{4}\left(\frac{2\sigma_\Delta^2}{m}+\alpha^2\frac{2\sigma_\delta^2}{m}\right)=\frac{\sigma_\Delta^2+\alpha^2\sigma_\delta^2}{N}$$

Thus, the quantity (13.2.7) is normal $N(0,\ 1)$. Also, the quantity (13.2.7) does not depend on (13.2.6) since the quantities

$$(\Delta_i-\bar{\Delta}_1)-\alpha(\delta_i-\bar{\delta}_1)\qquad (i=1,\ 2,\ \ldots,\ m),$$
$$(\Delta_j-\bar{\Delta}_2)-\alpha(\delta_j-\bar{\delta}_2)\qquad (j=m+1,\ \ldots,\ N)$$

do not depend on $\frac{\bar{\Delta}_1-\bar{\Delta}_2}{2}-\alpha(\bar{\delta}_1-\bar{\delta}_2)$, which can be proved by considering the product of the corresponding mathematical expectations.

In view of this, the quantity

$$t=\frac{\sqrt{N}\,a_1(a-\alpha)}{s}\tag{13.2.8}$$

has Student's distribution with $N-2$ degrees of freedom. Substituting s from (13.2.5) we get

$$t=\frac{a_1(a-\alpha)\sqrt{N-2}}{\sqrt{(s_y')^2+\alpha^2(s_x')^2-2\alpha s_{xy}'}}.\tag{13.2.9}$$

For given confidence coefficient, p_0, and number of degrees of freedom $N-2$, we obtain, from tables of Student's distribution, a number, t_0, such that $P(|t|\leqslant t_0)=p_0$. Then we have, with probability p_0,

$$a_1^2(a-\alpha)^2\leqslant\left[(s_y')^2+\alpha^2(s_x')^2-2\alpha s_{xy}'\right]\frac{t_0^2}{N-2},\tag{13.2.10}$$

and a confidence region for α is obtained by solving this inequality for α.

We will now show that for the condition

$$a_1^2>\frac{(s_x)^2 t_0^2}{N-2}\tag{13.2.11}$$

the equation

$$a_1^2(a-\alpha)^2=\left((s_y')^2+\alpha^2(s_x')^2-2\alpha s_{xy}'\right)\frac{t_0^2}{N-2} \qquad (13.2.12)$$

must have real roots, k_1 and k_2 $(k_2 \geqslant k_1)$, and the interval

$$I=[k_1, k_2] \qquad (13.2.13)$$

will be a confidence interval for α, with confidence coefficient p_α.

From (13.2.5) we have

$$(s_y')^2+\alpha^2(s_x')^2-2\alpha s_{xy}'>0 \quad \text{for all} \quad \alpha.$$

This means that for $\alpha=a$, the left hand side of (13.2.12) is equal to zero, and so less than the right hand side. Hence the expression

$$a_1^2(a-\alpha)^2-\left((s_y')^2+\alpha^2(s_x')^2-2\alpha s_{xy}'\right)\frac{t_0^2}{N-2} \qquad (13.2.14)$$

will be negative for $\alpha=a$.*) If (13.2.11) is satisfied then, after multiplying by $\frac{N-2}{t_0^2}$, expression (13.2.14) cannot be less than

$$(a-\alpha)^2(s_x')^2-\left((s_y')^2+\alpha^2(s_x')^2-2\alpha s_{xy}'\right)=$$
$$=\left((a-\alpha)^2-\alpha^2\right)(s_x')^2-(s_y')^2-2\alpha s_{xy}'=$$
$$=(a^2-2\alpha a)\left(s_x'^2+\frac{s_{xy}'}{a}\right)-a\,(s_{xy}')-(s_y')^2. \qquad (13.2.15)$$

Assuming that $s_x'^2+\frac{s_{xy}'}{a}\neq 0$, we see that there can be found $\alpha=a'$, such that the expression (13.2.15), and so, also, (13.2.14) must be positive. Putting (13.2.14) equal to zero we obtain an equation of the second degree with regard to α, to which corresponds a parabola which is below the axis $O\alpha$, when $\alpha=a$, and above the axis $O\alpha$, when $\alpha=a'$. Consequently, we can find a second point $\alpha=a''$ on the axis of abscissae such that, without loss of generality $a'<a<a''$. Then the points of intersection with the axis $O\alpha$, i.e. the roots k_1 and k_2, of the expression (13.2.14) will also be real, with $k_1<a<k_2$. Further, inequality (13.2.10) will hold for

---

* Editorial Note

A more direct proof is obtained by noting that, if (13.2.11) is satisfied, then the coefficient of α^2 in (13.2.14) is positive; hence the function (13.2.14) increases without limit as α approaches $+\infty$ or $-\infty$, and so there must be two real roots $k_1<a<k_2$ and, if $k_1 \leqslant \alpha \leqslant k_2$, (13.2.10) is satisfied.

$k_1 \leqslant \alpha \leqslant k_2$, so that (13.2.13) really does give the required confidence interval.

We now note that the inequality (13.2.11) will be satisfied with probability arbitrarily near to unity, if N is large and condition 5 is satisfied, for then a_1 will converge in probability to some positive constant, while $\frac{(s_x)^2 t_0^2}{N-2}$ will converge in probability to zero.

Now we will construct a confidence interval for β, it being assumed that α is known exactly.

We consider the quantities

$$b_\alpha = \bar{y} - \alpha\bar{x}; \quad \bar{x} = \frac{[x]}{N}; \quad \bar{y} = \frac{[y]}{N}.$$

We have

$$b_\alpha - \beta = (\bar{y} - \bar{Y}) - \alpha(\bar{x} - \bar{X}) = \bar{\Delta} - \alpha\bar{\delta},$$

where

$$\bar{\Delta} = \frac{[\Delta]}{N}; \quad \bar{\delta} = \frac{[\delta]}{N}.$$

Hence we conclude that the quantity

$$\frac{(b_\alpha - \beta)\sqrt{N}}{\sqrt{\sigma_\Delta^2 + \alpha^2\sigma_\delta^2}} \tag{13.2.16}$$

is normal $N(0, 1)$. It does not depend on (13.2.6), so that the quantity

$$t = \frac{\sqrt{N-2}\,(b_\alpha - \beta)}{\sqrt{(s_y')^2 + \alpha^2 (s_x')^2 - 2\alpha s_{xy}'}}$$

has Student's distribution with $N-2$ degrees of freedom. For given confidence coefficient, p_0, and number of degrees of freedom $N-2$, we find, from tables of Student's distribution, a number γ and obtain a confidence interval for β:

$$I = \left[b_\alpha - \gamma \sqrt{\frac{(s_y')^2 + \alpha^2 (s_x')^2 - 2\alpha s_{xy}'}{N-2}}, \right.$$
$$\left. b_\alpha + \gamma \sqrt{\frac{(s_y')^2 + \alpha^2 (s_x')^2 - 2\alpha s_{xy}'}{N-2}} \right].$$

3. Grouped Observations

In section 1 and section 2 we carried out the estimation of α and β on the basis of a dichotomy of the observations into two groups G_1 and G_2. Group G_1 consisted of the pairs of observations $(x_1, y_1), \ldots, (x_m, y_m)$, and G_2 of $(x_{m+1}, y_{m+1}), \ldots, (x_N, y_N)$. However, exactly the same methods could have been developed on the basis of an arbitrary division into general groups G_1 and G_2 of given sizes, provided only that the method of division does not depend on the errors $\delta_1, \ldots, \delta_N; \Delta_1, \ldots, \Delta_N$, i.e. on the sample values of the observations (x_k, y_k) $(k=1, 2, \ldots, N)$. We can retain the groups G_1 and G_2, but change the numbering of the observations. This is equivalent to the same type of division into two groups. The question of deciding what is, in itself, the best dichotomy, has no unique answer, since it is necessary to know in what sense we are using the word 'best'. If we state the question in terms of the quality of the estimator of α, then, since α has a point estimator $a=\frac{a_2}{a_1}$, it is natural to try to make a_1 (and hence also a_2) as large as possible, with probability near to unity, because fluctuations in the denominator will then have less effect on the fluctuations of the estimator a.

We have

$$a_1=\frac{(x_1+\cdots+x_m)-(x_{m+1}+\cdots+x_N)}{N}. \qquad (13.3.1)$$

If we were allowed to make the dichotomy on the basis of the observations themselves, it would be possible to note that we would obtain maximum $|a_1|$, if we arranged the observations in increasing order of magnitude: $x_1 \leqslant x_2 \leqslant \cdots \leqslant x_N$. In fact, if half of the numbers x_n must be given the sign + and the other half the sign -, then the greatest value of $|a_1|$ is obtained if the m smallest values have one sign and the m largest have the other. Although this rule introduces dependence on the observations, in practice, when N is large and the error variance is not large, it is possible to make use of the above formulae.

4. The Orthogonal Regression Line (Gradient) and its Applications

In section 1 of the introduction we acquainted ourselves with the problems of constructing a straight line which would minimize the sum of squares of the distance from points of a given system to the line. We will make the mathematico-statistical formulation of this problem more precise. Suppose that as system of points $P_1, \ldots, P_N$ in a plane possesses the following properties: there is a straight line l such that if we measure the distances Δ_i of P_i from l, attaching the sign + to one side of the line and - to the other, then the quantities $\Delta_1, \ldots, \Delta_N$ form a set of mutually independent normal variables $N(0, \sigma)$.

We take a rectangular system of co-ordinates XOY; let the point P_i have the co-ordinates (x_i, y_i) in this system and let the required line l have the equation

$$y = \alpha x + \beta, \tag{13.4.1}$$

where α and β are unknown. It is necessary to estimate α and β from the observations (x_i, y_i) $(i = 1, 2, \ldots, N)$.

We mention a further example in which such a statement of the problem is natural. From a known formula of analytical geometry we have

$$\Delta_i = \frac{y_i - \alpha x_i - \beta}{\sqrt{\alpha^2+1}}. \tag{13.4.2}$$

Therefore the likelihood function for $\Delta_1, \ldots, \Delta_N$ will have the form

$$L = (2\pi)^{-\frac{N}{2}} \sigma^{-N} \exp\left\{-\frac{1}{2(\alpha^2+1)\sigma^2} \sum_{i=1}^{N} (y_i - \alpha x_i - \beta)^2\right\}. \tag{13.4.3}$$

It is natural to minimize the expression:

$$\sum_{i=1}^{N} \left(\frac{y_i - \alpha x_i - \beta}{\sqrt{\alpha^2+1}}\right)^2 \tag{13.4.4}$$

i.e. α and β must be determined so that the sum of squares of the distances of the points (x_i, y_i) from the straight line $y = \alpha x + \beta$ will be a minimum. Such a problem was considered in example 6 of the introduction; the solution (in general, not unique) is given by the formulae (see (0.1.29)),

$$\operatorname{tg} 2\alpha' = \frac{2\sum_{i=1}^{N} (x_i - \bar{x})(y_i - \bar{y})}{\sum_{i=1}^{N} (x_i - \bar{x})^2 - \sum_{i=1}^{N} (y_i - \bar{y})^2}, \tag{13.4.5}$$

$$\bar{y} - \alpha' \bar{x} - \beta' = 0. \tag{13.4.6}$$

In most actual cases the points P_i are distributed roughly linearly and fall within a narrow strip, so that $\operatorname{tg} 2\alpha'$ is determined uniquely, and the required value, out of α' and $\alpha' + \frac{\pi}{2}$ (corresponding to the axis of maximum moment of inertia, as was shown in the introduction) is found uniquely. Optimal qualities, in a certain sense, and asymptotic normality of the estimators (α', β'), follows from the general properties of estimation by the method of maximum likelihood (see chapter III). The line obtained is called the orthogonal regression line, or gradient line.

By way of an example in which such a line plays an important rôle, it is possible to mention the problem of constructing a linear profile of a surface (see Linnik and Khousou [33]). In studying the profile of a surface having only a rough nature, and not well defined, we usually use much enlarged photographs of the micro-surface of the profile. Considerations of the theory of stochastic processes (random curves) lead us to suppose that there must exist an axis l, which is such that, if we use it as abscissa for the profile, we will obtain ordinates which follow a stationary normal stochastic process. This supposition is very well confirmed by observation.

If we take a series of abscissae $\xi_1, \ldots, \xi_N$ on the axis l at such distances from each other that correlations between the corresponding ordinates $\eta_1, \ldots, \eta_N$ are eliminated, then we obtain a series of points $P_1, \ldots, P_N$, satisfying the scheme shown at the beginning of this section. Then, the determination of the axis l, which we can call the mean line of profile, is reduced to the estimation of the coefficients in the equation of the linear orthogonal regression line from formulae (13.4.5) and (13.4.6). The linear orthogonal regression line is also applied in some problems in correlation theory (see, for example, the study of potato prices in Sweden in the book by Cramer [25], p. 505, and theoretical considerations by Creasy [27]).

CHAPTER XIV

MISCELLANEOUS ADDITIONAL RESULTS

1. Confidence Ellipsoids

We return to the scheme of reduction by elements (chapter VIII), retaining the notation of that chapter. We have

$$Y = X^{(0)} + XA, \qquad (14.1.1)$$

where $X^{(0)} = X^{(0)}_{N1}$ and $X = X_{Nn}$ are known matrices;

rank $(X) = n$, $(N > n)$; $Y = Y_{N1}$ is unknown, and $A = A_{n1} = \begin{Vmatrix} a_1 \\ \vdots \\ a_n \end{Vmatrix}$

is a matrix of unknown parameters (elements).

The observation matrix has the form $' = L_{N1} = Y + \Delta$, where

$\Delta = \Delta_{N1} = \begin{Vmatrix} \Delta_1 \\ \vdots \\ \Delta_N \end{Vmatrix}$ is a normal vector of random errors, with

$$E(\Delta) = 0; \quad B_\Delta = E(\Delta\Delta^T) = \sigma^2 P^{-1}, \qquad (14.1.2)$$

$P = P_{NN} = \begin{Vmatrix} p_1 & 0 & \dots & 0 \\ \cdot & \cdot & \cdot & \cdot \\ 0 & 0 & \dots & p_N \end{Vmatrix}$; $p_i > 0$ is a matrix of the known

weights of the observations: σ^2 is an unknown parameter.

In chapter VIII we have constructed confidence intervals for estimating $a_1, a_2, \dots, a_n$ separately; in chapter VII we also considered interval estimation of a linear form $l = g_1 a_1 + \dots + g_n a_n$

in our parameters, with known coefficients.

Now suppose that we wish to estimate m linear functions

$$h_r = g_{r1}a_1 + \dots + g_{rn}a_n; \quad r = 1, 2, \dots, m; \quad 1 \leqslant m \leqslant n, \tag{14.1.3}$$

in the parameters a_i, with known g_{rj}.

We introduce the matrix

$$G = G_{mn} = \|g_{rj}\| \tag{14.1.4}$$

and we write (14.1.3) in the form

$$H = H_{m1} = GA; \quad H = \begin{Vmatrix} h_1 \\ \vdots \\ h_m \end{Vmatrix}. \tag{14.1.5}$$

Without loss of generality, we will assume that rank $(G) = m$. We will construct a confidence region for $H = H_{m1}$. As in chapter VIII, we will denote the matrix $\begin{Vmatrix} \tilde{a}_1 \\ \vdots \\ \tilde{a}_n \end{Vmatrix}$, of estimators of A by the method of least squares, by the symbol $\tilde{A}$.

<u>Theorem 14.1.1. (J.V.Linnik [32]).</u>

Let $\tilde{H} = G\tilde{A}$, $K = K_{mm} = GC^{-1}G^T$ and let $Z = \begin{Vmatrix} z_1 \\ \vdots \\ z_m \end{Vmatrix}$ be the vector of the current co-ordinates $(z_1, \dots, z_m)$. Then the matrix is non-singular, and the confidence ellipsoid $\ni_{\gamma_0}$:

$$(Z - \tilde{H})^T K^{-1}(Z - \tilde{H}) = \gamma_0 [\tilde{p}\tilde{v}\tilde{v}] \tag{14.1.6}$$

covers the point $Z = H$ with probability p_0, and also

$$F_{m, N-n}(\gamma_0) = p_0, \tag{14.1.7}$$

where

$$F_{m, N-n}(x) = \frac{\Gamma\left(\frac{N-n+m}{2}\right)}{\Gamma\left(\frac{N-n}{2}\right)\Gamma\left(\frac{m}{2}\right)} \int_0^x \frac{u^{\frac{m}{2}-1}}{(1+u)^{\frac{N-n+m}{2}}} du \tag{14.1.8}$$

is Fisher's distribution function (see section 6, chapter II).

Proof. As in chapter VIII, we put

$$C = X^T P X, \qquad (14.1.9)$$

where $C = C_{nn}$ is a non-singular matrix and

$$\tilde{A} - A = C^{-1} X^T P \Delta. \qquad (14.1.10)$$

Also $\tilde{A}$ is an n-dimensional normal vector and rank $(G) = m \leqslant n$. Hence, by theorem 2.3.1, $\tilde{H} - H = G(\tilde{A} - A)$ will be an m-dimensional normal vector. Also

$$E(\tilde{H} - H) = 0, \qquad (14.1.11)$$

and the correlation matrix has the form

$$B_{\tilde{H}} = B_{(\tilde{H}-H)} = E\left[G(\tilde{A} - A)\left(G(\tilde{A} - A)\right)^T\right] =$$
$$= G B_{\tilde{A}} G^T = \sigma^2 G C^{-1} G^T = \sigma^2 K. \qquad (14.1.12)$$

Since $\tilde{H}$ is an m-dimensional normal vector and $K = K_{mm}$, K must be a non-singular matrix. We now construct the positive quadratic form

$$Q = \frac{1}{\sigma^2} (\tilde{H} - H)^T K^{-1} (\tilde{H} - H) \qquad (14.1.13)$$

and show that it is distributed as χ^2_m.

Let $f(x_1, \ldots, x_m)$ be the probability density function of the vector $\tilde{H} - H$.

It is known that, with $X = \left\| \begin{matrix} x_1 \\ \vdots \\ x_m \end{matrix} \right\|$

$$f(x_1, \ldots, x_m) = (2\pi)^{-\frac{m}{2}} \sigma^{-m} \left(\det(K)\right)^{-\frac{1}{2}} \exp\left\{-\frac{1}{2\sigma^2} X^T K^{-1} X\right\} \qquad (14.1.14)$$

(see section 2, chapter II). Also, for any $x > 0$, we have

$$P\{Q \leqslant x\} = \int_{\sigma^2 X^T K^{-1} X \leqslant x} \cdots \int f(x_1, \ldots, x_m)\, dx_1 \ldots dx_m.$$

Let $F = F_{mm}$ be an orthogonal matrix such that, by the substitution $X = FZ$, the quadratic form $\sigma^2 X^T K^{-1} X$ takes the diagonal form $Z^T D Z$, where

$$D = \sigma^2 F^T K^{-1} F = \begin{Vmatrix} d_1 & 0 & \dots & 0 \\ 0 & d_2 & \dots & 0 \\ \cdot & \cdot & \cdot & \cdot \\ 0 & 0 & \dots & d_n \end{Vmatrix}.$$

Then $d_i > 0$ and, since $\det(F) = \pm 1$ and the corresponding Jacobian is equal to unity, we get

$$P\{Q \leqslant x\} = \\ = (2\pi)^{-\frac{m}{2}} \left(\det(\sigma^2 K)\right)^{-\frac{1}{2}} \int \dots \int_{Z^T DZ \leqslant x} \exp\left\{-\frac{1}{2} Z^T D Z\right\} dz_1 \dots, dz_m.$$

Further, $\det(D) = d_1 d_2 \dots d_m = \left(\det(\sigma^2 K)\right)^{-1}$, so that

$$P\{Q \leqslant x\} = \\ = (2\pi)^{-\frac{m}{2}} (d_1 d_2 \dots d_m)^{\frac{1}{2}} \int \dots \int_{d_1 z_1^2 + \dots + d_m z_m^2 \leqslant x} \exp\left\{-\frac{1}{2}\left(\sum_{j=1}^{m} d_j z_j^2\right)\right\} dz_1 \dots dz_m.$$

Putting $z_j \sqrt{d_j} = w_j$ $(j = 1, 2, \dots, m)$, we find

$$P\{Q \leqslant x\} = \\ = (2\pi)^{-\frac{m}{2}} \int \dots \int_{w_1^2 + \dots + w_m^2 \leqslant x} \exp\left\{-\frac{1}{2}(w_1^2 + \dots + w_m^2)\right\} dw_1 \dots dw_m. \tag{14.1.15}$$

By the definition of χ_m^2 we have

$$P\{Q \leqslant x\} = P\{\chi_m^2 \leqslant x\},$$

which was to be proved.

As is known from chapter VIII, the vector $\tilde{A}$ does not depend stochastically on $[p\tilde{v}\tilde{v}]$, and this is also true for the vector $\tilde{H} - H$ and its function, the quadratic form Q. In view of this we have

$$\frac{Q}{[p\tilde{v}\tilde{v}]\,\sigma^{-2}} = \frac{(H - \tilde{H})^T K^{-1} (H - \tilde{H})}{[p\tilde{v}\tilde{v}]} = \frac{(\chi'_m)^2}{\chi_{N-n}^2}, \tag{14.1.16}$$

where the χ^2 -distributions in the numerator and denominator are independent.

Hence, for a given $\gamma_0 > 0$, the probability of the event

$$(H-\tilde{H})^T K^{-1}(H-\tilde{H}) \leqslant \gamma_0 [p\tilde{v}\tilde{v}] \qquad (14.1.17)$$

(which we will denote by $\mathfrak{A}$) is

$$P(\mathfrak{A}) = F_{m,\, N-n}(\gamma_0), \qquad (14.1.18)$$

where $F_{m,\, N-n}(x)$ is the appropriate Fisher's distribution. Covering the point $Z=H$ by the ellipsoid $\mathcal{E}_{\gamma_0}$ (see (14.1.6)) is equivalent to the event $\mathfrak{A}$, and so the theorem is proved.

In chapter XI we have already applied a special case of the ellipsoid $\mathcal{E}_{\gamma_0}$ in the problem of direct and reversed bearings. We will now consider some other special cases. If $G=E=E_{nn}$, $H=A$, then we require a confidence region for all of the parameters $(a_1, a_2, \ldots, a_n)$. In this case $K=C^{-1}$; $K^{-1}=C$, and the ellipsoid $\mathcal{E}_{\gamma_0}$ has the form

$$(Z-\tilde{A})^T C (Z-\tilde{A}) = \gamma_0 [p\tilde{v}\tilde{v}]. \qquad (14.1.19)$$

Another extremal case occurs in estimating a single parameter, a_i say. We put $G=\|0, 0, \ldots, 1, 0, \ldots, 0\|$ (unity in the i th position). Then

$$K = GC^{-1}G^T = \{C^{-1}\}_{ii}. \qquad (14.1.20)$$

The confidence ellipsoid $\mathcal{E}_{\gamma_0}$ takes the form

$$\frac{(z-\tilde{a}_i)^2}{\{C^{-1}\}_{ii}} = \gamma_0 [p\tilde{v}\tilde{v}], \qquad (14.1.21)$$

and its covering of the parameter a_i is the event $\mathfrak{A}$

$$\frac{|a_i-\tilde{a}_i|}{\sqrt{\{C^{-1}\}_{ii}\,[p\tilde{v}\tilde{v}]}} \leqslant \sqrt{\gamma_0}. \qquad (14.1.22)$$

If we consider, instead, the equivalent event

$$\frac{|a_i-\tilde{a}_i|}{\sqrt{\{C^{-1}\}_{ii}\dfrac{[p\tilde{v}\tilde{v}]}{N-n}}} \leqslant \sqrt{\gamma_0 (N-n)}, \qquad (14.1.23)$$

then $P(\mathfrak{A})$ will be evaluated from Student's law with $(N-n)$ degrees of freedom, and we obtain the same confidence intervals for estimating the a_i's separately as were given in chapter VIII.

We now note some points arising in the solution of equation (14.1.7)

$$F_{m,\,N-n}(\gamma_0)=p_0.$$

It is not difficult to show that Fisher's $F_{m,\,N-n}(x)$ can always be expressed in terms of elementary functions (see Linnik [32]).

In the case $m=n=2$, which we met in chapter XI in problems of bearings on a plane, there is immediately obtained (see (11.1.33) and (11.1.34)):

$$\gamma_0=\left(\frac{1}{1-p_0}\right)^{\frac{2}{N-2}}-1;$$

for large N, $\gamma_0=\frac{2}{N-2}\ln\frac{1}{1-p_0}+O\left(\frac{1}{N^2}\right)$. In other cases complicated expressions are obtained and we will get only asymptotic expressions for γ_0, for large N. This is most easily done by considering the probabilistic meaning of Fisher's distribution. We write equation (14.1.7) in the form

$$F_{m,\,N-n}(\gamma_0)=P\{(\chi_m')^2\leqslant\gamma_0\chi^2_{N-n}\}=p_0. \qquad (14.1.24)$$

Now we suppose that $m\leqslant n$ and n is bounded; $N\to\infty$. The quantities $(\chi_m')^2$ and χ^2_{N-n} are stochastically independent. For fixed n and $N\to\infty$ we put

$$\chi^2_{N-n}=N-n+\xi_N, \text{ where } E\xi_N=0 \quad \text{and} \quad \sigma(\xi_N)=O(\sqrt{N});$$

then (14.1.24) takes the form

$$F_{m,\,N-n}(\gamma_0)=P\left\{(\chi_m')^2\leqslant\gamma_0\left(1+\frac{\xi_N}{N-n}\right)(N-n)\right\}=p_0. \qquad (14.1.25)$$

Neglecting the deviate $\frac{\xi_N}{N-n}$ we see that

$$\gamma_0\sim\frac{\xi_0}{N-n},$$

where ξ_0 is found from tables of the χ^2_m distribution; if

$P\{\chi_m^2 \leqslant x\} = K_m(x)$, then

$$K_m(\xi_0) = p_0. \tag{14.1.26}$$

Hence it is not difficult to work out the lengths of the semi-axes of the confidence ellipsoid $Э_{\gamma_0}$.

We also note that exactly the same results for the confidence ellipsoid $Э_\gamma$ will be true if $X = X_{Nn}$ and the abscissae x_{rj} $(r = 1, 2, \ldots, N;\ j = 1, 2, \ldots, n)$ are chosen in any random way whatever, subject only to the condition that, with probability equal to one, rank $(X) = n$. In this case $C = X^T PX$ is also a random matrix and $\tilde{A} = C^{-1}X^T PL$ will no longer, in general, be a normal vector for normal L. However, the ellipsoid $Э_{\gamma_0}$ remains a confidence region with the same confidence coefficient. In fact, for any fixed matrix X of rank n it has the same (conditional) confidence coefficient p_0; therefore the overall probability of covering A is p_0. These results should not be confused with Wald's results (chapter XII) in which X is essentially random, but the equations $Y = XA$ no longer hold because of errors in measurement of the abscissae.

2. Dependent Observations

We will consider the same scheme of reduction by elements

$$Y = X_0 + XA;\quad L - X_0 - \Delta = XA, \tag{14.2.1}$$

where we regard the error vector $\Delta = \begin{Vmatrix} \Delta_1 \\ \vdots \\ \Delta_N \end{Vmatrix}$ as being normal, but now, not necessarily with independent components Δ_i. This will correspond to a scheme of stochastically dependent observations, i.e. with their errors stochastically dependent. We will suppose that the vector of mean values is zero (i.e. the errors Δ_i are unbiased), while the correlation matrix, B_Δ, of the Δ,

$$B_\Delta = \sigma^2 B_0 \tag{14.2.2}$$

is known with accuracy up to σ^2, i.e. B_0 is a known matrix. Then we can reduce the problem to the case of independent errors Δ_i, which has already been discussed.

Let $G = G_{NN}$ be a non-singular matrix. Pre-multiplying (14.2.1) by G we obtain:

$$GY = GX_0 + GXA; \quad GL - GX_0 - G\Delta = GXA. \qquad (14.2.3)$$

Here the matrices Y, X_0, X, L, and Δ have been replaced by these same matrices, pre-multiplied by G. We put

$$\Delta^{(1)} = \begin{Vmatrix} \Delta_1^{(1)} \\ \vdots \\ \Delta_N^{(1)} \end{Vmatrix} = G\Delta. \qquad (14.2.4)$$

By theorem 2.3.1, the correlation matrix of the new normal vector $\Delta^{(1)}$ is

$$B_{\Delta^{(1)}} = GB_\Delta G^T = \sigma^2 GB_0 G^T. \qquad (14.2.5)$$

We can find a non-singular (and even orthogonal) matrix G such that

$$GB_0G^T = \begin{Vmatrix} d_1 & 0 \dots & 0 \\ \cdot & \cdot \quad \cdot & \cdot \\ 0 & 0 \dots & d_N \end{Vmatrix} \qquad (14.2.6)$$

is a diagonal matrix. Then

$$B_{\Delta^{(1)}} = \sigma^2 GB_0G^T = \begin{Vmatrix} d_1\sigma^2 & 0 & \dots & 0 \\ 0 & d_2\sigma^2 & \dots & 0 \\ \cdot & \cdot & \cdot & \cdot \\ 0 & 0 & \dots & d_N\sigma^2 \end{Vmatrix}. \qquad (14.2.7)$$

Putting $d_r = \frac{1}{p_r}$ $(r = 1, 2, \dots, N)$, we see that the vector $\Delta^{(1)}$ has independent components with weights $p_1, p_2, \dots, p_N$ and the relations (14.2.3) give the usual scheme of reduction by elements with Y, X_0, X, L, Δ replaced by the matrices $GY, GX_0, GX, GL, G\Delta$. All the formulae and conclusions of chapter VIII remain valid. In particular, the system of normal equations for $\tilde{A}$ takes the form

$$C\tilde{A} = X^TG^TPGL; \quad C = X^TG^TPGX, \qquad (14.2.8)$$

and so on.

We will have a good deal of freedom of choice in constructing the matrix G, since we do not need it to be orthogonal. We can make use of this in analysing available data with dependent errors (for example, in the analysis of level circuits, when they are based on a reference mark, the position of which is not given exactly, but estimated from observations in some of these circuits).

We could also have tried applying the operation of pre-multiplication by the non-singular matrix G, transforming (14.2.1) into (14.2.3), to previous schemes, for example, in the case of independent observations of equal accuracy. However this would not have led to useful results. If the matrix G were not orthogonal we would have disturbed the stochastic independence of the observations, and if it were orthogonal the new observation vector would have had independent components, but the system of normal equations would be just the same as before. For if G is an orthogonal matrix, then $G^T = G^{-1}$, $P = E$, and (14.2.8) is equivalent to $C\tilde{A} = X^T L$; $C = X^T X$, i.e. it remains as before.

3. The Rôle of the Normal Law in the Theory of the Method of Least Squares

In chapter VI (sections 4-5) and chapter VIII we became acquainted with some extremal properties of the method of least squares applied to a normal error vector Δ with independent components. These followed from the joint efficiency of the estimators $(\tilde{a}_1, \ldots, \tilde{a}_n)$ of the elements $a_1, \ldots, a_n$ by the method of least squares. The question naturally arises: can the estimators $(\tilde{a}_1, \ldots, \tilde{a}_n)$ be jointly efficient in the case when the errors of observations are independent, but follow some other law, differing from the normal law.

The answer to this question is in the negative. It is possible to show that for a very wide class of unbiased estimators, the estimators found by the method of least squares can be jointly efficient only if the error vector Δ is normal (Petrov [40], pp. 56-7). Hence the existence of optimal properties for the method of least squares is closely connected with the normality of the error vector.

In order to solve this question we will consider the scheme of reduction by elements (chapter VIII) with the symbols of that chapter. For simplicity we will first consider observations of equal accuracy, and $X^{(0)} = 0$. We will need to use theorem 5, p. 92. We will assume that the likelihood function, L, of the observations $l_1, l_2, \ldots, l_N$ satisfies the conditions laid down in this theorem. We must have

$$\ln L = \sum_{r=1}^{N} \ln f\left(l_r - \sum_{j=1}^{n} a_j x_{rj},\ \sigma\right), \qquad (14.3.1)$$

where the probability density $f(x)$ is assumed to be continuous, non-zero and twice differentiable. The maximum likelihood equations for estimators $a'_1, \ldots, a'_n$ of the parameters $a_1, \ldots, a_n$ have the form

$$\frac{\partial \ln L}{\partial a'_j} = \sum_{r=1}^{N} \frac{\partial}{\partial a'_j} \ln f_r(\delta_r;\ \sigma) = 0, \qquad (14.3.2)$$

where

$$\delta_r = l_r - \sum_{j=1}^{n} a'_j x_{rj}. \qquad (14.3.3)$$

We introduce the matrices

$$\delta = \begin{Vmatrix} \delta_1 \\ \vdots \\ \delta_N \end{Vmatrix}; \quad A' = \begin{Vmatrix} a'_1 \\ \vdots \\ a'_n \end{Vmatrix};$$

X and L will have the same meaning as in chapter VI. Equations (14.3.3) can be written in the form $XA' = L - \delta$. Pre-multiplying by X^T we find

$$X^T X A' = X^T L - X^T \delta. \qquad (14.3.4)$$

Since $X^T X = C$ (the matrix of the normal system), we have

$$CA' = X^T L - X^T \delta$$

and

$$A' = C^{-1} X^T L - C^{-1} X^T \delta. \qquad (14.3.5)$$

Further,

$$C^{-1} X^T L = \tilde{A} = \begin{Vmatrix} \tilde{a}_1 \\ \vdots \\ \tilde{a}_n \end{Vmatrix}$$

is a single-column matrix of estimators by the method of least squares. Hence

$$A' = \tilde{A} - C^{-1} X^T \delta. \qquad (14.3.6)$$

Hence the identity of the estimators A' with the estimators by the method of least squares $\tilde{A}$ is equivalent to the relation

$$C^{-1} X^T \delta = 0,$$

or, since C^{-1} is non-singular,

$$X^T\delta = 0. \tag{14.3.7}$$

For such identity, the maximum likelihood equations (14.3.2) must have the unique set of solutions $(\tilde{a}_1, \ldots, \tilde{a}_n)$. We also have

$$\frac{\partial \ln f_r(\delta_r; \sigma)}{\partial a_j'} = \frac{f_r'(\delta_r; \sigma)}{f_r(\delta_r, \sigma)} \frac{\partial \delta_r}{\partial a_j'} = -\frac{f_r'(\delta_r; \sigma)}{f_r(\delta_r; \sigma)} x_{rj}. \tag{14.3.8}$$

Thus, these equations can be written in the form

$$\sum_{r=1}^{N} \frac{f_r'(\delta_r; \sigma)}{f_r(\delta_r; \sigma)} x_{rj} = 0. \tag{14.3.9}$$

Introducing the matrix

$$\varphi(\delta) = \varphi_{n1} = \left\| \begin{matrix} \frac{f_1'}{f_1}(\delta_1; \sigma) \\ \vdots \\ \frac{f_N'}{f_N}(\delta_N; \sigma) \end{matrix} \right\| = \left\| \begin{matrix} \varphi_1(\delta_r) \\ \vdots \\ \varphi_N(\delta_N) \end{matrix} \right\|, \tag{14.3.10}$$

we write equation (14.3.9) in the form

$$X^T\varphi(\delta) = 0. \tag{14.3.11}$$

We see that the equations $X^T\delta = 0$ and $X^T\varphi(\delta) = 0$ must be equivalent.

We will assume that this is true for any matrix $X = X_{Nn}$ of rank n and any set of numbers $(\delta_1, \ldots, \delta_N)$ Now we take a matrix of form

$$X=\begin{Vmatrix} 0 & \ldots\ldots & 0 & 0 & +1 \\ 0 & \ldots\ldots & 0 & +1 & -\frac{x}{n-1} \\ 0 & \ldots\ldots 0 & +1 & -1 & -\frac{x}{n-1} \\ \ldots & \ldots & \ldots & \ldots & \ldots \\ 0 & \ldots -1 & 0 & \ldots & -\frac{x}{n-1} \\ \ldots & \ldots & \ldots & \ldots & \ldots \\ 0 & +1 & \ldots & \ldots & 0 \\ +1 & -1 & \ldots 0 & \ldots & 0 \\ -1 & 0 & \ldots 0 & \ldots & 0 \end{Vmatrix} \qquad (14.3.12)$$

such that the sum of elements of each column, except the last, is equal to zero.

We will also consider the matrix

$$\delta=\begin{Vmatrix} x \\ 1 \\ \vdots \\ 1 \\ 1 \\ \vdots \\ 1 \end{Vmatrix} \begin{matrix} \left.\vphantom{\begin{matrix} x \\ 1 \\ \vdots \\ 1 \end{matrix}}\right\} n \\ \left.\vphantom{\begin{matrix} 1 \\ \vdots \\ 1 \end{matrix}}\right\} N-n \end{matrix}$$

Here x is a variable argument.

We have: rank $(X)=n$ for $x \neq 0$. Also, evidently, $X^T\delta=0$ for any x; whence $X^T\varphi(\delta)=0$. The last of these equations gives

$$\varphi_1(x)-\frac{x}{n-1}\sum_{r=2}^{n}\varphi_r(1)=0,$$

whence

$$\varphi_1(x)=\alpha_1 x \qquad (14.3.13)$$

with α_1 constant. Analogously, we have

$$\varphi_r(x) = \alpha_r x \qquad (r = 1, 2, \ldots, N). \tag{14.3.14}$$

Further, $\varphi_r(x) = \frac{f'_r}{f_r}$, so we have the differential equations

$$\frac{f'_r}{f_r} = \alpha_r x.$$

Integrating, we find: $\ln f_r = c_0 x^2 + c_1$, where c_i 's are constants depending only on r. Therefore

$$f_r = \exp(c_0 x^2 + c_1) = c_2 e^{c_0 x^2} \tag{14.3.15}$$

But f_r must be a probability density, so that

$$\int_{-\infty}^{\infty} f_r(x)\, dx = 1.$$

Hence it follows that c_0 must be negative. We put

$$c_0 = -\frac{1}{2\mu^2},$$

and then from (14.3.15) we find

$$c_2 = \frac{1}{\sqrt{2\pi}\,\mu},$$

so that $f_r(x)$ is the normal density $N(0, \mu)$. Since the errors were assumed to be unbiased and of equal accuracy, $\mu = \sigma$ and cannot depend on r.

We have proved the normality of f_r for equally accurate errors; it follows that this is also true for errors which are not of equal accuracy. In fact, we know, from section 1 of chapter VI, that cases when errors are not of equal accuracy can be transformed into cases with errors of equal accuracy, if the fundamental equation $L - \Delta = XA$ is pre-multiplied by $P^{\frac{1}{2}}$, so that we get

$$P^{\frac{1}{2}} L - P^{\frac{1}{2}} \Delta = P^{\frac{1}{2}} XA.$$

With the conditions stated above, the vector $P^{\frac{1}{2}}\Delta$ is normal, and consequently the vector Δ is normal.

Thus, the assertion - that the joint efficiency of estimators obtained by the method of least squares implies, under extremely wide conditions, the normality of the error vector - is proved. There is a deep connexion between the method of least squares and the normal distribution law.

4. Non-Normal Error Vector. A Formula of Gauss. Theorem of Kolmogorov, Petrov and Smirnov

We consider the scheme of reduction by elements

$$y_r = a_1 x_{r1} + \ldots + a_n x_{rn} \qquad (r = 1, \ldots, N), \tag{14.4.1}$$

$$y_r = l_r - \Delta_r, \tag{14.4.2}$$

or, in matrix form,

$$\begin{aligned} Y &= XA; \\ Y &= L - \Delta. \end{aligned} \qquad \text{rank } (X) = n, \tag{14.4.3}$$

We keep the conditions and notation of chapter VIII, but we will assume that the error vector

$$\Delta = \begin{Vmatrix} \Delta_1 \\ \Delta_2 \\ \vdots \\ \Delta_N \end{Vmatrix} \tag{14.4.4}$$

has independent components Δ_r, which are now not assumed to be normal. We will assume that

$$E(\Delta_r) = 0; \quad D(\Delta_r) = \frac{\sigma^2}{p_r}, \tag{14.4.5}$$

$$E(\Delta_r^4) = \frac{\mu_4}{p_r^2}, \tag{14.4.6}$$

where $p_r (r = 1, 2, \ldots, N)$ are known numbers (weights). A case like that defined in section 1 of chapter VII can easily be treated as a case of equally accurate measurements. We note that, for normal errors Δ_r, (14.4.6) follows from (14.4.5); for cases when the Δ_r are non-normal, this is not so. By replacing the observations l_r by the sample group means

$$\bar{l}_r = \frac{l_{r1} + \ldots + l_{rm}}{m}$$

of groups of independent observations we have

$$D(\overline{l}_r) = \frac{\sigma^2}{m}, \quad \text{if} \quad D(l_{rj}) = \sigma^2 \qquad (j = 1, \ldots, m).$$

Assume that the central moments of fourth order $\mu_4(l_{rj}) = \mu_4$ exist. It is easy to show that

$$\mu_4(\overline{l}_r) = \frac{3\sigma^4}{m^2} + \frac{\mu_4 - 3\sigma^4}{m^3}. \qquad (14.4.7)$$

For the normal law we have

$$\mu_4 = 3\sigma^4, \qquad (14.4.8)$$

so that in this case

$$\mu_4(\overline{l}_r) = \frac{\mu_4}{m^2},$$

Replacing l_r by the group mean $\overline{l}_r$, and giving this observation the weight $p_r = m$ (see section 6, chapter VI); the equation (14.4.6) is still satisfied. In the general case of non-normal observations, l_{rj}, on interchanging l_r and $\overline{l}_r$ (14.4.7) and (14.4.5) will be satisfied; in general, (14.4.6) will not be satisfied.

We know that, for a non-normal error vector Δ, it is no longer possible to guarantee the optimal properties of estimators obtained by the method of least squares, and, according to section 3 of this chapter, this corresponds to the essence of the matter. As was seen in section 2 of chapter VII, in those cases where conditions (14.4.5) are satisfied, it is only possible to guarantee minimal variance for the separate estimators among all linear unbiased estimators of the measured elements and linear functions of them. But minimal variance is itself a condition of the same type as least squares, and similar theorems to those for normal error vectors Δ, though non-trivial, give much less extensive results.

We must note once again, that from the solution of the normal equations

$$\tilde{A} = C^{-1}X^T PL.$$

We see that the estimators $\tilde{a}_1, \ldots, \tilde{a}_n$ of the parameters $a_1, \ldots, a_n$ are obtained in the form of linear functions of the independent observations $l_1, \ldots, l_N$, and therefore it is to be expected, from Liapounov's theorem (Theorem 2.7.1) that these estimators $\tilde{a}_1, \ldots, \tilde{a}_n$ will be approximately normal, even for a non-normal error vector Δ. In such cases the unbiasedness and minimal variance of $\tilde{a}_i$ among linear unbiased estimators of a_i will already have an advantageous significance in terms of probability, similar to that described in section 5 of chapter XI.

We return to formulae (14.4.5) and (14.4.6). In the case of a normal error vector Δ, we have $\mu_4 = 3\sigma^4$ and

$$E\left(\Delta_r^4\right) = \frac{3\sigma^4}{p_r}. \tag{14.4.9}$$

We know that, in this case, $\tilde{s}^2 = \frac{[p\tilde{v}\tilde{v}]}{N-n}$ is an unbiased estimator of σ^2, and $\tilde{s}^2$ is distributed as $\frac{\sigma^2}{N-n}\chi^2_{N-n}$. Since

$$D\left(\chi^2_{N-n}\right) = 2(N-n)\sigma^4 \tag{14.4.10}$$

(see section 6, chapter II), then

$$D\left(\tilde{s}^2\right) = \frac{1}{(N-n)^2} D\left([p\tilde{v}\tilde{v}]\right) = \frac{2\sigma^4}{N-n}. \tag{14.4.11}$$

Since $\mu_4 = 3\sigma^4$ for a normal error vector Δ, (14.4.11) can be written

$$D\left(\tilde{s}^2\right) = \frac{\mu_4 - \sigma^4}{N-n}. \tag{14.4.12}$$

Gauss ([7], section 39) obtained a generalization of formula (14.4.12) for the variance $D\left(\tilde{s}^2\right)$ in the case of a non-normal error vector under conditions (14.4.5) and (14.4.6) and (more naturally) the condition of equal accuracy $[p_r = 1,\ (r = 1, \ldots, N)]$. We will derive this formula of Gauss in matrix form.

Theorem 14.4.1 (K.F.Gauss).
Under conditions (14.4.5) and (14.4.6) we have

$$D\left(\tilde{s}^2\right) = \frac{\mu_4 - \sigma^4}{N-n} - \frac{\mu_4 - 3\sigma^4}{(N-n)^2}(n - \Omega), \tag{14.4.13}$$

where (in our usual notation)

$$\Omega = \sum_{r=1}^{N} \{u_{rr}\}^2, \tag{14.4.14}$$

$$U = P^{\frac{1}{2}} X C^{-1} X^T P^{\frac{1}{2}}. \tag{14.4.15}$$

Here, $C = X^T P X$ is the matrix of the normal system of equations.

Proof. We consider first the case of equally accurate measurements, $P=E$; it is easy to pass from this to a given case, as was described in section 1 of chapter VI. In the notation of chapter VI, we have, for this case, (see (6.6.2))

$$\tilde{V}=(U-E)\Delta; \quad U=XC^{-1}X^T \tag{14.4.16}$$

We also have, as was explained in chapter VI,

$$U^2=U; \quad U^T=U; \qquad \text{rank } (U)=n. \tag{14.4.17}$$

In chapter VI it was also explained that the symmetrical matrices U and $E-U$ are positive semi-definite. This fact will be very important later. We also have

$$\tilde{s}^2=\frac{[\tilde{v}\tilde{v}]}{N-n},$$
$$[\tilde{v}\tilde{v}]=\tilde{V}^T\tilde{V}=\Delta^T(U-E)^T(U-E)\Delta=\Delta^T(U-E)^2\Delta.$$

Further,

$$(U-E)^2=U^2-2U+E=U-2U+E=E-U.$$

Thus

$$[\tilde{v}\tilde{v}]=\Delta^T(E-U)\Delta. \tag{14.4.18}$$

We put $U=U_{NN}=\|u_{ij}\|$; then from (14.4.18) we have

$$[\tilde{v}\tilde{v}]=\sum_{r=1}^{N}\Delta_r^2-\sum_{i,j=1}^{N}u_{ij}\Delta_i\Delta_j. \tag{14.4.19}$$

Here $u_{ij}=u_{ji}$, since $U^T=U$. Re-writing (14.4.19) as

$$[\tilde{v}\tilde{v}]=\sum_{r=1}^{N}(1-u_{rr})\Delta_r^2-2\sum_{\substack{i<j\\ i,j=1,\ldots,N}}u_{ij}\Delta_i\Delta_j, \tag{14.4.20}$$

we have, since $E(\tilde{s}^2)=\sigma^2$,

$$D(\tilde{s}^2)=E(\tilde{s}^2-\sigma^2)^2=E(\tilde{s}^4)-2\sigma^2E\tilde{s}^2+\sigma^4=$$
$$=E(\tilde{s}^4)-2\sigma^4+\sigma^4=E(\tilde{s}^4)-\sigma^4.$$

Hence we obtain

$$D(\tilde{s}^2)=\frac{1}{(N-n)^2}E([\tilde{v}\tilde{v}]^2)-\sigma^4. \tag{14.4.21}$$

We will find $E([\tilde{v}\tilde{v}]^2)$. We note that the errors Δ_i are mutually independent, and $E(\Delta_i)=0$. This simplifies the calculations; we must take the square of the sum (of squares) (14.4.18) and find the mathematical expectation of this square. This will consist of terms containing products of the form

$$\Delta_r^2\Delta_\mu\Delta_\nu \quad (\mu<\nu) \text{ and } \Delta_i\Delta_j\Delta_\mu\Delta_\nu \quad (i<j,\ \mu<\nu).$$

We also have $E(\Delta_r^2\Delta_\mu\Delta_\nu)=0$, since the product contains the term Δ_ρ $(\rho=\mu$ or ν, $\rho\neq r)$ and therefore it has expected value equal to zero (see chapter II). From similar considerations, $E(\Delta_i\Delta_j\Delta_\mu\Delta_\nu)$ can be unequal to zero only in those cases when $i=\mu$ and $j=\nu$. The case $i=\nu$, $j=\mu$ cannot arise, since $i<j$ and $\mu<\nu$. Taking this into account, we obtain from (14.4.20)

$$E([\tilde{v}\tilde{v}]^2)=\sum_{r,t=1}^{N}(1-u_{rr})(1-u_{tt})E\,\Delta_r^2\Delta_t^2+ \\ +4\sum_{i<j}(u_{ij})^2 E\Delta_i^2\Delta_j^2. \qquad (14.4.22)$$

We have

$$E(\Delta_i^2\Delta_j^2)=E(\Delta_i^2)E(\Delta_j^2)=\sigma^4 \qquad (i<j) \qquad (14.4.23)$$

Also, $E(\Delta_r^2\Delta_t^2)=\sigma^4$ for $r\neq t$ and

$$E(\Delta_r^4)=\mu_4 \qquad (14.4.24)$$

for $r=t$. This allows (14.4.22) to be written as:

$$E([\tilde{v}\tilde{v}]^2)=(\mu_4-\sigma^4)\sum_{r=1}^{N}(1-u_{rr})^2+\sigma^4\left(\sum_{r=1}^{N}(1-u_{rr})\right)^2+ \\ +2\sigma^4\sum_{i,j=1}^{N}(u_{ij})^2-2\sigma^4\sum_{i=1}^{N}(u_{ii})^2. \qquad (14.4.25)$$

We will now prove the equations

$$\sum_{r=1}^{N}u_{rr}=n; \qquad \sum_{i,j=1}^{N}(u_{ij})^2=n. \qquad (14.4.26)$$

According to (14.4.17) we have

$$\sum_{r=1}^{N} u_{rr} = \mathrm{Sp}(U) = n. \qquad (14.4.27)$$

Next we consider the expression $\sum_{i,j=1}^{N} u_{ij}^2$ the sum of squares of all elements of the matrix U. We will prove the equation

$$\sum_{i,j=1}^{N} u_{ij}^2 = \mathrm{Sp}(UU^T). \qquad (14.4.28)$$

In fact, $\mathrm{Sp}(UU^T)$ is the sum of the diagonal elements of UU^T. But the diagonal elements are, as can be seen from the very definition of matrix multiplication, the sums of squares of elements in rows of the matrix U. This proves (14.4.28). Now, from (14.4.17) and (14.4.27) we find

$$U^T = U, \quad UU^T = U^2 = U; \quad \mathrm{Sp}(UU^T) = \mathrm{Sp}(U) = n,$$

which proves (14.4.26).

It is not so simple to evaluate the quantity

$$\sum_{i=1}^{N} (u_{ii})^2 = \Omega,$$

(see (14.4.22)). Inserting (14.4.26) and (14.4.27) into (14.4.22), we find

$$E([\tilde{v}\tilde{v}]^2) = (\mu_4 - \sigma^4)(N - 2n + \Omega) + \sigma^4 (N - n)^2 + 2\sigma^4 n - 2\sigma^4 \Omega.$$

Hence

$$E([\tilde{v}\tilde{v}]^2) = (\mu_4 - \sigma^4)(N - n) - (\mu_4 - 3\sigma^4)(n - \Omega) + \sigma^4 (N - n)^2.$$

Substituting this in (14.4.21) we reach (14.4.13), which proves the theorem for equally accurate observations.

For the general case, according to the statement in chapter VI, section 1, it is sufficient to replace X by $P^{\frac{1}{2}}X$, L by $P^{\frac{1}{2}}L$, in order to reduce it to the case of equally accurate observations. In this, $\tilde{V}$ is replaced by $P^{\frac{1}{2}}\tilde{V}$; $[\tilde{v}\tilde{v}] = \tilde{V}^T\tilde{V}$ by $\tilde{V}^T P \tilde{V} = [p\tilde{v}\tilde{v}]$, so that

$$\tilde{s}^2 = \frac{[p\tilde{v}\tilde{v}]}{N-n}. \qquad (14.4.29)$$

The matrix $C = X^T X$ is replaced by $X^T P X$ and $U = X^T C^{-1} X$ by $U = P^{\frac{1}{2}} X C^{-1} X^T P^{\frac{1}{2}}$. Gauss formula (14.4.13) remains valid. All properties of the matrix U, it goes without saying, remain valid, since U will play the rôle of the corresponding matrix for the system of equally accurate observations. These properties can also be verified directly.

If the vector Δ is normal, then the old formula (14.4.12) is obtained from Gauss' formula (14.4.13). In the general case, also, Gauss gave upper and lower bounds for the quantity Ω. Gauss' bounds, which lead to corresponding bounds for $D(\tilde{s}^2)$, have the form

$$\frac{n^2}{N} \leqslant \Omega \leqslant N. \qquad (14.4.30)$$

Gauss' lower bound, as we will learn later, cannot be improved in the general case, but the upper bound is very rough, as was shown by Kolmogorov, Petrov and Smirnov [23]; and, as can be seen from (14.4.13), it can sometimes give a trivial, negative lower limit for $D(\tilde{s}^2)$ (it is clear that $D(\tilde{s}^2) \geqslant 0$). These three authors gave an upper bound for Ω, which cannot be further improved in the general case, and obtained a lower bound to $D(\tilde{s}^2)$, which cannot be improved.

<u>Theorem 14.4.2 (A.N.Kolmogorov, A.A.Petrov, Y.M.Smirnov [23]).</u> In the general case we have the estimate

$$\Omega \leqslant n, \qquad (14.4.31)$$

which cannot be improved; so that for $\mu_4 - 3\sigma^4 \geqslant 0$

$$\frac{1}{N-n}\left(\mu_4 - \sigma^4 - \frac{n}{N}(\mu_4 - 3\sigma^4)\right) \leqslant D(\tilde{s}^2) \leqslant \frac{\mu_4 - \sigma^4}{N-n} \qquad (14.4.32)$$

and for $\mu_4 - 3\sigma^4 \leqslant 0$

$$\frac{\mu_4 - \sigma^4}{N-n} \leqslant D(\tilde{s}^2) \leqslant \frac{1}{N-n}\left(\mu^4 - \sigma^4 + \frac{n}{N}(3\sigma^4 - \mu_4)\right). \qquad (14.4.33)$$

We note that μ_4 is always greater than or equal to σ^4, so that the bounds are never trivial.

We will prove the inequalities

$$\frac{n^2}{N} \leqslant \Omega \leqslant n, \qquad (14.4.34)$$

but we will not prove that they cannot be improved. The last is based on an algebraic theorem of Maltsev [23] and [34].

Proof. It is required to prove that

$$\frac{n^2}{N} \leqslant \sum_{i=1}^{N} u_{ii}^2 \leqslant n. \tag{14.4.35}$$

We will first prove that

$$0 \leqslant u_{ii} \leqslant 1. \tag{14.4.36}$$

For if (14.4.36) is not satisfied, then at least one of the matrices U and $E-U$ would have negative diagonal elements u_{ii} or $1-u_{ii}$. But as was shown above, these matrices are semi-definite and therefore this is impossible, since it contradicts the conditions of semi-definiteness (see section 4 of chapter I). Thus (14.4.36) is true. Hence, by the Cauchy-Buniakovski inequality (see (1.1.1)),

$$\begin{gathered} N \sum_{i=1}^{N} u_{ii}^2 \geqslant \left(\sum_{i=1}^{N} u_{ii} \right)^2 = (\mathrm{Sp}\,(U))^2 = n^2; \\ \sum_{i=1}^{N} u_{ii}^2 \geqslant \frac{n^2}{N}. \end{gathered} \tag{14.4.37}$$

From (14.4.36) we see that $0 \leqslant u_{ii}^2 \leqslant u_{ii}$, and hence

$$\sum_{i=1}^{N} u_{ii}^2 \leqslant \sum_{i=1}^{N} u_{ii} = \mathrm{Sp}\,(U) = n, \tag{14.4.38}$$

which also proves (14.4.34). Further, (14.4.30) and (14.4.31) are obtained by substituting the inequalities (14.3.34) in Gauss' formula (14.4.13). The upper bound for Ω given by Gauss corresponds to using only the fact that $0 \leqslant u_{ii} \leqslant 1$, so that $\sum_{i=1}^{N} u_{ii}^2 \leqslant N$.

5. Cauchy's Method of Reduction of Observations

We will consider the scheme of reduction by elements. For simplicity, and without loss of generality, we put $X_0 = 0$, so that the system of fundamental equations takes the form (in the notation of chapter VIII)

$$Y = L - \Delta = XA,$$

or, in detail

$$y_r = l_r - \Delta_r = \sum_{j=1}^{n} x_{rj} a_j \qquad (r = 1, 2, \ldots, N). \qquad (14.5.1)$$

The observations are assumed to be independent. We have seen that, with a normal error vector Δ, the method of least squares has certain optimal properties among a wide class of other methods (see section 5, chapter VI), so that, in this sense, it possesses an advantage. But, despite the common use of simplified methods (for example, the Gauss' and Gauss-Doolittle methods - see section 12, chapter VI) the calculation of the solution of the normal system of equations stil presents difficulties. Sometimes, therefore, recourse is made to the other methods of estimating a_j from the observations l_r $(r = 1, 2, \ldots, N)$ and the fundamental equations (14.5.1).

The construction of the normal equations and the estimators of the parameters $(a_1, \ldots, a_n)$ obtained from them are, in the final analysis, methods of combining the N equations (14.5.1), which over-define the estimators, in such a way that the results could be obtained by the solution of a linear system of equations in the n parameters $(a_1, \ldots, a_n)$. There are many such methods, apart from the method of least squares, although, as was explained above, they will no longer have the optimal properties possessed by the method of least squares. One of these methods was suggested by Cauchy.

Here we will give a brief account of it and discuss some simple questions connected with its efficiency, relative to the method of least squares. *)

Cauchy's suggestion was as follows. Firstly we 'prepare' the system (14.5.1), i.e. we multiply each equation by $+1$ or -1 so as to make $x_{1j} > 0$ $(j = 1, 2, \ldots, N)$. We suppose that this has been done. Then all the equations are added, giving

$$(x_{11} + x_{21} + \ldots + x_{N1}) a_1 + (x_{12} + x_{22} + \ldots + x_{N2}) a_2 + \ldots + \\ + (x_{1n} + x_{2n} + \ldots + x_{Nn}) a_n = y_1 + \ldots + y_N. \qquad (14.5.2)$$

We will adhere to Cauchy's notation, putting

$$x_{1j} + x_{2j} + \ldots + x_{Nj} = Sx_j \qquad (j = 1, 2, \ldots, n). \qquad (14.5.3)$$

We then have

$$a_1 Sx_1 + \ldots + a_n Sx_n = Sy. \qquad (14.5.4)$$

---

* Here we use the diploma thesis of Bartenieva [3] on Cauchy's method, submitted to Leningrad State University in 1956

Since $x_{1j} > 0$, $Sx_1 > 0$. Dividing (14.5.4) by Sx_1, we obtain

$$a_1 + a_2 \frac{Sx_2}{Sx_1} + \dots + a_n \frac{Sx_n}{Sx_1} = \frac{Sy}{Sx_1}. \qquad (14.5.5)$$

Multiplying (14.5.5) successively by $x_{11}, x_{12}, \dots, x_{1N}$ and subtracting, from the N equations obtained, the equations of the system of equations (14.5.1), the terms in a_1 cancel and we get a system of N equations with $(n-1)$ unknowns $a_2, \dots, a_n$

$$\left(x_{12} - x_{11}\frac{Sx_2}{Sx_1}\right) a_2 + \dots + \left(x_{nn} - x_{11}\frac{Sx_n}{Sx_1}\right) a_n = y_1 - x_{11}\frac{Sy}{Sx_1},$$

$$\dots\dots\dots\dots\dots\dots\dots\dots$$

$$\left(x_{N2} - x_{N1}\frac{Sx_2}{Sx_1}\right) a_2 + \dots + \left(x_{Nn} - x_{N1}\frac{Sx_n}{Sx_1}\right) a_n = y_N - x_{N1}\frac{Sy}{Sx_1}.$$

We then produce another new system (with $n-2$ unknowns) by a similar series of operations, and so on. In general, we will finally obtain a system of N equations with a single unknown a_n

$$x'_{rn} a_n = y'_r \qquad (r = 1, 2, \dots, N), \qquad (14.5.6)$$

where $x'_{rn} \geqslant 0$ are derived coefficients and y'_r is a linear combination of the y_q's $(q = 1, 2, \dots, N)$, resulting from the working procedure.

Next, we substitute l_q for each unknown y_q in y'_r. We denote the result of this substitution by l'_r. Then we find a'_n from the equation

$$a'_n = \frac{Sl'_r}{Sx'_r}. \qquad (14.5.7)$$

In the preceding equations we put a'_n in place of a_n and l_q in place of y_q, we add them and find a'_{n-1}, and so on until we find a'_1.

In the course of the work it sometimes happens (in practice, quite often) that some of the coefficients of $a_k, a_{k+1}, \dots, a_n$ become very small; then the corresponding terms are usually neglected, and the procedure continued with the remainder. When the resultant estimates a'_i have been found, they are inserted into the equations and the other parameters determined as before.

We see that Cauchy's method (if small terms are not neglected) leads to linear estimators for $(a_1, \dots, a_n)$; the estimators $(a'_1, \dots, a'_n)$ for these parameters by Cauchy's method are linear functions of the observations $l_1, \ldots, l_N$.

Theorem 14.5.1.

The estimators $a_1', \ldots, a_n'$ of the parameters $a_1, \ldots, a_n$ by Cauchy's method are unbiased, if small terms have not been neglected.

Proof. The estimators a_i' are linear functions of the observations l_r if small terms have not been neglected. Substituting l_r for y_r $(r=1, 2, \ldots, N)$ and a_i' for a_i, all the expressions used in Cauchy's method become exact equations. Among these expressions there is an expression of the form

$$a_i' = L_i(l_1, \ldots, l_N) \qquad (i=1, 2, \ldots, n), \qquad (14.5.8)$$

where L_i is a linear function of the observations so that

$$E\big(L_i(l_1, \ldots, l_N)\big) = L_i(y_1, \ldots, y_N). \qquad (14.5.9)$$

But by substituting l_r for y_r in the right-hand side of (14.5.8) a_i' can be replaced by a_i, i.e.

$$E(a_i') = a_i,$$

which is what it is required to prove.

If small terms are neglected in the course of the calculations, then, in general, the estimates will be nearly unbiased.

We now turn to the question of the efficiency of estimators obtained by Cauchy's method; we will assume that small terms have not been neglected and will restrict ourselves to cases of one or two parameters a_1 and a_2, and equally accurate observations l_r.

In chapter VII (theorem 7.2.2) it has been proved that, even with a non-normal random error vector $(\Delta_1, \ldots, \Delta_N)$, provided only that the variance exists, the method of least squares gives efficient estimators of the parameters a_i with respect to all methods of estimation leading to linear unbiased estimators. Since Cauchy's method also gives such estimators, we have

$$D(a_i') \geqslant D(\tilde{a}_i) \qquad (i=1, 2, \ldots, n), \qquad (14.5.10)$$

where $\tilde{a}_i$, as before, denote the least squares estimator of a_i.

It is true that measuring the accuracy of an estimator by its variance is essentially the same as looking at it from the viewpoint of least squares, but, as was explained in chapter V, such an approach has a 'better' real meaning if the a_i' and $\tilde{a}_i$ are normal, or approximately normal. If the error vector $(\Delta_1, \ldots, \Delta_N)$ is normal, then $\tilde{a}_i$ and a_i'

are normal, since they are linear functions of the Δ_i 's. By Liapunov's theorem 2.7.1, even if it is non-normal (but the Δ_i 's are independent) the estimators a_i' and $\tilde{a}_i$ will, in general, be approximately normal, if N, the number of equations, is large compared with n, the number of parameters. Hence the inequality (14.5.10) will imply that, in general, the probability of a deviation from a_i', not greater than a given ε, will be greater for the estimator $\tilde{a}_i$ than for a_i'.

We turn to the system of equations, in one or two unknowns, which is being studied. For the system, with one unknown,

$$x_{r1}a_1 = y_r \qquad (r = 1, 2, \ldots, N) \qquad (x_{r1} \geqslant 0) \quad (14.5.11)$$

we have the estimators: $a_1' = \frac{Sl}{Sx_1}$ (Cauchy's method), $\tilde{a}_1 = \frac{[x_1 l]}{[x_1 x_1]}$ (method of least squares).

Hence

$$D(a_1') = \frac{N\sigma^2}{\left(\sum_{r=1}^{N} x_{r1}\right)^2}; \quad D(\tilde{a}_1) = \frac{\sigma^2}{[x_1 x_1]}. \qquad (14.5.12)$$

We call the ratio $\frac{D(\tilde{a}_1)}{D(a_1')}$ the <u>efficiency of the estimator</u> a_1'.

We have

$$e_1 = \frac{D(\tilde{a}_1)}{D(a_1')} = \frac{\left(\sum_{r=1}^{N} x_{r1}\right)^2}{N \sum_{r=1}^{N} x_{r1}^2}. \qquad (14.5.13)$$

According to general theory, this ratio must be less than unity. It is not difficult to be convinced of this by using the Cauchy-Buniakovski inequality (1.1.1)

$$\left(\sum_{r=1}^{N} x_{r1}\right)^2 \leqslant N \sum_{r=1}^{N} x_{r1}^2.$$

The equality sign arises only in the case when all the x_{r1} 's are equal to one another, i.e. if there are repeated observations all giving the same fundamental equation $x_{11}a_1 = y_1$. In this case $a_1' = \tilde{a}_1$, as can be seen from the formulae for these estimators. On the other hand, e_1 can be as small as desired. If we take, for example,

$x_{r1}=\frac{1}{r}$ $(r=1, 2, \ldots, N)$, a simple calculation shows that, for large N, we have $e_1 \approx \frac{6(\ln N)^2}{\pi^2 N}$.

In such cases the method of least squares is more useful than Cauchy's method. Generally, (14.5.13) gives information on the factor by which the use of Cauchy's method decreases the accuracy.

We now consider the system with two unknowns. Let the matrix X of the system have the form

$$X=\left\| \begin{matrix} x_{11} & x_{12} \\ x_{21} & x_{22} \\ \vdots & \vdots \\ x_{N1} & x_{N2} \end{matrix} \right\|; \quad \text{rank}\,(X)=2 \text{ and } x_{r1} \geqslant 0 \qquad (r=1, 2, \ldots, N).$$

Putting, as usual $x_j=(x_{1j}, x_{2j}, \ldots, x_{Nj})$, we have, as before

$$\left.\begin{aligned} D(\tilde{a}_1) &= \frac{[x_2x_2]\,\sigma^2}{[x_1x_1][x_2x_2]-[x_1x_2]^2}, \\ D(\tilde{a}_2) &= \frac{[x_1x_1]\,\sigma^2}{[x_1x_1][x_2x_2]-[x_1x_2]^2}. \end{aligned}\right\} \qquad (14.5.14)$$

We will now find the estimators a_1' and a_2' by Cauchy's method. We have

$$x_{r1}a_1+x_{r2}a_2=y_r, \qquad (r=1, 2, \ldots, N), \qquad (14.5.15)$$
$$x_{r1} \geqslant 0 \qquad (r=1, 2, \ldots, N).$$

We obtain the equations for a_2

$$\left(x_{12}-x_{11}\frac{Sx_2}{Sx_1}\right)a_2=y_1-x_{11}\frac{Sy}{Sx_1},$$
$$\cdots\cdots\cdots\cdots\cdots$$
$$\left(x_{N2}-x_{N1}\frac{Sx_2}{Sx_1}\right)a_2=y_N-x_{N1}\frac{Sy}{Sx_1}.$$

Let $\varepsilon_r=\pm 1$ be the sign of the quantity $x_{r2}-x_{r1}\frac{Sx_2}{Sx_1}$. In this case we have

$$\sum \varepsilon_r \left(x_{r2} - x_{r1}\frac{Sx_2}{Sx_1}\right) a_2 = \sum \varepsilon_r \left(y_r - x_{r1}\frac{Sy}{Sx_1}\right).$$

or

$$a_2\left(S(x_2\varepsilon) - S(x_1\varepsilon)\frac{Sx_2}{Sx_1}\right) = S(y\varepsilon) - S(x_1\varepsilon)\frac{Sy}{Sx_1}.$$

Whence we obtain the estimator of a_2

$$a_2' = \frac{S(l\varepsilon) - S(x_1\varepsilon)\dfrac{Sl}{Sx_1}}{S(x_2\varepsilon) - S(x_1\varepsilon)\dfrac{Sx_2}{Sx_1}} \tag{14.5.16}$$

and the estimator of a_1

$$a_1' = \frac{Sl - a_2' Sx_2}{Sx_1}. \tag{14.5.17}$$

We will consider the estimator a_2' more carefully. We have

$$a_2' = \frac{1}{S(x_2\varepsilon) - S(x_1\varepsilon)\dfrac{Sx_2}{Sx_1}}\left(\sum_{r=1}^{N} l_r\left(\varepsilon_r - \frac{S(x_1\varepsilon)}{Sx_1}\right)\right). \tag{14.5.18}$$

so that

$$D(a_2') = \frac{\sigma^2}{\left(S(x_2\varepsilon) - S(x_1\varepsilon)\dfrac{Sx_2}{Sx_1}\right)^2}\sum_{r=1}^{N}\left(\varepsilon_r - \frac{S(x_1\varepsilon)}{Sx_1}\right)^2. \tag{14.5.19}$$

Hence, from (14.5.14), the efficiency of the estimator a_2' is

$$e_1 = \frac{D(\tilde{a}_2)}{D(a_2')} = \frac{[x_1x_1][x_2x_2] - [x_1x_2]^2}{[x_1x_1]\left(S(x_2\varepsilon) - S(x_1\varepsilon)\dfrac{Sx_2}{Sx_1}\right)^2}\sum_{r=1}^{N}\left(\varepsilon_r - \frac{S(x_1\varepsilon)}{Sx_1}\right)^2. \tag{14.5.20}$$

From general theory, $0 \leqslant e_1 \leqslant 1$.

In order to answer the question - what is the proportion of accuracy lost by using Cauchy's method, as compared with the method of least squares ? - it is necessary to know the matrix X in order to evaluate the expression (14.5.20). In practical cases of series of equally accurate observations, $D(a_2')$ can be greater than $D(a_2)$ by a factor of 10 or more; the standard deviation can be greater by a factor of three or more. Nevertheless, the results can be sufficiently accurate, while the calculation is very simple; this leads to Cauchy's method being preferred to the method of least squares in many cases.

TABLE 30

Results of estimation of the parameters a_1 and a_2

Date: August 1955	Method of least squares	Cauchy's method
4—5	4,904 0,280	4,904 0,280
13—14	5,696 0,195	5,696 0,195
14—15	5,707 0,237	5,708 0,231
15—16	5,709 0,248	5,715 0,218
23—24	5,398 0,220	5,404 0,200
25—26	5,299 0,106	5,284 0,156
26—27	5,269 0,150	5,280 0,113
28—29	5,188 0,234	5,190 0,227

Bartenieva [3] has published data on the time correction from observations of stars at the Pulkovski laboratory, August 1955. The equations

$$u + A_r a = (\alpha - T)_r \qquad (r = 1, 2, \ldots, N),$$

hold, where A_r and α are taken from the star catalogue, and T is the observed moment of time. The parameters to be estimated are a, the azimuth of the instrument, and u, the time correction.

We put $u = a_1$; $a = a_2$. The results shown in Table 30 were obtained from a series of observations. They show that the accuracy of the observations was satisfactory (σ^2 small). It is true that it is not certain that the observations could be regarded as of equal accuracy; Cauchy's method, not using weights for the observations, was carried through exactly, but the method of least squares was applied on the assumption of equal accuracy, i.e. without calculation of weights. Hence a formula of type (14.5.20) could not now be applied to the comparison of the efficiencies of the methods.

BIBLIOGRAPHY

1. ABBÉ E., Über die Gesetzmässigkeit in der Verteilung der Fehler bei Beobachtungsreihen. Werke, Bd. 2, Jena, pp. 55-81 (1906).
2. ARLEY N. and BUCH K.R., Introduction to the theory of probability and statistics. John Wiley: New York; Chapman and Hall: London (1950).
3. BARTENIEVA L.S., The efficiency of Cauchy's method (Effektivnost metoda Koshi) (Diploma thesis), Leningrad State University (1956).
4. BERNSTEIN S.N., Theory of probability (Teoriya veroyatnostei) (4th edition), Gostekhizdat (1946).
5. WALD A., The fitting of straight lines if both variables are subject to errors, Ann.Math.Statistics, Vol. 11, No. 3, pp. 284-300 (1940).
6. GANTMACHER F.R., Theory of matrices (Teoriya matrits), Gostekhizat (1953).
7. GAUSS K.F., Theoria motus corporum coelestium, Hamburg (1809).
8. GAUSS K.F., Disquisitio de elementis ellipticis Palladis (1810).
9. GAUSS K.F., Theoria combinationis observationum erroribus minimis obnoxiae (1821).
10. HELMERT F., Die Ausgleichungsrechnung nach der Methode der kleinsten Quadrate, Leipzig - Berlin (1907).
11. GNEDENKO B.W., Course on the theory of probability (Kurs teorii veroyatnostei), 2nd edition, Gostekhizdat (1954).
12. GRUBBS F., Sample criteria for testing outlying observations, Ann. Math.Statistics, Vol. 21, No. 1, pp. 27-58 (1950).
13. HUZURBAZAR V.S., The likelihood equation, consistency, and maxima of the likelihood function. Ann.Eugenics, Vol. 14 (1948).
14. DUNIN-BARKOVSKI I.V. and SMIRNOV N.V., The theory of probability and mathematical statistics for technology, (Teoriya veroyatnostei i matematicheskaya statistika w tekhnike), Gostekhizdat (1955).
15. DAVID F.N., Probability theory for statistical methods, Cambridge (1951).
16. DUGUÉ D., Application des propriétés de la limite au sens du calcul des probabilités á l'étude de diverses questions de l'estimation, Journ. de l'Éc.Polytechnique, Vol. 3, No. 4 (1937).
17. ZIMOVNOV V.N., Problems in the estimation of the accuracy of the results of measurements (Voprosi otsenki tochnosti resultatov izmerenii), Geodezizdat (1951).

18. EDELSON N.L., The method of least squares (Sposob naimenshikh kvadratov), 2nd edition, Leningrad (1932).
19. EDELSON N.L., The method of least squares and the theory of the mathematical treatment of observations (Sposob naimenshikh kvadratov i teoriya matematicheskoi obrabotki nablyudenii), Geodezizdat (1947).
20. KENDALL M.G., The advanced theory of statistics, Vol. 1, 2: Griffin; London (1948).
21. KOLMOGOROV A.N., On the log-normal distribution law of sizes of subdivision of an aggregrate (0 logarifmicheski normalnom zakonye raspredeleniya razmerov chastitz pri droblenii), Dokl. Akad.Nauk USSR, Vol. 31, pp. 99-101 (1941).
22. KOLMOGOROV A.N., On the bases of the method of least squares (K obosnovaniyu metoda naimenshikh kvadratov), Uspekhi Matem. Nauk, Vol. 1, No. 1, pp. 57-70 (1946).
23. KOLMOGOROV A.N., PETROV A.A., SMIRNOV Y.M., A formula of Gauss in the method of least squares (Odna formula Gauss'a iz teorii metoda naimenshikh kvadratov), Izv. Akad.Nauk USSR, math.series, Vol. 11, No. 6, pp. 561-66 (1947).
24. CRAMER H., Contributions to the theory of statistical estimation, Skand.Aktuar. Vol. 29, pp. 85-94 (1946).
25. CRAMER H., Mathematical methods of statistics. Princeton University Press (1947).
26. KRASOVSKI F.N., Course of geodesy (Kurs geodezii), Parts I and II, G.L.Z. (1931).
27. CREASY M.A., Confidence limits for the gradient in the linear functional relationship, Journ. Roy.Stat.Soc., Ser.B, Vol. 18, No. 1, pp. 65-69 (1956).
28. KUROSH A.G., Course of higher algebra (Kurs vishei algebri) 5th edition, Gostekhizdat (1956).
29. LAPLACE P.S., Théorie analytique des probabilités, Paris (1812).
30. LEGENDRE A.M., Nouvelles méthodes pour la détermination des orbites des comètes, Paris (1806). Appendice sur la méthode des moindres carrés.
31. LOÈVE M., On sets of probability laws and their limit elements, Univ. Calif. Publ. in Statistics (1950).
32. LINNIK J.V., Some remarks on the method of least squares, with an appendix on the problem of direct and reverse bearings. (Nekotoriye zamechaniya k metodu naimenshikh kvadratov, s prilozkeniyem k zadacham priyamikh i obratnikh zasechek). Teoriya veroyatnostyei i yego primeneniya, Vol. 2, No. 3, pp. 349-359 (1957).
33. LINNIK J.V. and KHOUSON A.P., Mathematico-statistical description of the unevenness of the profile of a surface while it is being polished (Matematiko-statisticheskoye opisaniye nerovnostyei profilya poverkhnosti pri shlifovanii), Inzhinernyi sbornik, Akad.Nauk USSR, Vol. XX, pp. 154-159 (1954).
34. MALTSEV A.L., Remarks on the paper 'A formula of Gauss in the method of least squares' by A.N.Kolmogorov, A.A.Petrov and L.M.Smirnov (Zamechaniye k rabote A.N.Kolmogorova, A.A.Petrova i L.M.Smirnova: 'Odna formula Gauss' a iz teorii metoda naimenshikh kvadratov'), Izv. Akad.Nauk USSR, Math.series, Vol. 11, No. 6, pp. 567-568 (1947).

35. MALTSEV A.L., Bases of linear algebras (Osnovi lineinoyi algebri) Gostekhizdat (1956).
36. MARKOV A.A., The law of large numbers and the method of least squares (1898) (Zakon bolshikh chisel i metod naimenshikh kvadratov), Izbr.Trudi, Izd.Akad.Nauk USSR, pp. 233-251 (1951).
37. MARKOV A.A., Probability calculations (Ischislenye veroyatnostei), 4th edition, GIZ (1924).
38. NEYMAN J., Statistical estimation as a problem in the classical theory of probability (Statisticheskaya otsenka kak problema klassicheskoi teorii veroyatnostei), Uspekhi Akad.Nauk, No. 10, pp. 207-229 (1944).
39. NEMCHINOV V.S., Chebyshev polynomials and mathematical statistics (Polinomii Chebysheva i matematicheskaya statistika), Moscow (1946).
40. PETROV V.V., On the method of least squares and its extremal properties (O metodye naimenshikh kvadratov i yego ekstremalnikh svoistvakh), Uspekhi Matem.Nauk, Vol. 9, No. 1, pp. 41-62 (1954).
41. RAO C.R., On the linear combination of observations and the general theory of least squares, Sankhya, Vol. 17, Pt. 3, pp. 237-256 (1946).
42. RAO C.R., Advanced statistical methods in biometric research, John Wiley: New York (1952).
43. RAO C.R., Information and accuracy attainable in the estimation of statistical parameters, Bull.Calcutta Math.Soc., No. 37 (1945).
44. ROMANOVSKI V.I., Fundamental problems in the theory of errors (Osnobnye zadachi teorii oshibok), Gostekhizdat (1947).
45. SLUTSKI E.E., Tables for the calculation of the incomplete Gamma function and the probability function (Tablitsi dla vichisleniya nepolnoi Γ-funktsii i funktsii veroyatnosti) Izd.Akad. Nauk USSR (1950).
46. SMIRNOV V.I., Course of higher mathematics (Kurs vishei matematiki) Vol. III, Pt. I, section 4, Gostekhizdat (1949).
47. FICHTENHOLZ G.M., Course of differential and integral calculus (Kurs differentialnogo i integralnogo ischisleniya), Vol. III, Gostekhizdat (1949).
48. HALD A., Statistical theory with engineering applications, John Wiley; New York: Chapman and Hall; London (1952).
49. HOEFFDING W., A class of statistics with asymptotically normal distribution, Ann.Math.Statistics, Vol. 19, No. 3, pp. 293-325 (1948).
50. HIRVONEN R.A., Weights and weighting coefficients (Vesa i vesoviye koeffitsienti), Maanmiitaus, Vol. 30, No. 1-2, pp. 10-23 (1955), (in Finnish).
51. CHEBOTARIEV A.S., Method of least squares and foundations of the theory of probability (Sposob naimenshikh kvadratov c osnovami teorii veroyatnostei), ONTI (1936).
52. CHEBYSHEV P.L., On interpolation by the method of least squares (Ob interpolirovanii po sposobu naimenshikh kvadratov), Collected works, Vol. 1 (1859).
53. CHEBYSHEV P.L., Sur l'intégration des différentielles irrationnels, Journ.de math., ser. I, Vol. 18 (1853).

54. EZEKIEL M., Methods of correlation analysis, 2nd edition, Houghton Mifflin, New York (1941).
55. AITKEN A.C., On least squares and linear combination of observations, Proc.Roy.Soc.Edin., Vol. 55, pp. 42-48 (1935).
56. YUSHCHENKO A.P., The method of least squares (Sposob naimenshikh kvadratov), Izd. 'Moskvoi transport' (1956).
57. FISHER R.A. and YATES F., Statistical Tables for biological, agricultural and medical research. Oliver and Boyd; London and Edinburgh (1938).

APPENDIX

Student's t-distribution *)

Table I

k \ p	0,99	0,98	0,95	0,90	0,80	0,70	0,60
1	63,657	31,821	12,706	6,314	3,078	1,963	1,376
2	9,925	6,965	4,303	2,920	1,886	1,386	1,061
3	5,841	4,541	3,182	2,353	1,638	1,250	0,978
4	4,604	3,747	2,776	2,132	1,533	1,190	0,941
5	4,032	3,365	2,571	2,015	1,476	1,156	0,920
6	3,707	3,143	2,447	1,943	1,440	1,134	0,906
7	3,499	2,998	2,365	1,895	1,415	1,119	0,896
8	3,355	2,896	2,306	1,860	1,397	1,108	0,889
9	3,250	2,821	2,262	1,833	1,383	1,100	0,883
10	3,169	2,764	2,228	1,812	1,372	1,093	0,879
11	3,106	2,718	2,201	1,796	1,363	1,088	0,876
12	3,055	2,681	2,179	1,782	1,356	1,083	0,873
13	3,012	2,650	2,160	1,771	1,350	1,079	0,870
14	2,977	2,624	2,145	1,761	1,345	1,076	0,868
15	2,947	2,602	2,131	1,753	1,341	1,074	0,866
16	2,921	2,583	2,120	1,746	1,337	1,071	0,865
17	2,898	2,567	2,110	1,740	1,333	1,069	0,863
18	2,878	2,552	2,101	1,734	1,330	1,067	0,862
19	2,861	2,539	2,093	1,729	1,328	1,066	0,861
20	2,845	2,528	2,086	1,725	1,325	1,064	0,860
21	2,831	2,518	2,080	1,721	1,323	1,063	0,859
22	2,819	2,508	2,074	1,717	1,321	1,061	0,858
23	2,807	2,500	2,069	1,714	1,319	1,060	0,858
24	2,797	2,492	2,064	1,711	1,318	1,059	0,857
25	2,787	2,485	2,060	1,708	1,316	1,058	0,856
26	2,779	2,479	2,056	1,706	1,315	1,058	0,856
27	2,771	2,473	2,052	1,703	1,314	1,057	0,855
28	2,763	2,467	2,048	1,701	1,313	1,056	0,855
29	2,756	2,462	2,045	1,699	1,311	1,055	0,854
30	2,750	2,457	2,042	1,697	1,310	1,055	0,854
40	2,704	2,423	2,021	1,684	1,303	1,050	0,851
60	2,660	2,390	2,000	1,671	1,296	1,046	0,848
120	2,617	2,358	1,980	1,658	1,289	1,041	0,845
∞	2,576	2,326	1,960	1,645	1,282	1,036	0,842

* The table gives values, γ_p, of a random variable t, following Student's distribution with k degrees of freedom, determined by the condition

$$P(|t| \leqslant \gamma_p) = p.$$

In other words, the probability, P, that an observed value of t does not exceed γ_p in absolute value is equal to p.

Table II

Values of $\gamma = \frac{1}{(1-p_0)^{\frac{2}{n-2}}} - 1$ (see page 278).

n \ p_0	0,90	0,95	0,99	n \ p_0	0,90	0,95	0,99
3	99,0	399,	9998,	33	0,160	0,213	0,346
4	9,000	19,0	99,0	34	0,155	0,206	0,333
5	3,642	6,368	20,54	35	0,150	0,199	0,322
6	2,162	3,472	9,000	36	0,145	0,193	0,311
7	1,512	2,314	5,310	37	0,141	0,187	0,301
8	1,154	1,714	3,642	38	0,136	0,181	0,291
9	0,931	1,353	2,728	39	0,133	0,176	0,283
10	0,778	1,115	2,162	40	0,129	0,171	0,274
11	0,668	0,946	1,783	41	0,125	0,166	0,266
12	0,585	0,820	1,512	42	0,122	0,162	0,259
13	0,520	0,724	1,310	43	0,119	0,157	0,252
14	0,468	0,648	1,154	44	0,116	0,153	0,245
15	0,425	0,586	1,031	45	0,113	0,149	0,239
16	0,389	0,534	0,931	46	0,110	0,146	0,233
17	0,359	0,491	0,848	47	0,108	0,142	0,227
18	0,334	0,454	0,778	48	0,105	0,139	0,222
19	0,311	0,422	0,719	49	0,103	0,136	0,217
20	0,292	0,395	0,668	50	0,101	0,133	0,212
21	0,274	0,371	0,624	51	0,099	0,130	0,207
22	0,259	0,349	0,585	52	0,096	0,127	0,202
23	0,245	0,330	0,551	53	0,095	0,125	0,198
24	0,233	0,313	0,520	54	0,093	0,122	0,194
25	0,222	0,298	0,492	55	0,091	0,120	0,190
26	0,212	0,284	0,468	56	0,089	0,117	0,186
27	0,202	0,271	0,445	57	0,087	0,115	0,182
28	0,194	0,259	0,425	58	0,086	0,113	0,179
29	0,186	0,248	0,406	59	0,084	0,111	0,175
30	0,179	0,239	0,389	60 *)	0,083	0,109	0,172
31	0,172	0,229	0,374				
32	0,166	0,221	0,359				

* Approximate values of γ for large values of n can be obtained form the approximate formula

$$\gamma \approx -\frac{2}{n-2} \ln(1-p_0).$$

Table III

Lower limits, γ_1, and upper limits, γ_2, for the confidence interval

$$\gamma_1 s_1 < \sigma < \gamma_2 s_1 \qquad \left(s_1 = \sqrt{\frac{1}{n-1} \sum_{i=1}^{n} (x_i - \bar{x})^2} \right)^{*)}$$

k \ p	0,99		0,98		0,95		0,90	
	γ_1	γ_2	γ_1	γ_2	γ_1	γ_2	γ_1	γ_2
1	0,356	159	0,388	79,8	0,446	31,9	0,510	15,9
2	0,434	14,1	0,466	9,97	0,521	6,28	0,578	4,40
3	0,483	6,47	0,514	5,11	0,566	3,73	0,620	2,92
4	0,519	4,39	0,549	3,67	0,599	2,87	0,649	2,37
5	0,546	3,48	0,576	3,00	0,624	2,45	0,672	2,090
6	0,569	2,98	0,597	2,62	0,644	2,202	0,690	1,916
7	0,588	2,66	0,616	2,377	0,661	2,035	0,705	1,797
8	0,604	2,440	0,631	2,205	0,675	1,916	0,718	1,711
9	0,618	2,277	0,644	2,076	0,688	1,826	0,729	1,645
10	0,630	2,154	0,656	1,977	0,699	1,755	0,739	1,593
11	0,641	2,056	0,667	1,898	0,708	1,698	0,748	1,550
12	0,651	1,976	0,677	1,833	0,717	1,651	0,755	1,515
13	0,660	1,910	0,685	1,779	0,725	1,611	0,762	1,485
14	0,669	1,854	0,693	1,733	0,732	1,577	0,769	1,460
15	0,676	1,806	0,700	1,694	0,739	1,548	0,775	1,437
16	0,683	1,764	0,707	1,659	0,745	1,522	0,780	1,418
17	0,690	1,727	0,713	1,629	0,750	1,499	0,785	1,400
18	0,696	1,695	0,719	1,602	0,756	1,479	0,790	1,385
19	0,702	1,666	0,725	1,578	0,760	1,460	0,794	1,370
20	0,707	1,640	0,730	1,556	0,765	1,444	0,798	1,358
21	0,712	1,617	0,734	1,536	0,769	1,429	0,802	1,346
22	0,717	1,595	0,739	1,519	0,773	1,416	0,805	1,335
23	0,722	1,576	0,743	1,502	0,777	1,402	0,809	1,326
24	0,726	1,558	0,747	1,487	0,781	1,391	0,812	1,316
25	0,730	1,541	0,751	1,473	0,784	1,380	0,815	1,308
26	0,734	1,526	0,755	1,460	0,788	1,371	0,818	1,300
27	0,737	1,512	0,758	1,448	0,791	1,361	0,820	1,293
28	0,741	1,499	0,762	1,436	0,794	1,352	0,823	1,286
29	0,744	1,487	0,765	1,426	0,796	1,344	0,825	1,279
30	0,748	1,475	0,768	1,417	0,799	1,337	0,828	1,274
40	0,774	1,390	0,792	1,344	0,821	1,279	0,847	1,228
50	0,793	1,336	0,810	1,297	0,837	1,243	0,861	1,199
60	0,808	1,299	0,824	1,265	0,849	1,217	0,871	1,179
70	0,820	1,272	0,835	1,241	0,858	1,198	0,879	1,163
80	0,829	1,250	0,844	1,222	0,866	1,183	0,886	1,151
90	0,838	1,233	0,852	1,207	0,873	1,171	0,892	1,141
100	0,845	1,219	0,858	1,195	0,878	1,161	0,897	1,133
200	0,887	1,15	0,897	1,13	0,912	1,11	0,925	1,09

* An explanation of this table is given in example 1 at the end of chapter IV.

Table IV

Quantiles of the distribution of the quantities $v = \frac{x_{max} - \bar{x}}{s}$ or $v_1 = \frac{\bar{x} - x_{min}}{s}$

n \ p	0,10	0,05	0,025	0,01
3	1,406	1,412	1,414	1,414
4	1,645	1,689	1,710	1,723
5	1,791	1,869	1,917	1,955
6	1,894	1,996	2,067	2,130
7	1,974	2,093	2,182	2,265
8	2,041	2,172	2,273	2,374
9	2,097	2,237	2,349	2,464
10	2,146	2,294	2,414	2,540
11	2,190	2,343	2,470	2,606
12	2,229	2,387	2,519	2,663
13	2,264	2,426	2,562	2,714
14	2,297	2,461	2,602	2,759
15	2,326	2,493	2,638	2,800
16	2,354	2,523	2,670	2,837
17	2,380	2,551	2,701	2,871
18	2,401	2,577	2,728	2,903
19	2,426	2,600	2,754	2,932
20	2,447	2,623	2,778	2,959
21	2,467	2,644	2,801	2,984
22	2,486	2,664	2,823	3,008
23	2,504	2,683	2,843	3,030
24	2,520	2,701	2,862	3,051
25	2,537	2,717	2,880	3,071

Table V

Quantiles, r_p, of the distribution of the quantity $r = \frac{q^2}{s_1^2}$ *)

n \ p	0,001	0,01	0,05	n \ p	0,001	0,01	0,05
4	0,295	0,313	0,390	33	0,503	0,614	0,722
5	0,208	0,269	0,410	34	0,509	0,619	0,726
6	0,182	0,281	0,445	35	0,515	0,624	0,729
7	0,185	0,307	0,468	36	0,521	0,629	0,733
8	0,202	0,331	0,491	37	0,526	0,634	0,736
9	0,221	0,354	0,512	38	0,532	0,638	0,740
10	0,241	0,376	0,531	39	0,537	0,642	0,743
11	0,260	0,396	0,548	40	0,542	0,647	0,746
12	0,278	0,414	0,564	41	0,548	0,651	0,749
13	0,295	0,431	0,578	42	0,552	0,655	0,752
14	0,311	0,447	0,591	43	0,557	0,659	0,755
15	0,327	0,461	0,603	44	0,562	0,662	0,758
16	0,341	0,475	0,614	45	0,566	0,666	0,760
17	0,355	0,487	0,624	46	0,570	0,669	0,763
18	0,368	0,499	0,633	47	0,574	0,673	0,765
19	0,381	0,510	0,642	48	0,578	0,676	0,768
20	0,393	0,520	0,650	49	0,582	0,679	0,770
21	0,404	0,530	0,657	50	0,585	0,681	0,772
22	0,414	0,539	0,665	51	0,589	0,684	0,774
23	0,424	0,548	0,671	52	0,592	0,687	0,776
24	0,433	0,556	0,678	53	0,596	0,690	0,778
25	0,442	0,564	0,684	54	0,599	0,692	0,780
26	0,451	0,571	0,689	55	0,602	0,695	0,782
27	0,459	0,578	0,695	56	0,605	0,697	0,784
28	0,467	0,585	0,700	57	0,608	0,700	0,785
29	0,475	0,591	0,705	58	0,611	0,702	0,787
30	0,482	0,598	0,709	59	0,614	0,705	0,789
31	0,489	0,603	0,714	60	0,617	0,707	0,791
32	0,496	0,609	0,718				

* The quantiles were calculated by multiplying the values given in Hart's tables by $\frac{n-1}{2n}$ (see Hart, Significance levels for the ratio of the mean square successive difference to the variance, Ann.Math.Stat., Vol. 13, (1942), 445-447).